RESIDENTIAL HEATING, VENTILATING, AND AIR CONDITIONING

Design and Application

John E. Traister

Prentice Hall, Englewood Cliffs, New Jersey 07632

Library of Congress Cataloging-in-Publication Data

Traister, John E.
    Residential heating, ventilating, and air conditioning : design
and application / John E. Traister.
        p.   cm.
    Includes index.
    ISBN 0-13-774456-0
    1. Heating--Equipment and supplies--Design and construction.
    2. Air conditioning--Equipment and supplies--Design and
    construction. 3. Ventilation--Equipment and supplies--Design and
    construction.   I. Title.
    TH7345.T73   1989
    697--dc20   89-3936
                                                               CIP

Cover design: George Cornell
Manufacturing buyer: Robert Anderson

 © 1990 by Prentice-Hall, Inc.
A Division of Simon & Schuster
Englewood Cliffs, New Jersey 07632

This book can be made available to businesses
and organizations at a special discount when
ordered in large quantities. For more information
contact:

Prentice-Hall, Inc.
Special Sales and Markets
College Division
Englewood Cliffs, N.J. 07632

Printed in the United States of America
10 9 8 7 6 5 4 3 2 1

ISBN 0-13-774456-0

Prentice-Hall International (UK) Limited, *London*
Prentice-Hall of Australia Pty. Limited, *Sydney*
Prentice-Hall Canada Inc., *Toronto*
Prentice-Hall Hispanoamericana, S.A., *Mexico*
Prentice-Hall of India Private Limited, *New Delhi*
Prentice-Hall of Japan, Inc., *Tokyo*
Simon & Schuster Asia Pte. Ltd., *Singapore*
Editora Prentice-Hall do Brasil, Ltda., *Rio de Janeiro*

Contents

PREFACE   xi

1 INTRODUCTION TO RESIDENTIAL HVAC CONSTRUCTION   1

Types of Residential Construction, 2
Wood-frame Structures, 2
Masonry Structures, 3
Reinforced Concrete, 4
Prefabricated Structures, 4
Residential HVAC Systems, 4
Combustion, 7
General Planning, 9
Preliminary Conference, 10
Designing the System, 11

2 BLUEPRINT READING   13

Pictorial Drawings, 13
Orthographic-Projection Drawings, 16
Electrical Diagrams, 17

Electrical and Electronic Graphic Symbols, 17
Schematic Wiring Diagrams, 65
Electrical Wiring Diagrams, 67
HVAC Drawings, 69

3 PSYCHROMETRICS 72

Winter Air Conditioning, 76
Psychrometric Processes, 77

4 RESIDENTIAL HEATING EQUIPMENT 82

Electric Heat, 83
Hot-water Systems, 89

5 INTRODUCTION TO COMPUTER PROGRAMMING 90

Preliminary Planning, 91
Writing the Program, 93
HVAC Systems Cost Analysis and Other
    Available Software, 96

6 RESIDENTIAL HEATING CALCULATIONS 102

Preparing the Sketch, 104
Completing the Heat-loss
    Calculations, 105
Simplified Cooling Calculations, 114
Windows, 114
Walls and Doors, 119
Ceilings, 121
Floors, 122

7 HOT-WATER HEATING SYSTEMS 124

Hot-water Heating, 124
Basic Facts about Heating, 126
Air Supply for Boiler Rooms, 128
Equipment Located in Unconfined Spaces, 129
Equipment Located in Confined Spaces, 129

Hot-water Combination Units, 134
Installation Instructions, 135
Piping for Steam or Hot Water, 137
Electrical Wiring, 138

8 ADD-ON AIR-CONDITIONING SYSTEMS   141

Mounting the Condensing Unit, 143
Installing the Cooling Coil, 144
Installing the Refrigerant Tubing, 149
Installing the Electric Wiring, 152
Prestarting Checklist, 152
Start-up Procedure, 153

9 AIR-DISTRIBUTION DUCTS   154

Duct Design, 155
Static Pressure, 156
Friction Loss, 156
Sizing Ductwork Systems, 157
Outlet Selection, 170
Location of Supply-air Outlets, 170
Selection Considerations, 173
Return-air Inlets, 174
Ductwork Fabrication, 174
Round Duct, 176
Rectangular Duct, 177
Combined Duct Installations, 177
Planning the Installation, 177
Fabricating Fiberglass Duct, 179
Suspending Rectangular Duct, 188
Branch Take-offs, 193

10 INSTALLING HIGH-VELOCITY SYSTEMS   194

The System Components, 194
System Design, 196
Basic Installation Procedures, 197

11 ELECTRIC HEATING UNITS   204

Installing Combination Heating and Cooling
    Units, 205
Installing Radiant Heating Cable, 206
Installation in Plaster Ceilings, 206
Installing Concrete Cable, 208

12 WIRING FOR HEATING, VENTILATING, AND AIR CONDITIONING   211

Transformers, 212
Control Circuit Transformers, 213
Electrical Line Current Capacity, 213
Control Relay, 215
Temperature Controls, 215

13 HVAC CONTROLS   216

Manual Starters, 217
Magnetic Controllers, 218
Overload Protection, 221
Protective Enclosures, 225
National Electrical Code Requirements, 227
Two-wire Control, 227
Three-wire Control, 228
Control Relays, 230
Other Controlling Equipment, 232
Electronic Controls, 233

14 BALANCING THE SYSTEM   234

Heating System Balance, 234
Balancing Instruments, 235
Cooling System Balance, 237

15 RESIDENTIAL ESTIMATING   239

Basic Considerations, 239
Unit Pricing, 243

Installation Variables, 244
Material Cost and Pricing, 246
Direct Job Expense, 247
Overhead Costs, 249
Profit and Selling Price, 252
Estimating and Contracting Forms, 254
Computer Estimating, 254

16 OFFICE FACILITIES AND MANAGEMENT   256

Programs for HVAC Office Management, 259
Mailing Lists, 267
Computer Software, 270
HVAC Specifications, 272
Using the Glossary Feature, 272
Replace, Insert, and Delete Features, 273

17 HVAC DRAFTING   299

The Vari Typer, 300
Using Conventional Typewriter for Lettering, 300
Time-saving Mechanical Symbols, 301
Mechanical Details, 302
Make Use of New Tools and Developments, 303
Drafting Facilities, 303
Computer-aided HVAC Drafting Techniques, 304
Drawing Aids, 305
Hardware, 306
AutoCAD Applications, 307
Macintosh Plus, 308

INDEX   309

Preface

Each year billions of dollars in construction work involve the design and installation of heating, ventilating, and air-conditioning (HVAC) systems for new and existing buildings. Much of this work involves residential construction.

Traditionally, consulting engineers were seldom involved with the design of residential systems. The systems were usually laid out by the architect or "designed" on the job by the contractor or workers. In recent times, however, these systems have become more complex and additional study is required to adequately plan HVAC systems for residential construction. This book is intended to aid in the design and installation of such systems.

Chapters begin with the basics and progress into actual installation practices, including heat-loss and heat-gain calculations.

The book should find use in all HVAC contractors' offices. Consulting engineers will want the book as a reference for residential projects, and it will even prove beneficial to the many do-it-yourselfers.

The author appreciates the help received from the many manufacturers of HVAC equipment, contractors, and consulting engineering firms.

—*John E. Traister*

1
Introduction to Residential HVAC Construction

Few modern conveniences offer the comfort afforded by automatic heating and cooling systems in the home. In fact, it is possible to set a desired condition on one's control or thermostat, and practically forget about the system. If surrounding conditions are below the desired temperature, the system calls for heat and produces just the right amount. Conversely, if the home is too hot, the system switches automatically to the cooling cycle. Furthermore, the air is cleaned electronically, and a prescribed amount of fresh air is introduced into the system.

The energy source for heat was mainly wood up until the past 100 years or so. Now many types of systems use practically every type of fuel conceivable, including the following:

1. Wood
2. Coal
3. Oil
4. Gas
5. Electricity
6. Solar energy
7. Combinations of the preceding types of fuel

Of course, other heat sources are also used to a limited degree in industry, but the preceding ones are those used most commonly in residential heating and cooling systems.

TYPES OF RESIDENTIAL CONSTRUCTION

Those involved in the design and installation of heating, ventilating, and air-conditioning (HVAC) systems for residential construction must be able to visualize the building structure and its relation to the HVAC systems in order to plan and coordinate the layout of the equipment, ductwork, and the like. Therefore, HVAC or mechanical designers and workers should have, or acquire, a thorough knowledge of building construction for all types of structures and should be able to interpret the drawings or plans in terms of the complete project with all of its necessary components.

In general, the following are the basic types of residential building construction:

1. Wood frame
2. Masonry
3. Reinforced concrete
4. Prefabricated structures

Usually, two or more basic types of construction are incorporated into one building. For example, the basement foundation may consist of reinforced concrete, while the upper portion of the building is wood frame with masonry veneer.

WOOD-FRAME STRUCTURES

The most common form of residential building construction is the wood-frame type shown in Fig. 1-1. However, the finish on the outside walls of wood-frame buildings consists of many different materials, including masonry, fiberboard, plywood, and several other materials.

In general, wood framing consists of jointing vertical 2 × 4 members to plates and headers—the entire structure then rests on a solid foundation. The interior walls of the structure are usually finished with plaster, drywall, wood panels, or a number of other finishes. The outside walls are first insulated with fiberboard and then finished with wood or masonry. The void spaces between the interior and exterior walls are filled with insulation.

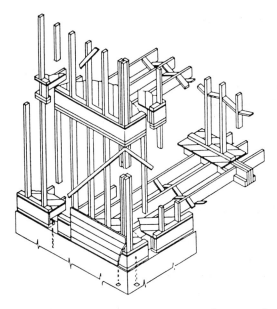

Figure 1-1   Wood framing is the most common type of structure for residential occupancies.

MASONRY STRUCTURES

The masonry structure is constructed by placing clay bricks, stones, cement blocks, or other materials, one upon the other, and bonding them together with cement mortar. Except for basement floor slabs, the floor, the ceiling, and the roof construction usually have a wood frame (see Fig. 1-2).

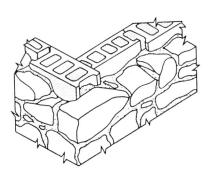

Figure 1-2   Typical masonry construction used for a residential foundation wall.

REINFORCED CONCRETE

Reinforced-concrete construction is sometimes used for residential foundations, although masonry structures of concrete blocks are more common today. Reinforced-concrete construction requires the building of forms, in which are placed the steel reinforcing bars or mesh necessary to reinforce the foundation, the walls, and the concrete slab. Concrete is then poured into or onto the forms. When hardened sufficiently, the forms are stripped off to reveal "bare" concrete, which may then be painted or left in its natural state (see Fig. 1-3).

PREFABRICATED STRUCTURES

Prefabricated structures have been used extensively over the past few years for residential buildings. Such construction usually has a wood frame with plywood exterior sheathing and drywall interior sheathing. Sections of floors, walls, and roofs are constructed at a central factory and then shipped to the building site, where they are assembled by building-trade workers. In some instances, as in the case of module homes, the ductwork and related heating and cooling equipment are also installed in the factory.

RESIDENTIAL HVAC SYSTEMS

All types of HVAC systems used in residential construction are described in detail in the chapters to follow. However, at this point, the reader should have a general understanding of each. Therefore, a brief description follows of the ones most commonly used.

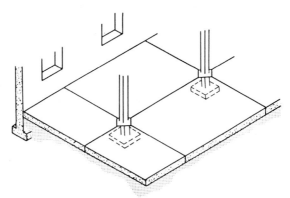

Figure 1-3   Reinforced concrete is sometimes used for basement walls as well as basement floor.

Hot-water baseboard heating. A zone hydronic (hot-water) heating system permits selection of different temperatures in each zone of the home. Baseboard heaters located along the outer walls of the rooms provide a blanket of warmth from floor to ceiling. Hot water is supplied from a central heating unit, which also supplies domestic hot water through a separate circuit. Hot-water boilers for the home are normally manufactured for use with oil, gas, or electricity as the fuel source.

The chief disadvantage of hot-water systems is that they use piping instead of ductwork. Therefore, if a central air-conditioning system is also desired, separate ductwork must be provided.

Electric baseboard heaters. Baseboard units utilize resistant heat as their basis of operation and have several advantages over other types of heat:

1. Fuel tanks and chimneys are not needed.
2. The initial installation cost is low.
3. Each room may be controlled separately by its own thermostat.

However, there are also disadvantages with this type of system:

1. Humidification is hard to control.
2. Heating units require constant cleaning to eliminate dust, which will burn and stain walls above heaters.

Combination heating/cooling units. The advantages of through-wall heating and cooling units are similar to those of electric baseboard heaters except that they also have cooling capability.

Heat pumps. A heat pump is a system in which refrigeration equipment takes heat from a source and transfers it to a conditioned space (when heating is desired), and removes heat from the space when cooling and dehumidification are desired.

Central heating units. Central heating and cooling units distribute heating and cooling from a centrally located source by means of circulating air. Heating fuels used include oil, gas, coal, wood, and electricity. The air is distributed via air ducts throughout the building.

Infrared heaters. These are assemblies that make use of the heat output of infrared lamps or other sources. Such heaters provide fast-response, high-temperature radiation and are particularly suited for use in locations in which it is difficult or impractical to maintain air temperatures at comfortable levels.

Fan-driven forced-air unit heaters. The heat source may be provided by either electric resistance heating or piped steam or hot water. Cooling may also be used in combination with the heat when cold water from a chiller is circulated through the coils of the unit.

High-velocity heating and cooling systems. High-velocity systems have been used in commercial buildings for quite some time, but due to the noise once common to this type of system, very few were installed in residential buildings. Now, however, new designs in this type of system have reduced the noise level to the point where it is quite acceptable for residential applications.

The compactness of the equipment and the small ductwork and outlets make this system well suited for use in existing structures where the installation of conventional forced-air ducts would require too much cutting and patching. On the other hand, the small 3-1/2-inch-diameter ducts of a residential high-velocity system can be "fished" through wall partitions, corners of closets, and similar places. The system's small air outlets (only 2-inch openings) can be placed nearly anywhere and still provide good air distribution.

Solar heat. A basic solar system consists of a solar (heat) collector that is usually arranged so that it faces south, a heat reflector mounted on the ground in front of the collector, a storage tank to hold the sun-heated water, a circulating pump, and piping. The operation of these components is simple. The storage tank is filled with water, which is pumped to the top of the heat collector. As the water flows over the collector, the sun heats it. At the bottom of the collector, the heated water is collected in a trough and then flows back to the storage tank.

The water may be pumped from the storage tank through a system of pipes to baseboard radiators in the living area; a heat exchanger in the water loop may transfer the heat to forced air for distribution via a duct system; or a heat pump may perform the exchange, using the water loop as both heat source and sink.

Radiant heating cable. Embedded heating cable is the most common large-area electric ceiling heating system in use today. The heating cable is laid out on a grid pattern and stapled to a layer of gypsum lath on the ceiling joists. Then the cable is covered with a layer of wet plaster, or another layer of gypsum board is placed over the cable. Heat cable is available on reels for easy payout as the grid is formed. The nonheating leads on the ends of the run of heating cable are brought up through the plates and fed down through the wall to the control thermostat or relay. Cables may be obtained in many lengths and spaced to satisfy room heating capacity requirements.

Miscellaneous heaters. Since about 1973, much experimenting has been done with alternative heating sources and of these, the wood furnace seems to have gained the most popularity in certain areas. Modern wood furnaces are automatically controlled and most require filling only once each day. Their efficiency is high where a plentiful wood supply is available at reasonable cost—such as for rural residents with a woodlot—these systems are difficult to surpass when it comes to saving energy and heating expenses. Although usually more expensive to install than conventional models, wood furnaces will quickly pay for themselves in fuel savings if, as mentioned previously, a cheap source of wood is available.

These and other types of heating, cooling, and ventilating systems are discussed in more detail in the chapters to follow, with particular emphasis on their design and application.

COMBUSTION

In dealing with residential heating systems, it is useful to have an elementary knowledge of combustion and fuels. In general, combustion is the very rapid chemical combination of two or more elements, accompanied by the production of light and heat. The atoms of some of the elements have a great attraction for those of other elements, and when they combine they rush together with such rapidity and force that heat and light are produced. For example, oxygen, which has a great attraction for nearly all other elements, has a particular fondness for carbon, and whenever these two elements come into contact at a sufficiently high temperature, they combine with great rapidity. The combustion of coal in a furnace is of this nature. The temperature of the furnace is raised by kindling the fire, and then the carbon of the coal begins to combine with oxygen taken from the air.

When carbon and oxygen combine, they form carbon dioxide, CO_2; when hydrogen and oxygen combine, they form water, H_2O. These are called the products of combustion. The oxygen required for combustion is usually obtained from the air, which is a mixture composed of approximately 23 parts of oxygen and 77 parts of nitrogen by weight. The nitrogen that enters the furnace with the oxygen takes no part in the combustion, but passes through the furnace and up the chimney without any change in its nature.

Air required for combustion. When carbon is burned to carbon dioxide, CO_2, one atom of carbon unites with two atoms of oxygen. Carbon has an atomic weight of 12 and oxygen has an atomic weight of 16, so that the molecular weight of CO_2 is $(1 \times 12) + (2 \times 16) = 44$; CO_2 is thus composed of $12/44 = 27.27$ percent carbon and $32/44 = 72.73$ percent oxygen. To burn a pound of carbon to CO_2, therefore, requires $32/12 = 2\text{-}2/3$

lb of oxygen. If the oxygen is taken from the air, it will take 2-2/3/0.23 = 11.6 lb of air to supply the 2-2/3 lb of oxygen. This is because only 23 percent of air is oxygen. Therefore, 1 lb of carbon requires 11.6 lb of air for complete combustion. Of this air, 2.67 lb is oxygen, which combines with the pound of carbon to form 3.67 lb of carbon dioxide. The 8.93 lb of nitrogen contained in the air passes off with the CO_2 as a product of combustion.

In dealing with the complete combustion of 1 lb of hydrogen, the product of the combustion is water, H_2O. H_2O is composed by weight of 2 parts hydrogen to 16 parts oxygen, requiring 16/2 = 8 lb of oxygen to unite with it. The air required to furnish 8 lb of oxygen is 8/0.23 = 34.8 lb.

Incomplete combustion. The amount of heat, in British thermal units (Btu), developed by the complete combustion of 1 lb of a fuel is called the calorific value of that fuel; it is also sometimes known as the hfat value or the heat of combustion. It may be determined most accurately by burning a known weight of the fuel with oxygen in an instrument known as a calorimeter. The gases resulting from the combustion are passed through a known weight of water and give up their heat to the water. By noting the rise of temperature of the water, it is possible to calculate the amount of heat absorbed, and thus to determine the heat that would be produced by the combustion of 1 lb of the fuel. The calorific values of the elements most commonly found in fuels are as follows:

	BTU/LB
Hydrogen, burned to water, H_2O	62,000
Carbon, burned to CO_2	14,600
Carbon, burned to CO	4,000
Sulfur, burned to SO_2	4,000

If the various percentages, by weight of the elements, composing a fuel are known, the approximate calorific value of that fuel may easily be calculated by the formula

$$X = 14,600C + 62,000(H-O/8) + 4000S$$

where

X = calorific value of fuel, in Btu per pound

C = percentage of carbon, expressed as a decimal

H = percentage of hydrogen, expressed as a decimal

O = percentage of oxygen, expressed as a decimal

S = percentage of sulfur, expressed as a decimal

For example, if a coal contains 85 percent carbon, 4 percent oxygen, 6 percent hydrogen, 1 percent sulfur, and 4 percent ash, the heat of combustion per pound may be found by the following formula:

$$X = 14,600 \times 0.85 + 62,000$$

$$(0.06 - 0.04/8) + 4000 \times 0.01 = 15,860 \text{ Btu}$$

With the exception of very large residences and tract-development houses, the size of the average residential HVAC system has not been large enough to justify the expense of preparing complete, detailed HVAC drawings and written specifications. Usually such systems are laid out by the architect or owners in the form of a sketchy layout of inlets and outlets, and the total loads for each room or area. The HVAC contractor or supervisor is then required to size the ductwork and make other necessary design calculations as the work progresses. Therefore, those involved in HVAC systems must have a good knowledge of the various codes, installation methods, and the like, to perform this work correctly and efficiently.

The primary use of early home HVAC systems was to provide interior heat during the colder seasons, but today's uses of HVAC systems provide comfort conditioning to include:

- Heating, ventilating, and air conditioning.
- Humidification and dehumidification.
- Air cleaning.
- Pool heating.
- Driveway and porch snow-melting facilities.
- Patio heating.
- Adequate, dependable, and trouble-free operation.
- Reasonable installation cost.
- Reasonable annual operating cost.
- Ease of service and maintenance.

GENERAL PLANNING

In planning any HVAC system, certain general factors must be considered regardless of the type of construction.

- Heating method.
- Cooling method.
- Supplemental heating and cooling.
- Type of building construction.

- Control and power wiring for systems.
- Equipment selection.

PRELIMINARY CONFERENCE

The person in charge of the HVAC system should arrange a meeting with the owners, architect, engineer, and HVAC contractor to determine the type of system and conveniences desired. At this time, the HVAC designer/ engineer or HVAC contractor should be prepared to make recommendations about all the HVAC conveniences available, and also the recommended type of fuel for the area in question. During this preliminary conference, much time can be saved if a standard form is used to collect the necessary data. Such a form should include the following:

1. *Temporary electrical facilities:* Who shall furnish the temporary electric facilities during construction to operate the necessary tools and machines required to install the HVAC system, and who will pay for the facilities?

2. *Air conditioning:* What type is wanted; that is, central or through-wall room units?

3. *Heating system:* Central or individual room heaters? Type of fuel? Forced air, hot water, and so on?

4. *Inlets and outlets:* Type and color of each?

5. *Type of ductwork:* Sheet metal or fiberglass?

After the preliminary discussion, the designer may want to verify certain conditions. This is also a good time to determine any shortage of materials from suppliers that may delay the work once the project is under construction.

The best way to lay out the HVAC system is to make drawings of the house. Obtain the original architectural drawings and, with these, trace an outline of the building's floor plan on tracing paper; these drawings will eventually comprise the HVAC drawings. Then sketch in all inlets and outlets at their desired or required location on the floor plan. After locating the equipment and laying out the routing of the ductwork, the entire system should be reviewed to be sure that everything meets the requirements of local and national codes and that the system is designed to meet the required heating and cooling conditions.

However, it is a rare HVAC job, indeed, that does not have one or more changes in the original contract before it is completed. These changes are usually the result of changes in building design, in type of equipment, or in the owner's requirements. These changes will have to be handled as the work progresses.

DESIGNING THE SYSTEM

Before heating and cooling loads can be determined, measurements of the building to be conditioned must be obtained. These measurements include the area of windows, doors, floor, ceiling, and the like, and may be taken from the architectural drawings or by actual measurement on the job, in the case of an existing building with no drawings available.

While taking these measurements and calculating the area of each component, a sketch should be made of the home's floor plan and other necessary details. Such a sketch will not only make identification of particular rooms or areas easier when the HVAC calculations are being made, it will also help to lay out the system components, such as diffusers, grilles, ductwork, and so on.

In making the sketch, floor plans obviously are not made to full size; rather, they are made to a reduced scale so that all distances on the drawing are smaller than the actual dimensions of the home, but reduced in the same proportion. The ratio, or relation between the size of drawing and the size of building, is indicated on the drawing (1/8 inch to 1 foot, for example), and the dimensions shown are the actual building dimensions, not the distance that is measured on the drawing.

One method of reducing dimensions in proportion is to choose a certain (small) distance and let that distance represent 1 foot in the building. This distance is then divided into 12 parts; each of these parts represents 1 inch. If half-inch divisions are required, these twelfths are subdivided further. When measurement is laid off on the drawing, it is made with a reduced foot rule calibrated as previously described, called an architect's scale. When a measurement is taken on the building itself, it is made with a standard rule or tape measure.

Architect's scales are available in many different ratios ranging from 1/16 inch = 1 foot to 1-1/2 inches = 1 foot. The scale 1/4 inch = 1 foot is the most common scale for residential drawings. Drawing paper ruled in 1/4-inch squares can be purchased to simplify the drawing.

If an existing home was originally designed by an architect, chances are that a complete set of working drawings will be available. If not, check

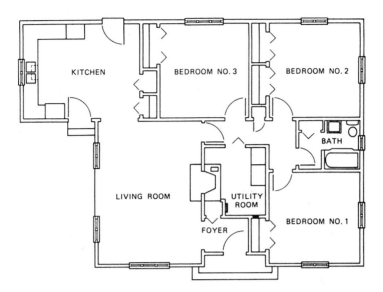

Figure 1-4 Typical floor plan of residence supplied by architect or designer.

with the architect for copies of the drawings, or the contractor who originally built the home may have a set that could be used for the heat-loss calculations. If all these sources fail to produce a set, complete measurements must be taken to draw the sketch.

Figure 1-4 is an example of what a drawing should resemble after it is completed. Begin by measuring the outside perimeter of the home, drawing the wall lines, and inserting dimensions. It would be helpful if someone was available to give assistance. Measure and locate all windows and doors on the drawing along with chimneys, carports, and so on. Continue by measuring all inside partitions, doors, and the like, and indicating their locations on the sketch.

It should be noted where there are storm windows and doors, the amount of insulation in the attic, outside walls, and under the roof in the ceiling. Further information to be taken from an existing home includes crawl space areas, basement areas, and other heated areas above and below the room(s) in question.

2
Blueprint Reading

Those involved with heating systems in any capacity will encounter many types of drawings and diagrams. For example, the engineer or designer will need to study the layout of areas to be heated to obtain important information for laying out ductwork and to calculate heat losses. Furthermore, he or she must be able to make sketches so the draftsmen may complete working drawings for the workers who perform the installation and maintenance of the system. Draftsmen must be able to read blueprints so they can interpret the engineer's sketches, and workers on the job must be able to read drawings and diagrams so that the various jobs are correctly performed. Therefore, a brief sampling of the various types of drawings that may be encountered in the HVAC field is in order.

PICTORIAL DRAWINGS

In pictorial drawings the objects are drawn in one view only; that is, three-dimensional effects are simulated on the flat plane of drawing paper by drawing several faces of an object in a single view. This type of drawing is very useful to describe objects and convey information to those who are not

well trained in blueprint reading or else to supplement conventional diagrams in certain special cases.

One example of a pictorial drawing would be an exploded view of a
motor starter used to control a fan-coil unit to show the physical relationship
of each part to the others, so that the starter could be disassembled and
reassembled during maintenance. See Fig. 2-1.

The types of pictorial drawings most often found in the HVAC industry
include:

1. Isometric drawing
2. Oblique drawing
3. Perspective drawing

All these drawings are relatively difficult to produce, and they are
normally used by manufacturers of heating components for showing their
products in catalogs, brochures, and similar publications. However, in
recent times, they are gradually being replaced by photographs where
possible.

By definition, an isometric drawing is a view projected onto a vertical
plane in which all the edges are foreshortened equally. Figure 2-2 shows an

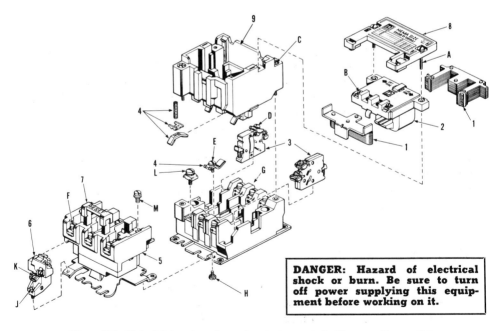

DANGER: Hazard of electrical
shock or burn. Be sure to turn
off power supplying this equipment before working on it.

Figure 2-1   Pictorial drawing of a motor starter control. (Courtesy Square D.)

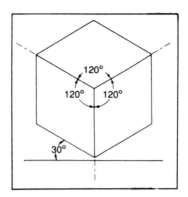

Figure 2-2   Isometric drawing of a cube.

isometric drawing of a cube. In this view, the edges are 120 degrees apart and are called the isometric axes, while the three surfaces shown are called the isometric planes. The lines parallel to the isometric axes are called the isometric lines.

Isometric drawings are usually preferred over the other two types mentioned for use in engineering departments to show certain details on installation drawings, because it is possible to draw isometric lines to scale with a 30- to 60-degree triangle.

The oblique drawing is similar to the isometric drawing in that one face of the object is drawn in its true shape, and the other visible faces are shown by parallel lines drawn at the same angle (usually 45 or 30 degrees) with the horizontal. However, unlike an isometric drawing, the lines drawn at a 30-degree angle are shortened to preserve the appearance of the object and are therefore not drawn to scale. The drawing in Fig. 2-3 is an oblique drawing of a cube.

The two methods of pictorial drawing described so far produce only approximate representations of objects as they appear to the eye, as each type produces some degree of distortion of any object so drawn. However, because of certain advantages, the previous two types are the ones most often found in engineering drawings.

Sometimes, as for a certain illustration or a more detailed instruction manual, it is desired to draw an exact pictorial representation of an object as it actually appears to the eye. A drawing of this type is called a perspective drawing; one such drawing, again of the cube, appears in Fig. 2-4.

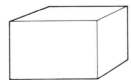

Figure 2-3   Oblique drawing of a cube.

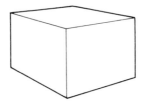

Figure 2-4 Perspective drawing of a cube.

ORTHOGRAPHIC-PROJECTION DRAWINGS

An orthographic-projection drawing is one that represents the physical arrangement and views of specific objects. These drawings give all plan views, elevation views, dimensions, and other details necessary to construct the project or object. For example, Fig. 2-5 suggests the form of a block, but it does not show the actual shape of the surfaces, nor does it show the dimensions of the object so that it may be constructed.

An orthographic projection of the block in Fig. 2-5 is shown in Fig. 2-6. One of the drawings in this figure shows the block as though the observer were looking straight at the front; one, as though the observer were looking straight at the left side; one, as though the observer were looking straight at the right side; and one, as though the observer were looking at the rear of the block. The remaining view is as if the observer were looking straight down on the block. These views, when combined with dimensions, will allow the object to be constructed properly from materials such as metal, wood, plastic, or whatever the specifications call for.

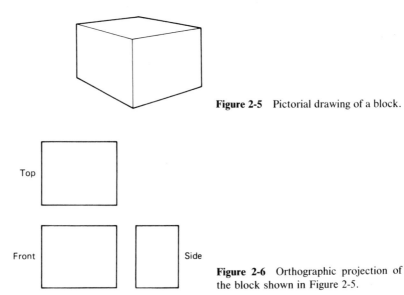

Figure 2-5 Pictorial drawing of a block.

Top

Front   Side

Figure 2-6 Orthographic projection of the block shown in Figure 2-5.

ELECTRICAL DIAGRAMS

Electrical diagrams are drawings intended to show, in diagrammatic form, electrical components and their related connections. Such drawings are seldom drawn to scale and show only the electrical association of the different components. In diagram drawings, symbols are used extensively to represent the various pieces of electrical equipment or components, and lines are used to connect these symbols—indicating the size, type, number of wires, and the like.

In general, the types of diagrams that will be encountered by those working with heating systems will include flow diagrams (Fig. 2-7), single-line block diagrams (Fig. 2-8), and schematic wiring diagrams (Fig. 2-9). All these types are frequently found in HVAC control diagrams.

ELECTRICAL AND ELECTRONIC GRAPHIC SYMBOLS

The purpose of a working drawing, as applied to the heating industry, is to show how a certain object, piece of equipment, or system is to be constructed, installed, modified, or repaired. An electronic testing instrument, for example, usually has drawings and specifications showing the mechanical arrangement of the chassis and housing and a schematic diagram

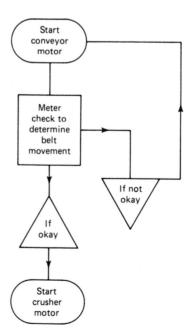

Figure 2-7 Typical flow diagram.

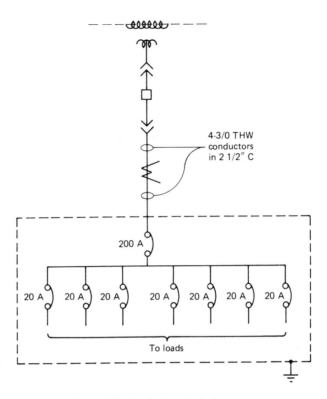

Figure 2-8   Single-line block diagram.

showing the various components, the power supply, and the connections between each. An electrical drawing of a system used in a building to indicate the routing of the control circuits usually shows the floor plans of each level, the routing of the conduit or conductors, the number and sizes of

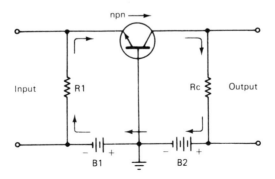

Figure 2-9   Schematic wiring diagram.

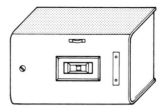

Figure 2-10 Pictorial drawing of a motor starter.

wires or cables, heating equipment, feeders, and other information for the proper installation of the system.

In preparing drawings for the electrical industry, symbols are used to simplify the work of those preparing the drawing. To illustrate this fact, look at the pictorial drawing of a motor starter in Fig. 2-10. Although this drawing clearly indicates the type of control, method of connections, and the like, such drawings would take hours for a draftsman to complete, costing more than could possibly be allotted for the conventional working drawing used in electrical construction. However, by using a drawing such as the one in Fig. 2-11, which utilizes symbols to indicate the various components, the drafting time can be cut back to only minutes, and, to the experienced worker, both drawings relay the exact same information.

Most engineers, designers, and draftsmen use symbols adopted by the United States of America Standards Institute (USASI) for use on electrical and electronic drawings. However, many designers and draftsmen frequently modify these symbols to suit their own particular requirements for the type of work they normally encounter. For this reason, most working drawings will have a symbol list or legend placed on the drawing to describe exactly what each symbol means, thus eliminating practically any doubt as to what is exactly required. A typical symbol list or legend appears in Fig. 2-12.

It is evident from the list in Fig. 2-12 that many symbols have the same basic form, but their meanings differ slightly because of the addition of a line, mark, or abbreviation. Therefore, a good procedure to follow in learning the different electrical symbols is to first learn the basic form and then apply the variations of that form to obtain the different meanings.

Note also that some of the symbols in Fig. 2-12 are abbreviations, such as XFER for transfer and WT for watertight. Others are simplified picto-

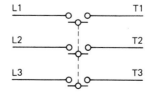

Figure 2-11 Schematic drawing of a motor starter using symbols to indicate various components. (Courtesy of Westinghouse.)

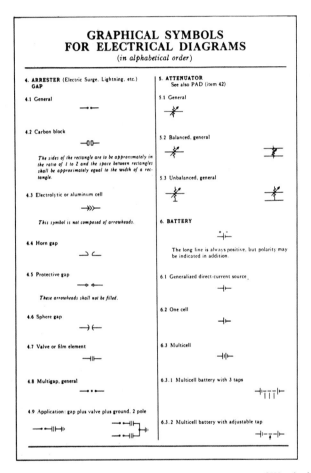

Figure 2-12   Typical electrical symbol list or legend. (Courtesy of Westinghouse.)

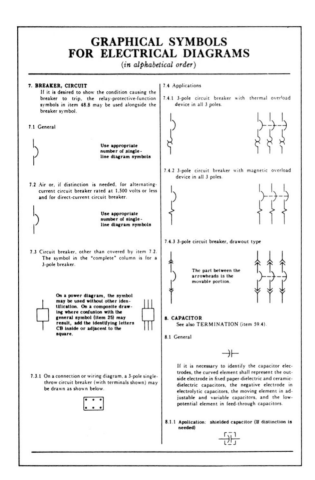

GRAPHICAL SYMBOLS
FOR ELECTRICAL DIAGRAMS
(in alphabetical order)

7. BREAKER, CIRCUIT
If it is desired to show the condition causing the breaker to trip, the relay-protective-function symbols in item 48.8 may be used alongside the breaker symbol.

7.1 General

Use appropriate number of single-line diagram symbols

7.2 Air or, if distinction is needed, for alternating-current circuit breaker rated at 1,500 volts or less and for direct-current circuit breaker.

Use appropriate number of single-line diagram symbols

7.3 Circuit breaker, other than covered by item 7.2. The symbol in the "complete" column is for a 3-pole breaker.

On a power diagram, the symbol may be used without other identification. On a composite drawing where confusion with the general symbol (item 25) may result, add the identifying letters CB inside or adjacent to the square.

7.3.1 On a connection or wiring diagram, a 3-pole single-throw circuit breaker (with terminals shown) may be drawn as shown below.

7.4 Applications

7.4.1 3-pole circuit breaker with thermal overload device in all 3 poles.

7.4.2 3-pole circuit breaker with magnetic overload device in all 3 poles.

7.4.3 3-pole circuit breaker, drawout type

The part between the arrowheads is the movable portion.

8. CAPACITOR
See also TERMINATION (item 59.4).

8.1 General

If it is necessary to identify the capacitor electrodes, the curved element shall represent the outside electrode in fixed paper-dielectric and ceramic-dielectric capacitors, the negative electrode in electrolytic capacitors, the moving element in adjustable and variable capacitors, and the low-potential element in feed-through capacitors.

8.1.1 Application: shielded capacitor (if distinction is needed)

Figure 2-12 (cont'd.)

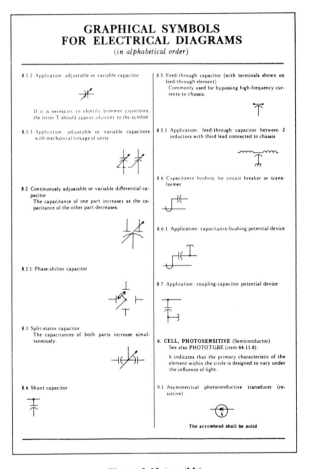

GRAPHICAL SYMBOLS
FOR ELECTRICAL DIAGRAMS
(in alphabetical order)

8.1.2 Application: adjustable or variable capacitor

If it is necessary to identify trimmer capacitors, the letter T should appear adjacent to the symbol.

8.1.3 Application: adjustable or variable capacitors with mechanical linkage of units

8.2 Continuously adjustable or variable differential capacitor
The capacitance of one part increases as the capacitance of the other part decreases.

8.2.1 Phase-shifter capacitor

8.3 Split-stator capacitor
The capacitances of both parts increase simultaneously.

8.4 Shunt capacitor

8.5 Feed-through capacitor (with terminals shown on feed-through element)
Commonly used for bypassing high-frequency currents to chassis.

8.5.1 Application: feed-through capacitor between 2 inductors with third lead connected to chassis

8.6 Capacitance bushing for circuit breaker or transformer

8.6.1 Application: capacitance-bushing potential device

8.7 Application: coupling-capacitor potential device

9. CELL, PHOTOSENSITIVE (Semiconductor)
See also PHOTOTUBE (item 64.11.6).
λ indicates that the primary characteristic of the element within the circle is designed to vary under the influence of light.

9.1 Asymmetrical photoconductive transducer (resistive)

The arrowhead shall be solid

Figure 2-12 (cont'd.)

GRAPHICAL SYMBOLS
FOR ELECTRICAL DIAGRAMS
(in alphabetical order)

9.2 Symmetrical photoconductive transducer; selenium cell

9.3 Photovoltaic transducer; barrier photocell; blocking-layer cell

10. CHASSIS FRAME
(See also GROUND (item 28))

The chassis or frame is not necessarily at ground potential.

11. COIL, BLOWOUT

The broken line - — - indicates where line connection to a symbol is made and is not a part of the symbol.

12. COIL, OPERATING
See also INDUCTOR; WINDING (item 31).

Always indicate the device designation within the circle.

13. CONNECTION, MECHANICAL MECHANICAL INTERLOCK
The preferred location of the mechanical connection is as shown in the various applications, but other locations may be equally acceptable.

13.1 Mechanical connection (short dashes)

13.2 Mechanical connection or interlock with fulcrum (short dashes)

13.3 Mechanical interlock, other

INDICATE BY A NOTE

14. CONNECTOR DISCONNECTING DEVICE
The connector symbol is not an arrowhead. It is larger and the lines are drawn at a 90-degree angle.

14.1 Female (or stationary) contact

14.2 Male (or moving) contact

14.3 Connector assembly, movable or stationary portion; jack, plug, or receptacle

Use appropriate number of contact symbols

14.3.1 Commonly used for a jack or receptacle (usually stationary)

Use appropriate number of contact symbols

14.3.2 Commonly used for a plug (usually movable)

Use appropriate number of contact symbols

14.4 Separable connectors (engaged)

Use appropriate number of contact symbols

14.4.1 Application: engaged 4-conductor connectors; the plug has 1 male and 3 female contacts

14.4.2 Application: engaged 4-conductor connectors, the plug has 1 male and 3 female contacts with individual contact designations shown in the complete-symbol column

Figure 2-12 (cont'd.)

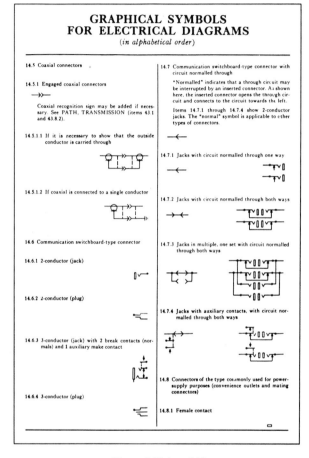

GRAPHICAL SYMBOLS
FOR ELECTRICAL DIAGRAMS
(in alphabetical order)

14.5 Coaxial connectors

14.5.1 Engaged coaxial connectors

Coaxial recognition sign may be added if necessary. See PATH, TRANSMISSION (items 43.1 and 43.8.2).

14.5.1.1 If it is necessary to show that the outside conductor is carried through

14.5.1.2 If coaxial is connected to a single conductor

14.6 Communication switchboard-type connector

14.6.1 2-conductor (jack)

14.6.2 2-conductor (plug)

14.6.3 3-conductor (jack) with 2 break contacts (normals) and 1 auxiliary make contact

14.6.4 3-conductor (plug)

14.7 Communication switchboard-type connector with circuit normalled through

"Normalled" indicates that a through circuit may be interrupted by an inserted connector. As shown here, the inserted connector opens the through circuit and connects to the circuit towards the left.

Items 14.7.1 through 14.7.4 show 2-conductor jacks. The "normal" symbol is applicable to other types of connectors.

14.7.1 Jacks with circuit normalled through one way

14.7.2 Jacks with circuit normalled through both ways

14.7.3 Jacks in multiple, one set with circuit normalled through both ways

14.7.4 Jacks with auxiliary contacts, with circuit normalled through both ways

14.8 Connectors of the type commonly used for power-supply purposes (convenience outlets and mating connectors)

14.8.1 Female contact

Figure 2-12 (cont'd.)

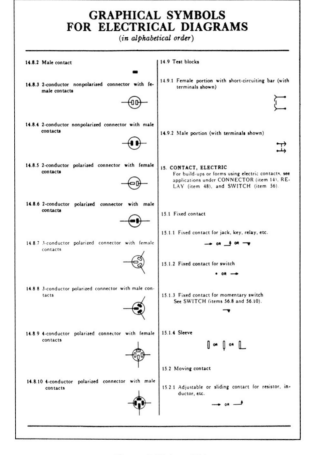

GRAPHICAL SYMBOLS
FOR ELECTRICAL DIAGRAMS
(in alphabetical order)

14.8.2 Male contact

14.8.3 2-conductor nonpolarized connector with female contacts

14.8.4 2-conductor nonpolarized connector with male contacts

14.8.5 2-conductor polarized connector with female contacts

14.8.6 2-conductor polarized connector with male contacts

14.8.7 3-conductor polarized connector with female contacts

14.8.8 3-conductor polarized connector with male contacts

14.8.9 4-conductor polarized connector with female contacts

14.8.10 4-conductor polarized connector with male contacts

14.9 Test blocks

14.9.1 Female portion with short-circuiting bar (with terminals shown)

14.9.2 Male portion (with terminals shown)

15. CONTACT, ELECTRIC
For build-ups or forms using electric contacts, see applications under CONNECTOR (item 14), RELAY (item 48), and SWITCH (item 56).

15.1 Fixed contact

15.1.1 Fixed contact for jack, key, relay, etc.

15.1.2 Fixed contact for switch

15.1.3 Fixed contact for momentary switch
See SWITCH (items 56.8 and 56.10).

15.1.4 Sleeve

15.2 Moving contact

15.2.1 Adjustable or sliding contact for resistor, inductor, etc.

Figure 2-12 (cont'd.)

GRAPHICAL SYMBOLS
FOR ELECTRICAL DIAGRAMS
(in alphabetical order)

15.2.2 Locking

15.2.3 Nonlocking

As applied to a removable circuit-breaker unit, (a) is an auxiliary contact that is closed when the unit is in the connected position. As applied to a housing or enclosure, (a) is an auxiliary contact that is closed when the removable circuit-breaker unit is in the connected position. See latest issue of American Standard C37.2 for further details.

15.2.4 Segment; bridging contact
See SWITCH (items 56.12.3 and 56.12.4).

⟳ or ⟲

In the parallel-line contact symbols shown below, the length of the parallel lines shall be approximately 1½ times the width of the gap (except for item 15.6).

15.2.5 Vibrator reed

15.3.1 Closed contact (break)

15.2.6 Vibrator split reed

15.3.2 Open contact (make)

15.2.7 Rotating contact (slip ring) and brush

15.3.3 Transfer

15.3 Basic contact assemblies

The standard method of showing a contact is by a symbol indicating the circuit condition it produces when the actuating device is in the deenergized or nonoperated position. The actuating device may be of a mechanical, electrical, or other nature, and a clarifying note may be necessary with the symbol to explain the proper point at which the contact functions, for example, the point where a contact closes or opens as a function of changing pressure, level, flow, voltage, current, etc. In cases where it is desirable to show contacts in the energized or operated condition and where confusion may result, a clarifying note shall be added to the drawing.

Auxiliary switches or contacts for circuit breakers, safety enclosed trucks, removable circuit-breaker units, housings, enclosures, etc., may be designated as follows:
(a) Closed when device is in energized or operated position;
(b) Closed when device is in de-energized or non-operated position.
(aa) Closed when operating mechanism of main device is in energized or operated position.
(bb) Closed when operating mechanism of main device is in de-energized or nonoperated position.

15.3.4 Make-before-break

15.4 Application: open contact with time closing (TC or TDC) feature

15.5 Application: closed contact with time opening (TO or TDO) feature

15.6 Time sequential closing

Figure 2-12 (cont'd.)

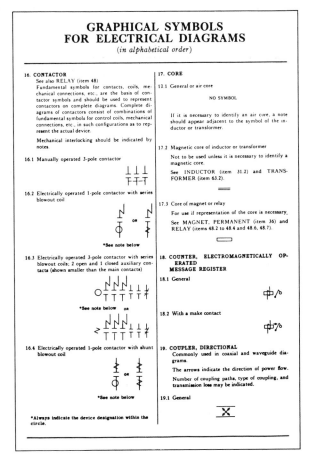

GRAPHICAL SYMBOLS
FOR ELECTRICAL DIAGRAMS
(in alphabetical order)

16. CONTACTOR
See also RELAY (item 48)
Fundamental symbols for contacts, coils, mechanical connections, etc., are the basis of contactor symbols and should be used to represent contactors on complete diagrams. Complete diagrams of contactors consist of combinations of fundamental symbols for control coils, mechanical connections, etc., in such configurations as to represent the actual device.

Mechanical interlocking should be indicated by notes.

16.1 Manually operated 3-pole contactor

16.2 Electrically operated 1-pole contactor with series blowout coil

See note below

16.3 Electrically operated 3-pole contactor with series blowout coils; 2 open and 1 closed auxiliary contacts (shown smaller than the main contacts)

See note below or

16.4 Electrically operated 1-pole contactor with shunt blowout coil

See note below

*Always indicate the device designation within the circle.

17. CORE

17.1 General or air core

NO SYMBOL

If it is necessary to identify an air core, a note should appear adjacent to the symbol of the inductor or transformer.

17.2 Magnetic core of inductor or transformer

Not to be used unless it is necessary to identify a magnetic core.

See INDUCTOR (item 31.2) and TRANSFORMER (item 63.2).

17.3 Core of magnet or relay

For use if representation of the core is necessary.

See MAGNET, PERMANENT (item 36) and RELAY (items 48.2 to 48.4 and 48.6, 48.7).

18. COUNTER, ELECTROMAGNETICALLY OPERATED MESSAGE REGISTER

18.1 General

18.2 With a make contact

19. COUPLER, DIRECTIONAL
Commonly used in coaxial and waveguide diagrams.

The arrows indicate the direction of power flow.

Number of coupling paths, type of coupling, and transmission loss may be indicated.

19.1 General

Figure 2-12 (cont'd.)

GRAPHICAL SYMBOLS
FOR ELECTRICAL DIAGRAMS
(in alphabetical order)

19.2 Applications

19.2.1 E-plane aperture coupling, 30-decibel transmission loss

19.2.2 Loop coupling, 30-decibel transmission loss

19.2.3 Probe coupling, 30-decibel transmission loss

19.2.4 Resistance coupling, 30-decibel transmission loss

20. COUPLING
Commonly used in coaxial and waveguide diagrams

20.1 Coupling by aperture with an opening of less than full waveguide size

Always indicate the type of coupling by designation: E, H or HE within the circle.

E indicates that the physical plane of the aperture is perpendicular to the transverse component of the major E lines.

H indicates that the physical plane of the aperture is parallel to the transverse component of the major E lines.

HE indicates coupling by all other kinds of apertures.

Transmission loss may be indicated.

20.1.1 Application: E-plane coupling by aperture to space

20.1.2 Application: E-plane coupling by aperture; 2 ends of transmission path available

20.1.3 Application: E-plane coupling by aperture; 3 ends of transmission path available

20.1.4 Application: E-plane coupling by aperture; 4 ends of transmission path available

20.2 Coupling by loop to space

20.2.1 Coupling by loop to guided transmission path

20.2.2 Application: coupling by loop from coaxial to circular waveguide with direct-current grounds connected

20.3 Coupling by probe to space
See OPEN CIRCUIT (item 59.2).

20.3.1 Application: coupling by probe to a guided transmission path

20.3.2 Application: coupling by probe from coaxial to rectangular waveguide with direct-current grounds connected

Figure 2-12 (cont'd.)

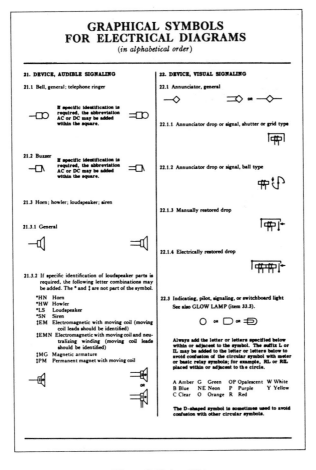

GRAPHICAL SYMBOLS
FOR ELECTRICAL DIAGRAMS
(in alphabetical order)

21. DEVICE, AUDIBLE SIGNALING

21.1 Bell, general; telephone ringer

If specific identification is required, the abbreviation AC or DC may be added within the square.

21.2 Buzzer

If specific identification is required, the abbreviation AC or DC may be added within the square.

21.3 Horn; howler; loudspeaker; siren

21.3.1 General

21.3.2 If specific identification of loudspeaker parts is required, the following letter combinations may be added. The * and ‡ are not part of the symbol.

*HN   Horn
*HW   Howler
*LS   Loudspeaker
*SN   Siren
‡EM   Electromagnetic with moving coil (moving coil leads should be identified)
‡EMN Electromagnetic with moving coil and neutralizing winding (moving coil leads should be identified)
‡MG   Magnetic armature
‡PM   Permanent magnet with moving coil

22. DEVICE, VISUAL SIGNALING

22.1 Annunciator, general

22.1.1 Annunciator drop or signal, shutter or grid type

22.1.2 Annunciator drop or signal, ball type

22.1.3 Manually restored drop

22.1.4 Electrically restored drop

22.3 Indicating, pilot, signaling, or switchboard light
See also GLOW LAMP (item 33.3).

Always add the letter or letters specified below within or adjacent to the symbol. The suffix L or IL may be added to the letter or letters below to avoid confusion of the circular symbol with meter or basic relay symbols; for example, RL or RIL placed within or adjacent to the circle.

A Amber   G Green   OP Opalescent W White
B Blue   NE Neon   P Purple   Y Yellow
C Clear   O Orange R Red

The D-shaped symbol is sometimes used to avoid confusion with other circular symbols.

Figure 2-12 (cont'd.)

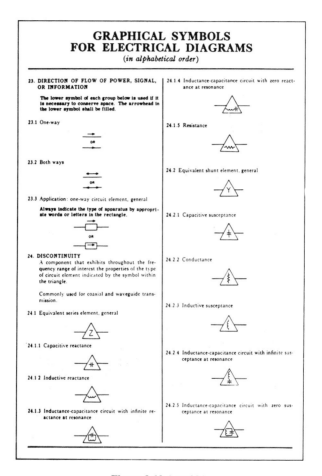

Figure 2-12 (cont'd.)

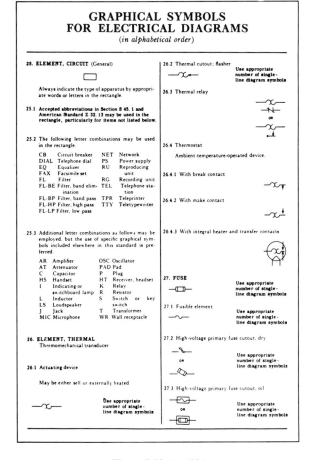

GRAPHICAL SYMBOLS
FOR ELECTRICAL DIAGRAMS
(in alphabetical order)

25. ELEMENT, CIRCUIT (General)

Always indicate the type of apparatus by appropriate words or letters in the rectangle.

25.1 Accepted abbreviations in Section S 45. 1 and American Standard Z 32. 13 may be used in the rectangle, particularly for items not listed below.

25.2 The following letter combinations may be used in the rectangle.

CB	Circuit breaker	NET	Network
DIAL	Telephone dial	PS	Power supply
EQ	Equalizer	RU	Reproducing
FAX	Facsimile set		unit
FL	Filter	RG	Recording unit
FL-BE	Filter, band elim-	TEL	Telephone sta-
	ination		tion
FL-BP	Filter, band pass	TPR	Teleprinter
FL-HP	Filter, high pass	TTY	Teletypewriter
FL-LP	Filter, low pass		

25.3 Additional letter combinations as follows may be employed, but the use of specific graphical symbols included elsewhere in this standard is preferred.

AR	Amplifier	OSC	Oscillator
AT	Attenuator	PAD	Pad
C	Capacitor	P	Plug
HS	Handset	HT	Receiver, headset
I	Indicating or	K	Relay
	switchboard lamp	R	Resistor
L	Inductor	S	Switch or key
LS	Loudspeaker		switch
J	Jack	T	Transformer
MIC	Microphone	WR	Wall receptacle

26. ELEMENT, THERMAL
Thermomechanical transducer

26.1 Actuating device

May be either self or externally heated

Use appropriate number of single-line diagram symbols

26.2 Thermal cutout; flasher

Use appropriate number of single-line diagram symbols

26.3 Thermal relay

26.4 Thermostat

Ambient-temperature-operated device.

26.4.1 With break contact

26.4.2 With make contact

26.4.3 With integral heater and transfer contacts

27. FUSE

Use appropriate number of single-line diagram symbols

27.1 Fusible element

Use appropriate number of single-line diagram symbols

27.2 High-voltage primary fuse cutout, dry

Use appropriate number of single-line diagram symbols

27.3 High-voltage primary fuse cutout, oil

Use appropriate number of single-line diagram symbols

Figure 2-12 (cont'd.)

GRAPHICAL SYMBOLS
FOR ELECTRICAL DIAGRAMS
(in alphabetical order)

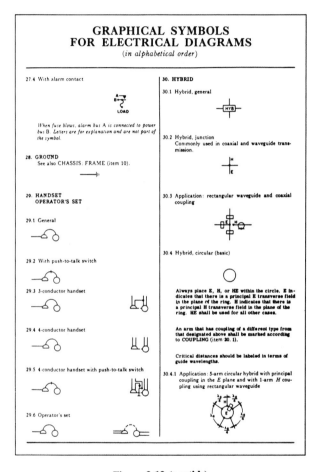

27.4 With alarm contact

When fuse blows, alarm bus A is connected to power bus B. Letters are for explanation and are not part of the symbol.

28. GROUND
   See also CHASSIS; FRAME (item 10).

29. HANDSET
   OPERATOR'S SET

29.1 General

29.2 With push-to-talk switch

29.3 3-conductor handset

29.4 4-conductor handset

29.5 4-conductor handset with push-to-talk switch

29.6 Operator's set

30. HYBRID

30.1 Hybrid, general

30.2 Hybrid, junction
   Commonly used in coaxial and waveguide transmission.

30.3 Application: rectangular waveguide and coaxial coupling

30.4 Hybrid, circular (basic)

Always place E, H, or HE within the circle. E indicates that there is a principal E transverse field in the plane of the ring. H indicates that there is a principal H transverse field in the plane of the ring. HE shall be used for all other cases.

An arm that has coupling of a different type from that designated above shall be marked according to COUPLING (item 20.1).

Critical distances should be labeled in terms of guide wavelengths.

30.4.1 Application: 5-arm circular hybrid with principal coupling in the E plane and with 1-arm H coupling using rectangular waveguide

Figure 2-12 (cont'd.)

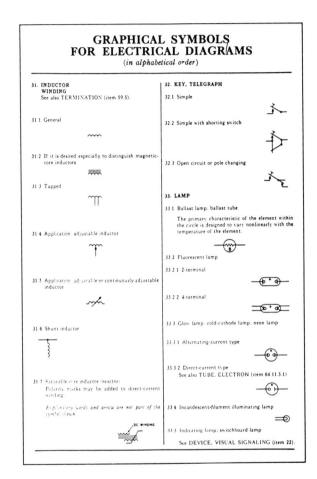

GRAPHICAL SYMBOLS
FOR ELECTRICAL DIAGRAMS
(in alphabetical order)

31. INDUCTOR WINDING
See also TERMINATION (item 59.5).

31.1 General

31.2 If it is desired especially to distinguish magnetic-core inductors

31.3 Tapped

31.4 Application: adjustable inductor

31.5 Application: adjustable or continuously adjustable inductor

31.6 Shunt inductor

31.7 Saturable-core inductor (reactor)
Polarity marks may be added to direct-current winding.

Explanatory words and arrow are not part of the symbol shown.

DC WINDING

32. KEY, TELEGRAPH

32.1 Simple

32.2 Simple with shorting switch

32.3 Open circuit or pole changing

33. LAMP

33.1 Ballast lamp; ballast tube

The primary characteristic of the element within the circle is designed to vary nonlinearly with the temperature of the element.

33.2 Fluorescent lamp

33.2.1 2-terminal

33.2.2 4-terminal

33.3 Glow lamp; cold-cathode lamp; neon lamp

33.3.1 Alternating-current type

33.3.2 Direct-current type
See also TUBE, ELECTRON (item 64.11.5.1)

33.4 Incandescent-filament illuminating lamp

33.5 Indicating lamp; switchboard lamp

See DEVICE, VISUAL SIGNALING (item 22).

Figure 2-12 (cont'd.)

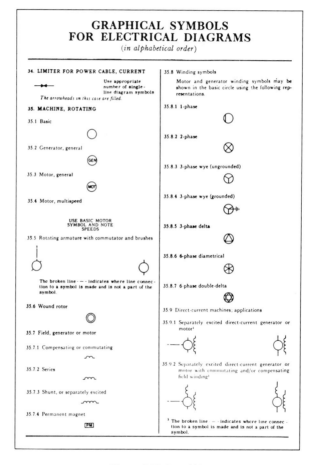

**GRAPHICAL SYMBOLS
FOR ELECTRICAL DIAGRAMS**
(in alphabetical order)

34. LIMITER FOR POWER CABLE, CURRENT

Use appropriate number of single-line diagram symbols

The arrowheads in this case are filled.

35. MACHINE, ROTATING

35.1 Basic

35.2 Generator, general

35.3 Motor, general

35.4 Motor, multispeed

USE BASIC MOTOR SYMBOL AND NOTE SPEEDS

35.5 Rotating armature with commutator and brushes

The broken line – — - indicates where line connection to a symbol is made and is not a part of the symbol.

35.6 Wound rotor

35.7 Field, generator or motor

35.7.1 Compensating or commutating

35.7.2 Series

35.7.3 Shunt, or separately excited

35.7.4 Permanent magnet

35.8 Winding symbols

Motor and generator winding symbols may be shown in the basic circle using the following representations.

35.8.1 1-phase

35.8.2 2-phase

35.8.3 3-phase wye (ungrounded)

35.8.4 3-phase wye (grounded)

35.8.5 3-phase delta

35.8.6 6-phase diametrical

35.8.7 6-phase double-delta

35.9 Direct-current machines; applications

35.9.1 Separately excited direct-current generator or motor[1]

35.9.2 Separately excited direct-current generator or motor with commutating and/or compensating field winding[1]

[1] The broken line – — - indicates where line connection to a symbol is made and is not a part of the symbol.

Figure 2-12 (cont'd.)

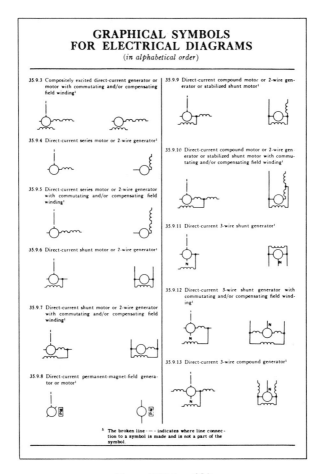

GRAPHICAL SYMBOLS
FOR ELECTRICAL DIAGRAMS
(in alphabetical order)

35.9.3 Compositely excited direct-current generator or motor with commutating and/or compensating field winding[1]

35.9.4 Direct-current series motor or 2-wire generator[1]

35.9.5 Direct-current series motor or 2-wire generator with commutating and/or compensating field winding[1]

35.9.6 Direct-current shunt motor or 2-wire generator[1]

35.9.7 Direct-current shunt motor or 2-wire generator with commutating and/or compensating field winding[1]

35.9.8 Direct-current permanent-magnet-field generator or motor[1]

35.9.9 Direct-current compound motor or 2-wire generator or stabilized shunt motor[1]

35.9.10 Direct-current compound motor or 2-wire generator or stabilized shunt motor with commutating and/or compensating field winding[1]

35.9.11 Direct-current 3-wire shunt generator[1]

35.9.12 Direct-current 3-wire shunt generator with commutating and/or compensating field winding[1]

35.9.13 Direct-current 3-wire compound generator[1]

[1] The broken line - - - indicates where line connection to a symbol is made and is not a part of the symbol.

Figure 2-12 (cont'd.)

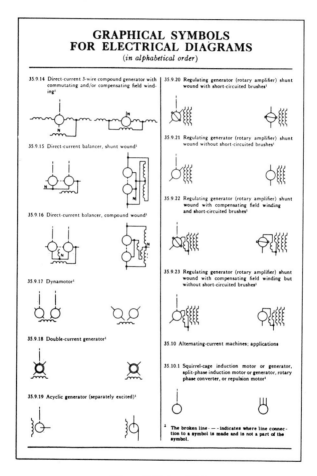

Figure 2-12 (cont'd.)

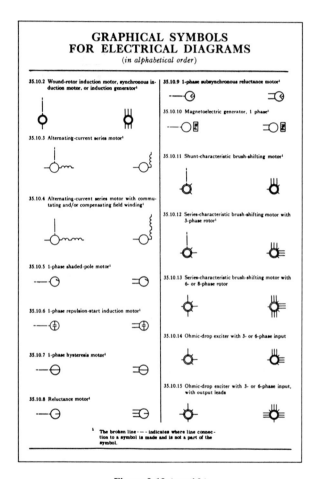

Figure 2-12 (cont'd.)

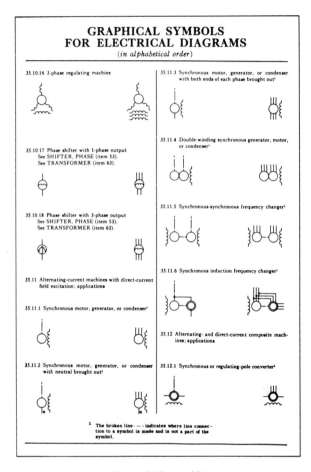

GRAPHICAL SYMBOLS
FOR ELECTRICAL DIAGRAMS
(in alphabetical order)

35.10.16 3-phase regulating machine

35.11.3 Synchronous motor, generator, or condenser with both ends of each phase brought out[1]

35.10.17 Phase shifter with 1-phase output
See SHIFTER, PHASE (item 53).
See TRANSFORMER (item 63).

35.11.4 Double-winding synchronous generator, motor, or condenser[1]

35.10.18 Phase shifter with 3-phase output
See SHIFTER, PHASE (item 53).
See TRANSFORMER (item 63).

35.11.5 Synchronous-synchronous frequency changer[1]

35.11 Alternating-current machines with direct-current field excitation; applications

35.11.1 Synchronous motor, generator, or condenser[1]

35.11.6 Synchronous induction frequency changer[1]

35.12 Alternating- and direct-current composite machines; applications

35.11.2 Synchronous motor, generator, or condenser with neutral brought out[1]

35.12.1 Synchronous or regulating-pole converter[1]

[1] The broken line - — - indicates where line connection to a symbol is made and is not a part of the symbol.

Figure 2-12 (cont'd.)

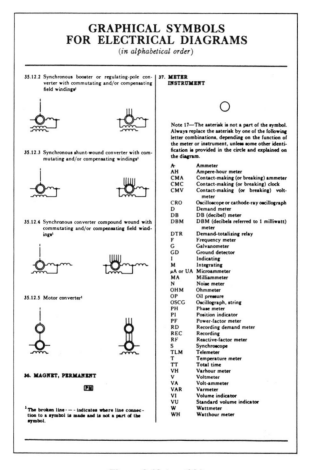

GRAPHICAL SYMBOLS
FOR ELECTRICAL DIAGRAMS
(in alphabetical order)

35.12.2 Synchronous booster or regulating-pole converter with commutating and/or compensating field windings[1]

35.12.3 Synchronous shunt-wound converter with commutating and/or compensating windings[1]

35.12.4 Synchronous converter compound wound with commutating and/or compensating field windings[1]

35.12.5 Motor converter[1]

36. MAGNET, PERMANENT

[1] The broken line - — - indicates where line connection to a symbol is made and is not a part of the symbol.

37. METER
INSTRUMENT

Note 17—The asterisk is not a part of the symbol. Always replace the asterisk by one of the following letter combinations, depending on the function of the meter or instrument, unless some other identification is provided in the circle and explained on the diagram.

A-	Ammeter
AH	Ampere-hour meter
CMA	Contact-making (or breaking) ammeter
CMC	Contact-making (or breaking) clock
CMV	Contact-making (or breaking) voltmeter
CRO	Oscilloscope or cathode-ray oscillograph
D	Demand meter
DB	DB (decibel) meter
DBM	DBM (decibels referred to 1 milliwatt) meter
DTR	Demand-totalizing relay
F	Frequency meter
G	Galvanometer
GD	Ground detector
I	Indicating
M	Integrating
μA or UA	Microammeter
MA	Milliammeter
N	Noise meter
OHM	Ohmmeter
OP	Oil pressure
OSCG	Oscillograph, string
PH	Phase meter
PI	Position indicator
PF	Power-factor meter
RD	Recording demand meter
REC	Recording
RF	Reactive-factor meter
S	Synchroscope
TLM	Telemeter
T	Temperature meter
TT	Total time
VH	Varhour meter
V	Voltmeter
VA	Volt-ammeter
VAR	Varmeter
VI	Volume indicator
VU	Standard volume indicator
W	Wattmeter
WH	Watthour meter

Figure 2-12 (cont'd.)

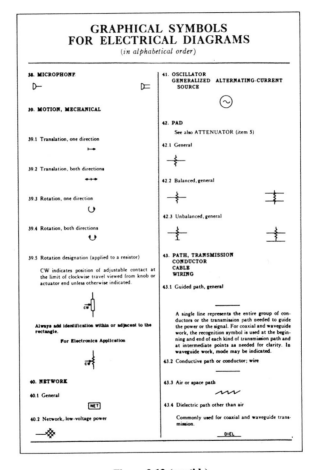

GRAPHICAL SYMBOLS
FOR ELECTRICAL DIAGRAMS
(in alphabetical order)

38. MICROPHONE

39. MOTION, MECHANICAL

39.1 Translation, one direction

39.2 Translation, both directions

39.3 Rotation, one direction

39.4 Rotation, both directions

39.5 Rotation designation (applied to a resistor)

CW indicates position of adjustable contact at the limit of clockwise travel viewed from knob or actuator end unless otherwise indicated.

Always add identification within or adjacent to the rectangle.

For Electronics Application

40. NETWORK

40.1 General

40.2 Network, low-voltage power

41. OSCILLATOR
GENERALIZED   ALTERNATING-CURRENT
SOURCE

42. PAD

See also ATTENUATOR (item 5)

42.1 General

42.2 Balanced, general

42.3 Unbalanced, general

43. PATH, TRANSMISSION
CONDUCTOR
CABLE
WIRING

43.1 Guided path, general

A single line represents the entire group of conductors or the transmission path needed to guide the power or the signal. For coaxial and waveguide work, the recognition symbol is used at the beginning and end of each kind of transmission path and at intermediate points as needed for clarity. In waveguide work, mode may be indicated.

43.2 Conductive path or conductor; wire

43.3 Air or space path

43.4 Dielectric path other than air

Commonly used for coaxial and waveguide transmission.

DIEL

Figure 2-12 (cont'd.)

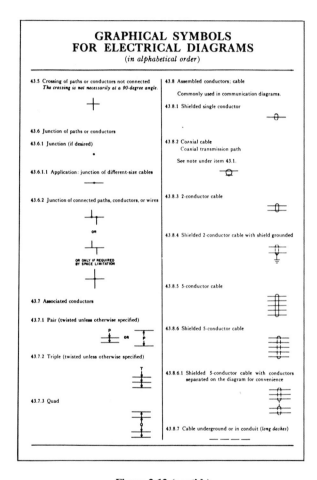

GRAPHICAL SYMBOLS
FOR ELECTRICAL DIAGRAMS
(in alphabetical order)

43.5 Crossing of paths or conductors not connected
The crossing is not necessarily at a 90-degree angle.

43.6 Junction of paths or conductors

43.6.1 Junction (if desired)

43.6.1.1 Application: junction of different-size cables

43.6.2 Junction of connected paths, conductors, or wires

OR

OR ONLY IF REQUIRED
BY SPACE LIMITATION

43.7 Associated conductors

43.7.1 Pair (twisted unless otherwise specified)

P OR P

43.7.2 Triple (twisted unless otherwise specified)

43.7.3 Quad

43.8 Assembled conductors; cable

Commonly used in communication diagrams.

43.8.1 Shielded single conductor

43.8.2 Coaxial cable
Coaxial transmission path

See note under item 43.1.

43.8.3 2-conductor cable

43.8.4 Shielded 2-conductor cable with shield grounded

43.8.5 5-conductor cable

43.8.6 Shielded 5-conductor cable

43.8.6.1 Shielded 5-conductor cable with conductors separated on the diagram for convenience

43.8.7 Cable underground or in conduit *(long dashes)*

Figure 2-12 (cont'd.)

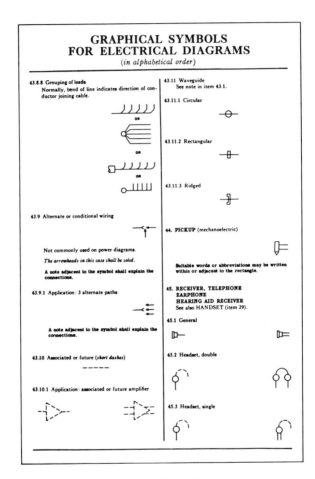

**GRAPHICAL SYMBOLS
FOR ELECTRICAL DIAGRAMS**

(in alphabetical order)

43.8.8 Grouping of leads
Normally, bend of line indicates direction of conductor joining cable.

OR

OR

OR

43.9 Alternate or conditional wiring

Not commonly used on power diagrams.

The arrowheads in this case shall be solid.

A note adjacent to the symbol shall explain the connections.

43.9.1 Application: 3 alternate paths

A note adjacent to the symbol shall explain the connections.

43.10 Associated or future (*short dashes*)

43.10.1 Application: associated or future amplifier

43.11 Waveguide
See note in item 43.1.

43.11.1 Circular

43.11.2 Rectangular

43.11.3 Ridged

44. PICKUP (mechanoelectric)

Suitable words or abbreviations may be written within or adjacent to the rectangle.

**45. RECEIVER, TELEPHONE
EARPHONE
HEARING AID RECEIVER**
See also HANDSET (item 29).

45.1 General

45.2 Headset, double

45.3 Headset, single

Figure 2-12 (cont'd.)

GRAPHICAL SYMBOLS
FOR ELECTRICAL DIAGRAMS
(in alphabetical order)

46. RECTIFIER

46.1 Electron-tube rectifier

See TUBE, ELECTRON (item 64).

46.1.1 Pool-type-cathode power rectifier

46.2 Metallic rectifier; asymmetrical varistor; crystal diode; electrolytic rectifier

Arrow shows direction of forward (easy) current as indicated by direct-current ammeter. *The arrowhead in this case shall be filled.*

46.2.1 Full-wave bridge type

46.3 On connection or wiring diagrams, rectifier may be shown with terminals and polarity marking. Heavy line may be used to indicate nameplate or positive polarity end.

47. REGULATOR, SPEED (Contact-making governor) Contacts open or closed as required; (shown here as closed).

48. RELAY

See also CONTACTOR (item 16)

Fundamental symbols for contacts, mechanical connections, coils, etc., are the basis of relay symbols and should be used to represent relays on complete diagrams.

The following letter combinations may be used with any relay symbol. The requisite number of these combinations may be used when a relay possesses more than one special feature.

AC Alternating-current or ringing relay
D   Differential
DB Double biased (biased in both directions)
DP Dashpot
EP Electrically polarized
†FO Fast operate
†FR Fast release
MG Marginal
NB No bias
NR Nonreactive
P   Magnetically polarized using biasing spring, or having magnet bias
SA Slow operate and slow release
SO Slow operate
SR Slow release
SW Sandwich wound to improve balance to longitudinal currents

† Used where unusually fast operation or fast releasing is essential to the circuit operation.

The proper poling for a polarized relay shall be shown by the use of + and − designations applied to the winding leads. The interpretation of this shall be that current in the direction indicated shall move or tend to move the armature toward the contact shown nearest the core on the diagram. If the relay is equipped with numbered terminals, the proper terminal numbers shall also be shown.

48.1 Basic

48.2 Relay coil

 or ⌇ or

Always indicate the device designation within the circle.

48.2.1 Semicircular dot indicates inner end of winding

Figure 2-12 (cont'd.)

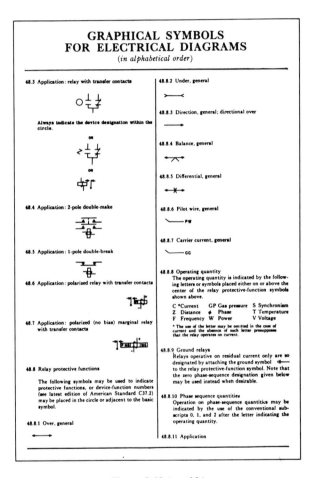

Figure 2-12 (cont'd.)

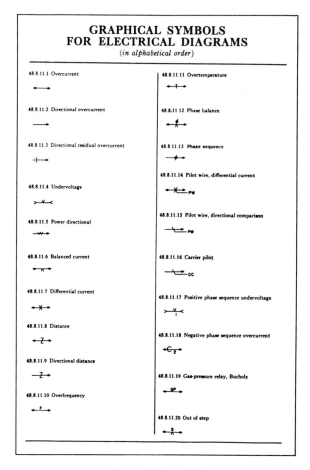

GRAPHICAL SYMBOLS
FOR ELECTRICAL DIAGRAMS
(in alphabetical order)

48.8.11.1 Overcurrent

48.8.11.11 Overtemperature

48.8.11.2 Directional overcurrent

48.8.11 12 Phase balance

48.8.11.3 Directional residual overcurrent

48.8.11.13 Phase sequence

48.8.11.14 Pilot wire, differential current

48.8.11.4 Undervoltage

48.8.11.15 Pilot wire, directional comparison

48.8.11.5 Power directional

48.8.11.6 Balanced current

48.8.11.16 Carrier pilot

48.8.11.7 Differential current

48.8.11.17 Positive phase sequence undervoltage

48.8.11.8 Distance

48.8.11.18 Negative phase sequence overcurrent

48.8.11.9 Directional distance

48.8.11.19 Gas-pressure relay, Bucholz

48.8.11.10 Overfrequency

48.8.11.20 Out of step

Figure 2-12 (cont'd.)

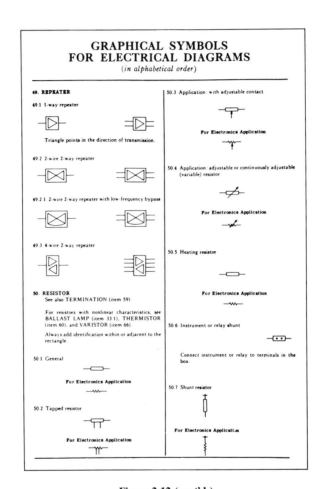

GRAPHICAL SYMBOLS
FOR ELECTRICAL DIAGRAMS
(in alphabetical order)

49. REPEATER

49.1 1-way repeater

Triangle points in the direction of transmission.

49.2 2-wire 2-way repeater

49.2.1 2-wire 2-way repeater with low-frequency bypass

49.3 4-wire 2-way repeater

50. RESISTOR
See also TERMINATION (item 59).

For resistors with nonlinear characteristics, see BALLAST LAMP (item 33.1), THERMISTOR (item 60), and VARISTOR (item 66).

Always add identification within or adjacent to the rectangle.

50.1 General

For Electronics Application

50.2 Tapped resistor

For Electronics Application

50.3 Application: with adjustable contact

For Electronics Application

50.4 Application: adjustable or continuously adjustable (variable) resistor

For Electronics Application

50.5 Heating resistor

For Electronics Application

50.6 Instrument or relay shunt

Connect instrument or relay to terminals in the box.

50.7 Shunt resistor

For Electronics Application

Figure 2-12 (cont'd.)

GRAPHICAL SYMBOLS
FOR ELECTRICAL DIAGRAMS
(in alphabetical order)

51. RESONATOR
Excluding piezoelectric and magnetostriction devices.

51.1 General

Commonly used for coaxial and waveguide transmission.

51.2 Applications

51.2.1 Resonator with mode suppression coupled by an E-plane aperture to a guided transmission path and by a loop to a coaxial path.

51.2.2 Tunable resonator having adjustable Q coupled by a probe to a coaxial system.

51.2.3 Tunable resonator with direct-current ground connected to an electron device and adjustably coupled by an E-plane aperture to a rectangular waveguide.

52. SHIELD
SHIELDING (short dashes)
Normally used for electric or magnetic shielding. When used for other shielding, a note should so indicate. For typical applications see:
CAPACITOR (item 8.1.1)
PATH, TRANSMISSION (items 43.8.1, 43.8.4, and 43.8.6)
TRANSFORMER (items 63.2.1 and 63.2.2)
TUBE, ELECTRON (item 64.7)

53. SHIFTER, PHASE
For power circuits see MACHINE, ROTATING (items 35.10.17 and 35.10.18).

53.1 General

53.2 3-wire or 3-phase

53.2.1 Application: adjustable

54. SOUNDER, TELEGRAPH

55. SUPPRESSION, MODE
Commonly used in coaxial and waveguide transmission.

56. SWITCH
See also FUSE (item 27); CONTACT, ELECTRIC (item 15);

Fundamental symbols for contacts, mechanical connections, etc., may be used for switch symbols.

The standard method of showing switches is in a position with no operating force applied. For switches that may be in any one of two or more positions with no operating force applied and for switches actuated by some mechanical device (as in air-pressure, liquid-level, rate-of-flow, etc., switches), a clarifying note may be necessary to explain the point at which the switch functions.

When the basic switch symbols in items 56.1 through 56.4 are shown on a diagram in the closed position, terminals must be added for clarity.

Figure 2-12 (cont'd.)

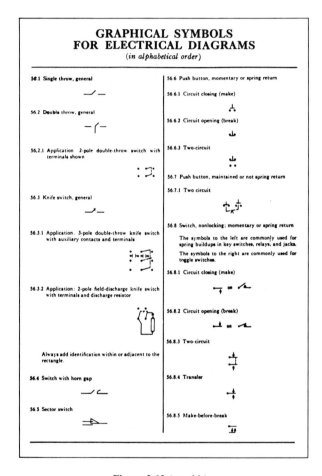

GRAPHICAL SYMBOLS
FOR ELECTRICAL DIAGRAMS
(in alphabetical order)

56.1 Single throw, general	56.6 Push button, momentary or spring return
	56.6.1 Circuit closing (make)
56.2 Double throw, general	
	56.6.2 Circuit opening (break)
56.2.1 Application 2-pole double-throw switch with terminals shown	56.6.3 Two-circuit
	56.7 Push button, maintained or not spring return
56.3 Knife switch, general	56.7.1 Two circuit
56.3.1 Application. 3-pole double-throw knife switch with auxiliary contacts and terminals	56.8 Switch, nonlocking; momentary or spring return
	The symbols to the left are commonly used for spring buildups in key switches, relays, and jacks. The symbols to the right are commonly used for toggle switches.
	56.8.1 Circuit closing (make)
56.3.2 Application: 2-pole field-discharge knife switch with terminals and discharge resistor	
	56.8.2 Circuit opening (break)
	56.8.3 Two-circuit
Always add identification within or adjacent to the rectangle.	
56.4 Switch with horn gap	56.8.4 Transfer
56.5 Sector switch	56.8.5 Make-before-break

Figure 2-12 (cont'd.)

GRAPHICAL SYMBOLS
FOR ELECTRICAL DIAGRAMS
(in alphabetical order)

56.9 Switch, locking

The symbols to the left are commonly used for spring buildups in key switches, relays, and jacks.

The symbols to the right are commonly used for toggle switches.

56.9.1 Circuit closing (make)

56.9.2 Circuit opening (break)

56.9.3 Transfer, 2-position

56.9.4 Transfer, 3-position

56.9.5 Make-before-break

56.10 Switch, combination locking and nonlocking
See also item 56.11.
Commonly used for toggle-switches.

56.10.1 3-position 1-pole: circuit closing (make), off, momentary circuit closing (make)

56.10.2 3-position 2-pole: circuit closing (make), off, momentary circuit closing (make)

56.11 Switch, key-type, applications

56.11.1 2-position with locking transfer and break contacts

56.11.2 3-position with nonlocking transfer and locking break contacts

56.11.3 3-position, multicontact combination

56.11.4 2-position, half of key switch normally operated, multicontact combination

56.12 Selector or multiposition switch

The position in which the switch is shown may be indicated by a note or designation of switch position.

56.12.1 General (for power and control diagrams)
Any number of transmission paths may be shown.

56.12.2 Break-before-make, nonshorting (nonbridging) during contact transfer

Figure 2-12 (cont'd.)

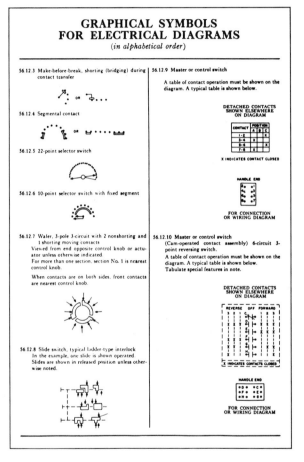

**GRAPHICAL SYMBOLS
FOR ELECTRICAL DIAGRAMS**
(*in alphabetical order*)

Figure 2-12 (cont'd.)

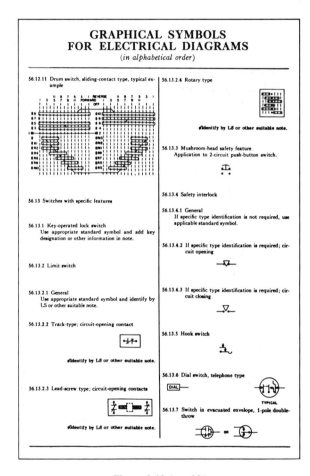

GRAPHICAL SYMBOLS
FOR ELECTRICAL DIAGRAMS
(*in alphabetical order*)

56.12.11 Drum switch, sliding-contact type, typical example

56.13 Switches with specific features

56.13.1 Key-operated lock switch
Use appropriate standard symbol and add key designation or other information in note.

56.13.2 Limit switch

56.13.2.1 General
Use appropriate standard symbol and identify by LS or other suitable note.

56.13.2.2 Track-type; circuit-opening contact

*Identify by LS or other suitable note.

56.13.2.3 Lead-screw type; circuit-opening contacts

*Identify by LS or other suitable note.

56.13.2.4 Rotary type

*Identify by LS or other suitable note.

56.13.3 Mushroom-head safety feature
Application to 2-circuit push-button switch.

56.13.4 Safety interlock

56.13.4.1 General
If specific type identification is not required, use applicable standard symbol.

56.13.4.2 If specific type identification is required; circuit opening

56.13.4.3 If specific type identification is required; circuit closing

56.13.5 Hook switch

56.13.6 Dial switch, telephone type

TYPICAL

56.13.7 Switch in evacuated envelope, 1-pole double-throw

Figure 2-12 (cont'd.)

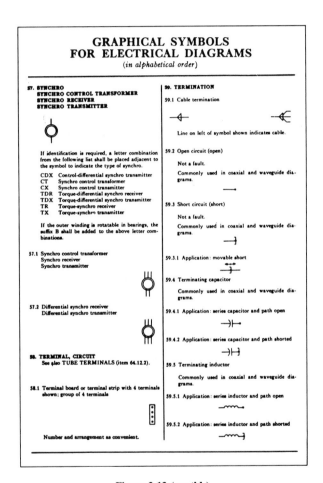

GRAPHICAL SYMBOLS
FOR ELECTRICAL DIAGRAMS
(in alphabetical order)

57. SYNCHRO
SYNCHRO CONTROL TRANSFORMER
SYNCHRO RECEIVER
SYNCHRO TRANSMITTER

If identification is required, a letter combination from the following list shall be placed adjacent to the symbol to indicate the type of synchro.

CDX   Control-differential synchro transmitter
CT   Synchro control transformer
CX   Synchro control transmitter
TDR   Torque-differential synchro receiver
TDX   Torque-differential synchro transmitter
TR   Torque-synchro receiver
TX   Torque-synchro transmitter

If the outer winding is rotatable in bearings, the suffix B shall be added to the above letter combinations.

57.1 Synchro control transformer
Synchro receiver
Synchro transmitter

57.2 Differential synchro receiver
Differential synchro transmitter

58. TERMINAL, CIRCUIT
See also TUBE TERMINALS (item 64.12.2).

58.1 Terminal board or terminal strip with 4 terminals shown; group of 4 terminals

Number and arrangement as convenient.

59. TERMINATION

59.1 Cable termination

Line on left of symbol shown indicates cable.

59.2 Open circuit (open)

Not a fault.

Commonly used in coaxial and waveguide diagrams.

59.3 Short circuit (short)

Not a fault.

Commonly used in coaxial and waveguide diagrams.

59.3.1 Application: movable short

59.4 Terminating capacitor

Commonly used in coaxial and waveguide diagrams.

59.4.1 Application: series capacitor and path open

59.4.2 Application: series capacitor and path shorted

59.5 Terminating inductor

Commonly used in coaxial and waveguide diagrams.

59.5.1 Application: series inductor and path open

59.5.2 Application: series inductor and path shorted

Figure 2-12 (cont'd.)

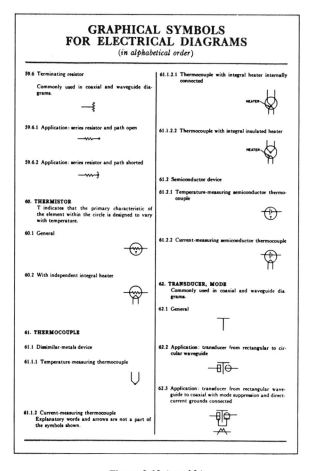

**GRAPHICAL SYMBOLS
FOR ELECTRICAL DIAGRAMS**
(*in alphabetical order*)

59.6 Terminating resistor

Commonly used in coaxial and waveguide diagrams.

59.6.1 Application: series resistor and path open

59.6.2 Application: series resistor and path shorted

60. THERMISTOR
T indicates that the primary characteristic of the element within the circle is designed to vary with temperature.

60.1 General

60.2 With independent integral heater

61. THERMOCOUPLE

61.1 Dissimilar-metals device

61.1.1 Temperature-measuring thermocouple

61.1.2 Current-measuring thermocouple
Explanatory words and arrows are not a part of the symbols shown.

61.1.2.1 Thermocouple with integral heater internally connected

61.1.2.2 Thermocouple with integral insulated heater

61.2 Semiconductor device

61.2.1 Temperature-measuring semiconductor thermocouple

61.2.2 Current-measuring semiconductor thermocouple

62. TRANSDUCER, MODE
Commonly used in coaxial and waveguide diagrams.

62.1 General

62.2 Application: transducer from rectangular to circular waveguide

62.3 Application: transducer from rectangular waveguide to coaxial with mode suppression and direct-current grounds connected

Figure 2-12 (cont'd.)

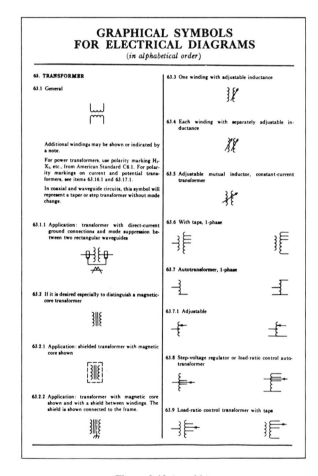

Figure 2-12 (cont'd.)

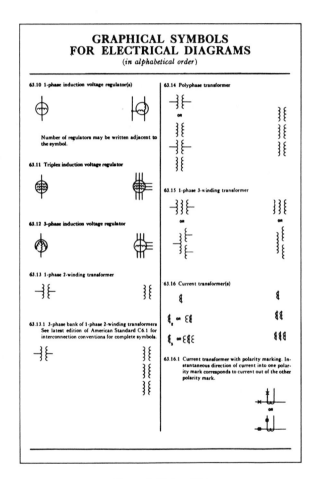

**GRAPHICAL SYMBOLS
FOR ELECTRICAL DIAGRAMS**
(in alphabetical order)

Figure 2-12 (cont'd.)

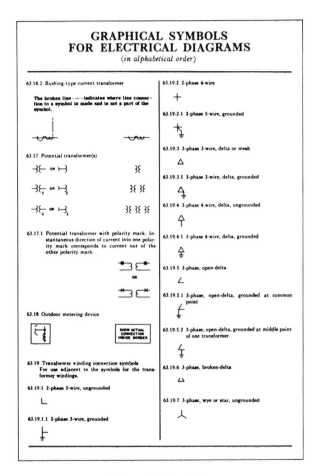

**GRAPHICAL SYMBOLS
FOR ELECTRICAL DIAGRAMS**
(*in alphabetical order*)

Figure 2-12 (cont'd.)

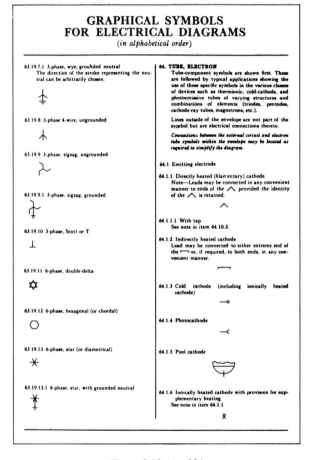

Figure 2-12 (cont'd.)

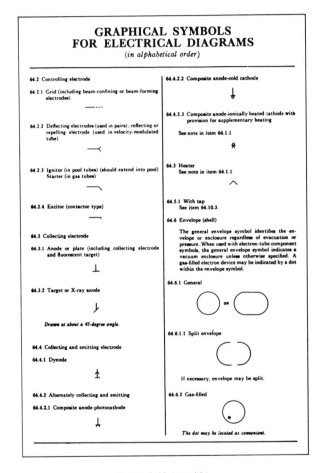

GRAPHICAL SYMBOLS
FOR ELECTRICAL DIAGRAMS
(in alphabetical order)

64.2 Controlling electrode

64.2.1 Grid (including beam-confining or beam-forming electrodes)

64.2.2 Deflecting electrodes (used in pairs); reflecting or repelling electrode (used in velocity-modulated tube)

64.2.3 Ignitor (in pool tubes) (should extend into pool) Starter (in gas tubes)

64.2.4 Excitor (contactor type)

64.3 Collecting electrode

64.3.1 Anode or plate (including collecting electrode and fluorescent target)

64.3.2 Target or X-ray anode

Drawn at about a 45-degree angle.

64.4 Collecting and emitting electrode

64.4.1 Dynode

64.4.2 Alternately collecting and emitting

64.4.2.1 Composite anode-photocathode

64.4.2.2 Composite anode-cold cathode

64.4.2.3 Composite anode-ionically heated cathode with provision for supplementary heating

See note in item 64.1.1

64.5 Heater
See note in item 64.1.1

64.5.1 With tap
See item 64.10.3.

64.6 Envelope (shell)

The general envelope symbol identifies the envelope or enclosure regardless of evacuation or pressure. When used with electron-tube component symbols, the general envelope symbol indicates a vacuum enclosure unless otherwise specified. A gas-filled electron device may be indicated by a dot within the envelope symbol.

64.6.1 General

OR

64.6.1.1 Split envelope

If necessary, envelope may be split.

64.6.2 Gas-filled

The dot may be located as convenient.

Figure 2-12 (cont'd.)

GRAPHICAL SYMBOLS
FOR ELECTRICAL DIAGRAMS
(in alphabetical order)

64.7 Shield
See item 64.10.10.

This is understood to shield against electric fields unless otherwise noted.

64.7.1 Any shield against electric fields that is within the envelope and that is connected to an independent terminal

64.7.2 Outside envelope of X-ray tube

64.8 Coupling
See COUPLING (item 20) and PATH, TRANSMISSION (items 43.8.2 and 43.11).

64.8.1 Coupling by loop (electromagnetic type)

Coupling loop may be shown inside or outside envelope as desired, but if inside it should be shown grounded.

64.9 Resonators (cavity type)

64.9.1 Single-cavity envelope and grid-type associated electrodes

64.9.2 Double-cavity envelope and grid-type associated electrodes

64.9.3 Multicavity magnetron anode and envelope

64.10 General notes

64.10.1 If new symbols are necessary, they should be formed where possible from component symbols. For example, see DYNODE (item 64.4.1), which combines the anode and photocathode convention.

64.10.2 A connection to anode, dynode, pool cathode, photocathode, deflecting electrode, composite anode-photocathode, and composite anode-cold cathode shall be to the center of that symbol. Connection to any other electrode may be shown at either end or both ends of the electrode symbol.

64.10.3 A diagram for a tube having more than one heater or filament shall show only one heater or filament symbol ⋀ unless they have entirely separate connections. If a heater or filament tap is made, either brought out to a terminal or internally connected to another element, it shall be connected at the vertex of the symbol, regardless of the actual division of voltage across the heater or filament.

64.10.4 Standard symbols, such as the inclined arrow for tunability and connecting dotted lines for ganged components, may be added to a tube symbol to extend the meaning of the tube symbol, provided such added feature or component is integral with the tube.

64.10.5 Electric components, such as resistors, capacitors, or inductors, which are integral parts of the tube and are important to its functional operation, shall be shown in the standard manner.

64.10.6 Multiple equipotential cathodes that are directly connected inside the tube shall be shown as a single cathode.

64.10.7 A tube having two or more grids tied internally shall be shown with symbols for each grid, except when the grids are adjacent in the tube structure. Thus, the diagram for a twin pentode having a common screeh-grid connection for each section and for a converter tube having the No. 3 and No. 5 grids connected internally will show separate symbols for each grid. However, a triode where the control grid is physically in the form of two grid windings would show only one grid.

64.10.8 A tube having a grid adjacent to a plate but internally connected to the plate to form a portion of it shall be shown as having a plate only.

Figure 2-12 (cont'd.)

GRAPHICAL SYMBOLS
FOR ELECTRICAL DIAGRAMS
(in alphabetical order)

64.10.9 Associated parts of a circuit, such as focusing coils, deflecting coils, field coils, etc., are not a part of the tube symbol but may be added to the circuit in the form of standard symbols. For example, resonant-type magnetron with permanent magnet may be shown:

64.10.10 External and internal shields, whether integral parts of tubes or not, shall be omitted from the circuit diagram unless the circuit diagram requires their inclusion.

64.10.11 In line with standard drafting practice, straight-line crossovers are recommended.

64.11 Typical applications

64.11.1 Triode with directly heated filamentary cathode and envelope connection to base terminal

64.11.2 Equipotential-cathode pentode showing use of elongated envelope

64.11.3 Equipotential-cathode twin triode illustrating elongated envelope and rule of item 64.10.3.

64.11.4 Typical wiring figure
This figure illustrates how tube symbols may be placed in any convenient position in a circuit.

64.11.5 Cold-cathode gas-filled tube

64.11.5.1 Rectifier; voltage regulator for direct-current operation
See also GLOW LAMP (item 33.3).

64.11.6 Phototube

64.11.6.1 Single-unit, vacuum type

64.11.6.2 Multiplier type

64.11.7 Cathode-ray tube

64.11.7.1 With electric-field deflection

64.11.7.2 For magnetic deflection

Figure 2-12 (cont'd.)

GRAPHICAL SYMBOLS
FOR ELECTRICAL DIAGRAMS
(in alphabetical order)

64.11.8 Mercury-pool tube
See also RECTIFIER (item 46.1.1).

64.11.8.1 With ignitor and control grid

64.11.8.2 With exciter, control grid, and holding anode

64.11.8.3 Single-anode pool-type vapor rectifier with ignitor

64.11.8.4 6-anode metallic-tank pool-type vapor rectifier with exciter, showing rigid-terminal symbol for control connection to tank (pool cathode is insulated from tank)

Anode symbols are located as convenient.

64.11.9 Magnetron

64.11.9.1 Resonant type with coaxial output

64.11.9.2 Transit-time split-plate type with stabilizing deflecting electrodes and internal circuit

64.11.9.3 Tunable, aperture coupled

64.11.10 Velocity-modulation (velocity-variation) tube

64.11.10.1 Reflex klystron, integral cavity, aperture coupled

64.11.10.2 Double-cavity klystron, integral cavity, permanent external-ganged tuning, loop coupled (coupling loop may be shown inside if desired. See item 64.8.1)

64.11.11 Transmit-receive (TR) tube
Gas filled, tunable integral cavity, aperture coupled, with starter.

Figure 2-12 (cont'd.)

GRAPHICAL SYMBOLS
FOR ELECTRICAL DIAGRAMS
(in alphabetical order)

64.11.12 X-ray tube

64.11.12.1 With filamentary cathode and focusing grid (cup). The anode may be cooled by fluid or radiation.

64.11.12.2 With control grid, filamentary cathode, and focusing cup

64.11.12.3 With grounded electrostatic shield

64.11.12.4 Double focus with rotating anode (see note in item 64.10.9)

64.11.12.5 With multiple accelerating electrode, electrostatically and electromagnetically focused (see note in item 64.10.9)

64.12 Basing and terminal connections for connection (wiring) diagrams

Not normally used for schematic diagrams.

64.12.1 Basing orientation symbols

64.12.1.1 For tubes with keyed bases
Explanatory word and arrow are not a part of the symbol shown.

64.12.1.2 For tubes with bayonets, bosses, and other reference points

64.12.2 Tube terminals
The usage of the rigid-envelope-terminal symbol of item 64.12.2.2 includes the indication of any external metallic envelope or conducting coating or casing that has a contact area (as in cathode-ray tubes, metallic "pencil" tubes, etc.). However, where contact to such external metallic elements is made through a base terminal, a dot junction is employed as in item 64.12.3.1 to indicate that voltage applied to this base terminal may make the envelope alive.

Terminal symbols may be added to the composite device symbols where desired without changing the meaning or becoming a part of the symbol.

64.12.2.1 Base terminals
Explanatory words and arrows are not a part of the symbol.

Figure 2-12 (cont'd.)

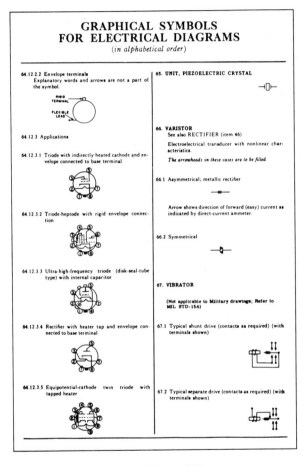

Figure 2-12 (cont'd.)

graphs, such as 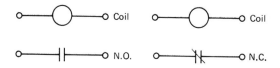 for externally operated disconnect switch, or Ⓝ┘ for a nonfusible safety switch, using both pictographs and abbreviations.

The most common abbreviations found in control diagrams include the following:

SP single pole
ST single throw
DP double pole
DT double throw
3P three pole
2P two pole
NC normally closed contact
NO normally open contact

Normally closed contact means the contact is closed when the relay coil is not energized. Normally open contact means the contact is open when the relay coil is not energized. Contacts will change position when the relay coil is energized. The normally closed contacts will open, and the normally open contacts will close.

Some examples of control symbols and abbreviations are shown in the illustrations that follow. For example, the drawing in Fig. 2-13 represents a single-pole, single-throw (SPST) switch; the contact on the left is normally open, while the one on the right is normally closed. The circuit in Fig. 2-14 represents a single-pole, double-throw (SPDT) switch, while the one in Fig. 2-15 shows double-pole, single-throw (DPST) contacts, one group of the normally open type and the other of the normally closed type. A double-pole, double-throw (DPDT) circuit is shown in Fig. 2-16, while a three-pole, double-throw (3PDT) circuit is represented in Fig. 2-17.

Figure 2-13   Single-pole, single-throw switch.

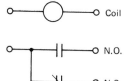

Figure 2-14   Single-pole, double-throw switch.

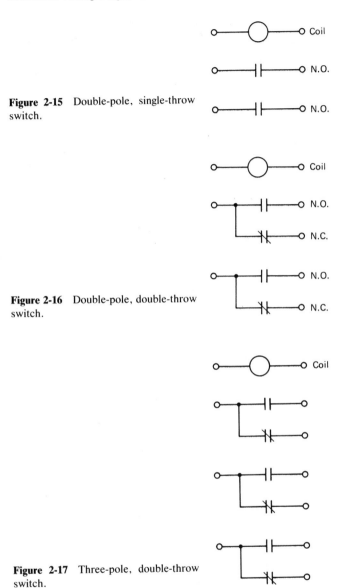

Figure 2-15 Double-pole, single-throw switch.

Figure 2-16 Double-pole, double-throw switch.

Figure 2-17 Three-pole, double-throw switch.

SCHEMATIC WIRING DIAGRAMS

Schematic wiring diagrams represent components in the control system by symbols, the wiring and connection to each, and other detailed information. Sometimes the conductors are shown in an assembly of several wires, which appear as one line on the drawing. When this method is used, each wire should be numbered where it enters the assembly and should keep the same number when it comes out of the assembly to be connected to some component in the system. When reading or using such drawings, if the schematic does not follow this procedure, mark and number the wires yourself.

Although the symbols represent certain components, an exact description of each is usually listed in schedules or else noted on the drawings. Such drawings are seldom, if ever, drawn to scale as an architectural or cabinet drawing would be. They appear in diagrammatic form. In the better drawings, however, the components are arranged in a neat and logical sequence so that they are easily traced and understood.

Electronic schematic diagrams indicate the scheme of plan according to which electronic or control components are connected for a specific purpose. Diagrams are not normally drawn to scale, and the symbols rarely look exactly like the component. Lines joining the symbols representing electronic or control components indicate that the components are connected.

To serve all its intended purposes, the schematic diagram must be accurate. Also, it must be understood by all qualified personnel, and it must provide definite information without ambiguity.

The schematics for a control circuit should indicate all circuits in the device. If they are accurate and well prepared, it will be easy to read and follow an entire closed path in each circuit. If there are interconnections, they will be clearly indicated.

In nearly all cases the conductors connecting the electronic symbols will be drawn either horizontally or vertically. Rarely are they ever slanted.

A dot at the junction of two crossing wires means a connection between the two wires. An absence of a dot in most cases indicates that the wires cross without connecting.

Schematic diagrams are, in effect, shorthand explanations of the manner in which an electronic circuit or group of circuits operates. They make extensive use of symbols and abbreviations. The more commonly used symbols were explained earlier in this chapter. These symbols must be learned to be able to interpret control drawings with the necessary speed required in the field or design department. The use of symbols presumes that the person reading the diagram is reasonably familiar with the operation of the device, and that he or she will be able to assign the correct meaning to the symbols. If the symbols are unusual, a legend will normally be provided to clarify matters.

Every component on a complete schematic diagram usually has a number to identify the component. Supplementary data about such parts are supplied on the diagram or on an accompanying list in the form of a schedule, which describes the component in detail or refers to a common catalog number familiar in the trade.

To interpret schematic diagrams, remember that each circuit must be complete in itself. Each component should be in a closed loop connected by conductors to a source of electric current such as a transformer or line voltage. There will always be a conducting path leading from the source to the component and a return path leading from the component to the source. The path may consist of one or more conductors. Other components may also be in the same loop or in additional loops branching off to other devices. For each electronic component, it must be possible to trace a completed conducting loop to the source.

ELECTRICAL WIRING DIAGRAMS

Complete schematic electrical wiring diagrams used in highly complex heating-control circuits are also represented by symbols. Every wire is either shown by itself or included in an assembly of several wires that appear as one line on the drawing. Figure 2-18 shows a complete schematic wiring diagram for a three-phase, ac magnetic nonreversing motor starter.

Note that this diagram shows the various devices in symbol form and indicates the actual connections of all wires between the devices. The three-wire supply lines are indicated by L_1, L_2, and L_3. The motor terminals of motor M are indicated by T_1, T_2, and T_3. Each line has a thermal overload-protection device (OL) connected in series with normally open line contactors C_1, C_2, and C_3, which are controlled by the magnetic starter coil, C. Each contactor has a pair of contacts that close or open during operation.

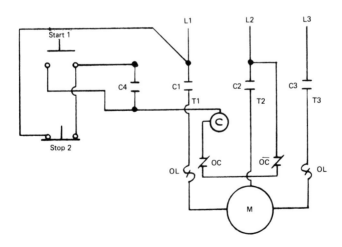

Figure 2-18   Schematic wiring diagram for a three-phase, ac magnetic nonreversing motor starter.

The control station, consisting of start push button 1 and stop push button 2, is connected across lines L_1 and L_2. An auxiliary contactor C_4 is connected in series with the stop push button and in parallel with the start push button. The control circuit also has normally closed overload contactors (OC) connected in series with the magnetic starter coil (C).

Figure 2-19 shows a typical single-line diagram of an industrial power-distribution system. In analyzing this diagram, the utility company will bring its lines to a substation outside the plant building. Air switches, lightning

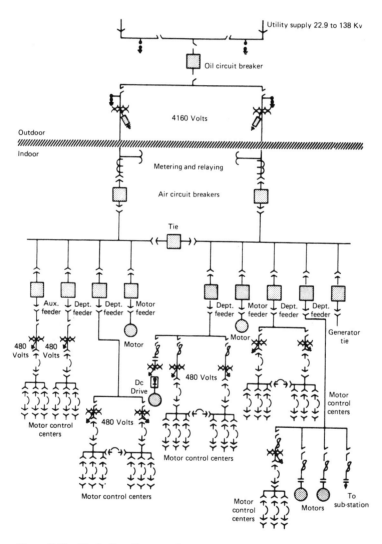

Figure 2-19   Single-line diagram of an industrial power-distribution system.

arresters, single-throw switches, and an oil circuit breaker are provided there. This substation also reduces the primary voltage to 4,160 volts by transformers. Again, lightning arresters and other various disconnecting means are shown.

HVAC DRAWINGS

Mechanical drawings for building construction include plumbing, heating, ventilating, air conditioning, and temperature-control systems. Most of these drawings are highly diagrammatical and are used to locate pipes, fixtures, ductwork, equipment, and the like.

The exact method of showing mechanical layouts on drawings for building construction will vary with the draftsman, engineer, or construction firm. The following is typical for most mechanical drawings.

Plumbing drawings.   Plumbing drawings cover the installation of the plumbing system within a building and on the premises. They cover the complete design and layout of the plumbing system and show floor-plan layouts, cross sections of the building, and detailed drawings.

All domestic cold-water piping is normally laid out on the building floor plans as shown in Fig. 2-20. Note that all valves, stops, and other connections are indicated by symbols. The water lines are indicated by broken lines; one style indicates a cold-water line while another indicates a hot-water line. Always check the legend or symbol list on each set of plumbing drawings, as these symbols could be reversed or altogether different.

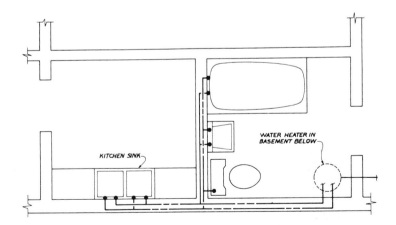

Figure 2-20   Method of showing domestic cold-water piping on a working diagram.

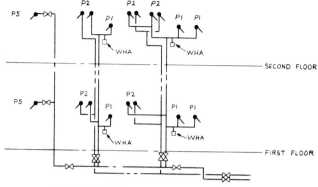

DOMESTIC H & C.W. RISER (TYPICAL) DIAGRAM Nº1
NO SCALE

Figure 2-21 A piping riser diagram.

MECHANICAL DRAWING SYMBOLS

NOTE: THESE ARE STANDARD SYMBOLS AND MAY NOT ALL APPEAR ON THE PROJECT DRAWINGS; HOWEVER, WHEREVER THE SYMBOL ON THE PROJECT DRAWINGS OCCURS, THE ITEM SHALL BE PROVIDED AND INSTALLED.

Symbol	Description	Symbol	Description
——S——	STEAM PIPE	MBH	THOUSAND BTU PER HOUR
———C———	CONDENSATE RETURN PIPE	GPM	GALLONS PER MINUTE
——HWS——	HOT WATER SUPPLY PIPE	CFM	CUBIC FEET PER MINUTE
——HWR——	HOT WATER RETURN PIPE		ROUND
——CWS——	CHILLED WATER SUPPLY PIPE		SQUARE
——CWR——	CHILLED WATER RETURN PIPE	SA	SUPPLY AIR
——HCS——	COMB HOT - CHILLED WATER SUPPLY	RA	RETURN AIR
——HCR——	COMB HOT - CHILLED WATER RETURN	OA	OUTSIDE AIR
——CS——	CONDENSER WATER SUPPLY PIPE	EA	EXHAUST AIR
——CR——	CONDENSER WATER RETURN PIPE	HSWR	HIGH SIDEWALL REGISTER
——D——	DRAIN PIPE FROM COOLING COIL	HSWG	HIGH SIDEWALL GRILLE
——FOS——	FUEL OIL SUPPLY PIPE	LSWR	LOW SIDEWALL REGISTER
——FOR——	FUEL OIL RETURN PIPE	LSWG	LOW SIDEWALL GRILLE
——R——	REFRIGERANT PIPE	CSR	CEILING SUPPLY REGISTER
PIPE RISING		CR	CEILING REGISTER
PIPE TURNING DOWN		CG	CEILING GRILLE
UNION		FR	FLOOR REGISTER
REDUCER - CONCENTRIC		FG	FLOOR GRILLE
REDUCER - ECCENTRIC		CD	CEILING DIFFUSER
STRAINER		TV	TURNING VANES
GATE VALVE		AE	AIR EXTRACTOR
GLOBE VALVE		SD	SPLITTER DAMPER
VALVE IN RISER		MD	MANUAL DAMPER
CHECK VALVE		FD	FIRE DAMPER
PRESSURE REDUCING VALVE		DL	DUCT LINER IN DUCT
PRESSURE RELIEF VALVE		AHU	AIR HANDLING UNIT
SQUARE HEAD COCK		BU	BLOWER UNIT
BALANCING VALVE		FCU	FAN COIL UNIT
3-WAY CONTROL VALVE		HWC	HOT WATER CONVECTOR
2-WAY CONTROL VALVE		UV	UNIT VENTILATOR
PITCH PIPE MINIMUM 1"/40'		WH	WALL HEATER
ANCHOR LOCATION		UH	UNIT HEATER
FLEXIBLE PIPE CONNECTION		WF	WALL FIN RADIATION
IN-LINE PUMP		PRV	POWER ROOF VENTILATOR
BOTTOM TAKE-OFF		UVS	UTILITY VENT SET
TOP TAKE-OFF		PF	PROPELLER FAN
PRESSURE GAUGE		T	THERMOSTAT
THERMOMETER		T$_N$	NIGHT THERMOSTAT
HOT WATER RISER		T$_M$	THERMOSTAT - HEATING ONLY
CHILLED WATER RISER		T$_C$	THERMOSTAT - COOLING ONLY
FAN COIL UNIT			THERMOSTAT - REMOTE BULB
EQUIPMENT AS INDICATED		6'-8"	MOUNTING HEIGHT ABOVE FINISHED FLOOR
AIR INTO REGISTER		NIC	NOT IN CONTRACT
AIR OUT OF REGISTER			
AIR FLOW THRU UNDERCUT OR LOUVERED DOOR			SUPPLY AIR DUCT SECTION
TURNING VANES			RETURN OR EXHAUST DUCT SECTION
AIR EXTRACTOR			FLEXIBLE DUCT CONNECTION

Figure 2-22 Complete HVAC symbol list.

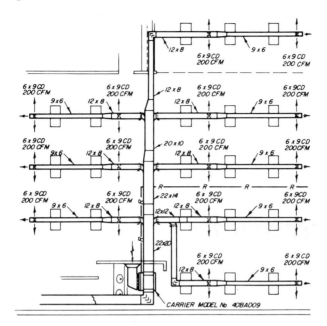

Figure 2-23 Practical applications of symbols shown in Figure 2-22.

Drains and vents in the drawing in Fig. 2-20 are shown by symbols only; no piping is shown in this plan view. When a more detailed description of such drains is called for, a piping rising diagram is sometimes used, such as the one in Fig. 2-21. It diagrammatically shows the arrangement of the drain and vent pipes.

Pipes sizes and other pertinent details are usually indicated by numerals or notes, respectively, and appear immediately adjacent to the component or equipment described. Schedules and written specifications complete the set of plumbing drawings. The schedules normally include the manufacturer's catalog number, pipe connection, size of pipe, and so on, of all plumbing fixtures and similar equipment.

HVAC drawings. Many piping and sheet-metal drawings are encountered on HVAC drawings, this being the most popular method of conveying the necessary information from the designer to the workers on the job. Air ducts are used to carry hot or cooled air to various areas in the home, while piping is used to carry steam and hot water for this type of heating.

A complete list of HVAC symbols is shown in Fig. 2-22, and practical applications are shown in Fig. 2-23.

3
Psychrometrics

Psychrometrics, as applied to HVAC design, deals with measuring and determining the properties of both inside and outside air. The study is also used to establish the conditions of air that will be most comfortable in a given air-conditioning situation.

Many time-consuming calculations are required to measure the properties of air if no aids are used. Fortunately, the psychrometric chart has been developed which greatly simplifies the process. Furthermore, since the computer handles calculations at a rapid pace, it should certainly be considered for such calculations.

In dealing with psychrometrics, certain essential terms must be understood; namely, dry-bulb temperature, wet-bulb temperature, relative humidity, dewpoint, and grains of moisture. These terms are briefly defined as follows:

Dry-bulb temperature. The temperature of air (either inside or out) as measured by a conventional thermometer.

Wet-bulb temperature. The temperature of air (either inside or out) as measured by a conventional thermometer with a wet cloth covering the glass bulb. Before taking the measurement, however, the thermometer is normally fitted with a wire or cord so that it may be rotated or otherwise moved rapidly through the air to be measured.

Relative humidity.   The actual amount of moisture in the air in relation to the maximum moisture the air can hold.

Grains of moisture.   The unit of measurement used to determine the amount of moisture in the air.

Dewpoint temperature.   The temperature at which moisture condenses on a surface.

In relation to the psychrometric chart, these terms can quickly tell many things about the condition of the air. The grains of moisture in the air can be determined either by dewpoint alone or in combination with dry-bulb, wet-bulb, or relative humidity.

The illustration below will help you to locate the lines and scales on the psychrometric chart that represent the terms previously defined. In

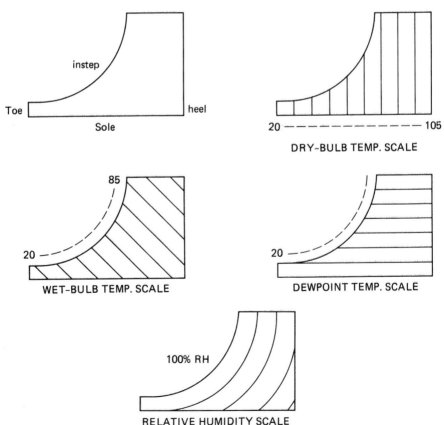

reviewing the chart in the figure, note that it resembles a shoe, with the toe on the left and the heel on the right.

The dry-bulb temperature scale extends along the bottom of the chart (sole) from toe to heel. The dry-bulb lines extend straight up from the sole, and each line represents a degree of temperature.

The wet-bulb temperature scale extends along the instep from the toe to the top of the shoe, while the wet-bulb lines extend diagonally downward to the sole and back of the shoe. Again, each line represents a degree of temperature.

The condensation or dewpoint scale is the same as the wet-bulb scale. However, the dewpoint lines extend horizontally to the back of the shoe. Each line represents each dewpoint temperature.

The relative humidity lines are located along the side of the shoe and follow about the same curve as the instep. The actual instep line is the 100 percent relative humidity line.

The grains of moisture scale follows along the back of the shoe from the heel to the top. The lines are the same as the dewpoint lines.

The following examples will help to illustrate a few of the previously discussed relationships. Let's assume a wet-bulb temperature of 65 degrees F, and a relative humidity of 50 percent. To find the dry-bulb temperature:

1. Locate 65F on wet-bulb scale.
2. Draw a line diagonally downward to the 50 percent rh line.
3. Locate the dry-bulb line that is closest to the intersection of the 65F wet-bulb line and 50 percent rh line.
4. Follow the dry-bulb line straight down to the dry-bulb scale.
5. Read the dry-bulb temperature at that point. Dry-bulb temperature is 78F.

Therefore, at 65F wet-bulb temperature and 50 percent rh, the dry-bulb temperature is 78F.

In the previous example, wet-bulb temperature and relative humidity were used to find dry-bulb temperature. In the next example, relative humidity and dry-bulb temperature will be used to determine the dewpoint temperature.

DRY-BULB, RELATIVE HUMIDITY—DEWPOINT

Given: Dry-bulb   78F
        Relative Humidity   50 percent

In the previous example, it was determined that the dry-bulb temperature was 78 degrees F, with a relative humidity of 50 percent. To find the dewpoint:

1. Find the intersection of the 78F dry-bulb and 50 percent rh lines.
2. Proceed horizontally to the instep line.
3. Read 58F dewpoint temperature.

Therefore, with a dry-bulb temperature of 78 degrees F, and 50 percent relative humidity, the dewpoint temperature is 58 degrees F.

Grains of moisture can also be found on the psychrometric chart by using a procedure similar to that described in the preceding example. Simply find the intersection of the lines listed here and then follow across the chart to the grains of moisture scale.

Finally, moisture can be measured per pound of air or per cubic foot of air. To find the moisture in a cubic foot of air, using the conditions (78F dry-bulb and 65F wet-bulb), proceed as follows:

1. Find the intersection of 78F dry-bulb and 65F wet-bulb.
2. Proceed horizontally along the grains of moisture line to the grains of moisture scale.
3. Read 72 grains.
4. Find the cubic foot scale along the sole of the shoe. The scale starts at 12.5 cubic feet and ends at 14.0 cubic feet. The cubic feet lines extend diagonally from the sole of the shoe to the instep.
5. Again locate the intersection of the 78F dry-bulb and 65F wet-bulb lines.
6. Draw a line parallel to the cubic foot line, from intersection located in item 5, to the sole of the shoe. The line crosses the sole at a point that is over halfway between 13.5 and 14 on the cubic foot scale, say 13.8 cubic feet.
7. Divide 72 grains by 13.8 cubic feet.
8. Moisture in air = 72/13.8 = 5 grains per cubic foot.

So, at 78F dry-bulb and 65F wet-bulb, the moisture in the air can be read as 72 grains per pound, or 5 grains per cubic foot.

In order to obtain full use of the psychrometric chart, it is necessary to understand the working application of several of the basic psychrometric terms that can be determined from it. These basic terms are humidity, dewpoint, and wet-bulb.

Relative humidity, as used in relation to comfort air conditioning, indicates the amount of moisture in the air. Through tests and observations, engineers have discovered that a certain combination of moisture and air temperature is more comfortable than other combinations in different seasons. By applying this knowledge to the psychrometric chart, it is possible to determine what must be done to the outside air before it can be supplied to the room to maintain the most comfortable combination of moisture and temperature in that space.

WINTER AIR CONDITIONING

Let's assume an outdoor dry-bulb temperature of 30 degrees F, along with an outdoor relative humidity of 20 percent. This is a typical outdoor winter weather condition in many parts of the country.

To find the combination of moisture and dry-bulb temperature that falls within the indoor comfort conditions for winter (30 percent to 35 percent rh and 72F to 75F):

1. Place a dot on the psychrometric chart at the intersection of 30F dry-bulb, and 20 percent rh.
2. Place a dot at the intersection of a dry-bulb and relative humidity that falls within the indoor comfort condition range for winter, say 30 percent rh and 72F.
3. Draw a line between the two dots.
4. By following the line from the first to the second intersection, it is possible to see several changes that must be made to bring the air to the desired temperature and relative humidity:
   a. Since relative humidity increases, from 20 percent to 30 percent moisture must be added to the air.
   b. Since the dry-bulb temperature is raised from 35F to 72F, heat must be added.

The same is done for summer air conditioning except the outdoor dry-bulb temperature is 85F and the outdoor relative humidity is 70 percent.

Relative humidity and the psychrometric chart have another practical application: they are used to determine conditions where condensation will form on cold surfaces. For example, the relative humidity at which condensation will not form on a window surface with a temperature of 30 degrees F, and an indoor air temperature of 72 degrees F, may be found by:

1. Use window temperature as dewpoint temperature, and locate 30F on dewpoint scale.
2. Find the intersection of 30F dewpoint and 72F dry-bulb.
3. Read the relative humidity at that point. Relative humidity is approximately 20 percent. This means that if humidity is above 20 percent, moisture will form.

In addition to being useful in areas that are air conditioned, a knowledge of dewpoint is also practical when dealing with unconditioned areas. Air-conditioning supply ducts that run through unconditioned areas are likely to develop condensation.

The dewpoint can be found if the dry-bulb temperature is known in the unconditioned space along with the wet-bulb temperature. Furthermore, the cold-air supply duct surface temperature must be known. To find the dewpoint temperature and whether or not condensation will form on the duct:

1. Locate the intersection of 90F dry-bulb and 75F wet-bulb and move horizontally to the dewpoint scale. The dewpoint is approximately 69F.

2. Use the duct surface temperature as the duct surface dewpoint or condensation temperature. The duct surface condensation temperature is 69F, as given.

3. The temperature at which condensation begins to form on the duct is 69F. Any duct temperature below 69F will cause condensation.

The most common method used to prevent condensation is to wrap the duct with insulation and then apply a vapor seal.

Wet-bulb temperature, in relation to the psychrometric chart, is used to determine the moisture content in the air. Since it is a comparatively simple process to determine the wet-bulb temperature, the wet-bulb scale values on the psychrometric chart become important in helping to determine the value of other psychrometric terms.

PSYCHROMETRIC PROCESSES

The psychrometric processes described herein show the relationship of psychrometric terms to the changes in the air that take place as it goes through the air-conditioning process.

In many air-conditioning systems, air is taken from the room and then returned to the air conditioner, where it is conditioned and then sent back to the room. For a typical air-conditioning process the air in the room picks up heat and moisture when it is mixed with outdoor air. The heat and moisture are taken away as the mixture goes through the air-conditioning apparatus. Then the mixture of air goes back to the room at a condition that is both cool and dry enough to maintain the required room temperature and humidity conditions.

To fully understand this process it is necessary to know the basic types of heating and cooling changes that can be interpreted on the psychrometric chart. These types of changes are latent and sensible heating and cooling.

Latent heat is identified as either latent heat of vaporization or of fusion. Latent heat of vaporization is the amount of heat needed to change a liquid to a vapor. Latent heat of fusion is the amount of heat that must be removed to change a liquid to a solid.

When the latent heat principle is applied to air, the more heat that is added, the higher the moisture content becomes. As latent heat is removed, the moisture content becomes lower.

Sensible heat is any heat that raises the temperature but not the moisture content of a substance. It is called sensible heat because it can be detected by the senses.

When the sensible heat principle is applied to air, the changes are related to air temperature. The air temperature increases as sensible heat is added and decreases as it is taken away.

An air-conditioning process in which sensible heat and latent heat are added at the same time is identified as a heating and humidifying process. For example, air that is to be heated and humidified must go through a heating coil and water spray coil. If air enters the heating coil at 60F dry-bulb, 45F wet-bulb, 23F dewpoint, and 28 percent relative humidity, and leaves the spray coil at 80F db, 62F wb, 50F dp, and 35 percent rh, a reverse psychrometric pattern occurs. Simultaneous cooling and dehumidifying also occur. The line which represents these processes has been given a special label. It is called the sensible heat factor line. This line represents the change that takes place involving both sensible and latent heat. For example, to find the sensible heat of a system with the following conditions:

Cooling load	10 tons
Desired room conditions	80F db
	67F wb
Supply air conditions	60F db
	58F wb

1. Plot the given conditions on a psychrometric chart and draw a straight line between the two points.
2. Continue the line to the sensible heat factor scale at the right-hand side of the chart.
3. Read .80 on the sensible heat factor scale. This means that 80 percent of the heat loss is sensible.

Another form of cooling is evaporative cooling. This is the process in which sensible heat is removed and latent heat is added to the air. This process can be plotted on the psychrometric chart as a diagonal line extending upward and to the left. This type of cooling requires a spray coil. As air passes through the water spray, it gives up heat to the water that is cooler. The vapor that results is carried in the air stream. This way the air is cooled and humidified at the same time.

Still another process that can be plotted on the psychrometric chart is air mixture. A mixture of outdoor air and return air can be plotted on the psychrometric chart, and the resulting air mixture temperature can immediately be determined. Once this is known, it is possible to determine the treatment that is required. For example, given:

Total air quantity required	10,000 cfm
Return air quantity	9,000 cfm
Return air temperature	80 F db and 63F eb
Outdoor air quantity	1,000 cfm
Outdoor air temperature	90 db and 75F wb

To find the dry-bulb temperature and the wet-bulb temperature of air mixture:

1. Plot return air and outdoor air conditions on the psychrometric chart and connect with a line.
2. Determine the percentage of return air used:

Total air	10,000 cfm
Return air	9,000 cfm
Percent return air used	9,000/
	10,000 = .90

3. Determine the dry-bulb temperature difference between return air and outdoor air: 90F − 80F = 10F
4. Determine the mixture of dry-bulb and wet-bulb temperatures:
   a. Multiply the dry-bulb temperature difference by the percent return air: 10 × .90 = 9
   b. Subtract 9 from the outdoor air dry-bulb temperature: 90 − 9 = 81. Mixture dry-bulb temperature = 81F.
   c. Proceed up the 81F dry-bulb line and intersect the line connecting the return air and outdoor air temperatures. Read the wet-bulb temperature at the point of intersection. Wet-bulb temperature of the mixture is 63.5F.

Another process is the bypass process. Bypass air flows through a coil but does not actually touch the coil's surface. If the velocity of the air passing over the coil surface is low, more of the air contacts the surface than when the velocity is high. In actual practice, bypass factors for cooling coils are determined before installation through tests and calculations.

Many cooling coils are rated according to apparatus dewpoint and, obviously, this temperature is important in selecting and testing the coils also.

In addition to the process described previously, there are two psychrometric concepts that require further description. These are specific volume and enthalpy. Specific volume involves the space occupied by air, and enthalpy relates to total heat content of the air.

Specific volume is the number of cubic feet occupied by one pound of air at various conditions of temperature and pressure. Another area concerning specific volume is air density. Since air density affects equipment such as fans and fan motors, specific volume is important in its relationship to fan and motor size.

With regard to the psychrometric chart, the specific volume scale extends along the sole of the chart from 12.5 cubic feet to 14.5 cubic feet. The specific volume lines represent cubic feet per pound of air and appear diagonally from the instep to the sole of the chart.

For example, find the specific volume when the air temperature is 56 degrees F.

1. Find 56F db on dry-bulb scale at the bottom of the psychrometric chart.
2. Read 13.0 cubic feet at that point. Specific volume is 13.0 cubic feet per pound of air.

In psychrometric terms, enthalpy defines the heat and moisture in the air. It is measured in Btu/lb of air. The enthalpy lines on the psychrometric chart are the same as the wet-bulb lines. They can be used to measure the change that takes place in a given psychrometric process.

For example, find the sensible heat removed from an area with the following specifications:

Initial dry-bulb temperature   78F
Initial wet-bulb temperature   65F
Final dry-bulb temperature   55F
Final wet-bulb temperature   50F

1. Read enthalpy at the intersection of the horizontal and vertical lines of the triangle. Enthalpy is 26 Btu.
2. Read enthalpy at final condition of the air. Enthalpy is 21.3 Btu.
3. Sensible heat removed is 23 − 20.3 = 2.7 Btu/lb of air.

The psychrometric processes described previously included cooling and humidifying, cooling and dehumidifying, and heating and humidifying. All are accomplished by using water spray coils inside of a spray chamber.

Cooling and humidifying are also known as an evaporative cooling process. It is plotted on the psychrometric chart as a line that follows up the wet-bulb line. The spray water lowers the dry-bulb temperature and raises the dewpoint until the dry-bulb, dewpoint, and wet-bulb temperatures are the same.

Cooling and dehumidifying are used to remove sensible heat and latent heat as air passes through the chilled water sprays and the dry-bulb, wet-bulb, and dewpoint are removed.

One necessary step is the cooling tower operation, which disposes of heat removed from the refrigerant by the water in the condenser. The water goes from the condenser to the cooling tower where it is sprayed into the air flowing through the cooling tower. The air picks up heat from the water and releases it into the atmosphere.

Finally, the heating and humidification process uses recirculating water sprays and a steam-water heater. As the water passes through the heater, it picks up heat. Then the water is sprayed into the stream of cool air. This causes the water to give up some of its heat, as the water evaporates. This finally will add moisture to the air.

4
Residential Heating Equipment

A properly designed heating system is one of the greatest comforts and conveniences any home can offer. Besides automatically maintaining a comfortable temperature inside the home when it's cold outside, a heating system can provide the correct amount of moisture in the air; remove dirt, bacteria, smoke, pollen, and other impurities; and provide continually circulating fresh air. By the same token, a cooling system not only keeps a home cool during hot weather, it also controls the humidity—keeping it at a comfortable level.

In selecting heating and cooling equipment for the home, however, there are other factors that must be considered besides comfort. The living habits of the family who resides in the home is one big factor. How much time is actually spent at home? How much unoccupied space is in the house? Does one member of the household—like an elderly relative—like the temperature in his or her room to be at least 78 degrees F, while the rest of the family prefers 70 degrees F? How many bedrooms are vacant most of the time? All of these are factors to consider when selecting an HVAC system for the home.

To some extent, the construction features of the house to be conditioned will dictate the type of heating system to use. Other questions to consider are:

1. Does the house have a basement?
2. Is it feasible to install ductwork in the existing structure, or would this type of installation require too much cutting and patching?
3. Does the owner want (and can afford) the best, or should the system be of fundamental design—one to which the owners can add later?
4. Will the home require maintaining a constant temperature 24 hours a day, or do family members need heat quickly when they return home in the evening?

Another consideration is the type of fuel to use. The selection will mostly be determined by the location of the house, as the distance from the house to fuel sources affects the fuel cost. But initial fuel cost is not always a good indication of the type to select. A fuel that costs more initially but provides clean and automatically controlled heat could be the cheapest in the long run. This may not always be the case, but should be considered.

ELECTRIC HEAT

Less than 25 years ago, electric heating units were used only for supplemental heat in small, seldom-used areas of the home, such as a laundry room or workshop, or in vacation homes on chilly autumn nights. Today, however, electric heat is used extensively in both new and renovated homes.

In addition to the fact that electricity is the cleanest fuel available, electric heat is usually the least expensive to install and maintain. Individual room heaters are very inexpensive compared to furnaces and ductwork required in oil and gas forced-air systems, no chimney is required, no utility room is necessary since there is no furnace or boiler, and the installation time and labor are less. Combine all these features and we have a heating system that ranks with the best.

Several types of electric heating units are available (see Fig. 4-1) and a description of each will help you decide which will best suit your needs, and also help in repair and maintenance of such units.

Electric baseboard heaters. Electric baseboard heaters are mounted on the floor along the baseboard, preferably on outside walls under windows for the most efficient operation. It is absolutely noiseless in operation and is the type most often used for heating residential occupancies. The ease with which each room or area may be controlled separately is another great advantage of this heater. Living areas can be heated to, say, 70 degrees F; bedroom heat lowered to, say 55 degrees F, for sleeping comfort; and unused areas may be turned off completely.

Electric baseboard units may be mounted on practically any surface (wood, plaster, drywall, and so on), but if polystyrene foam insulation is

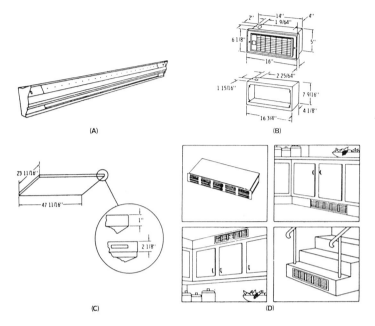

Figure 4-1 Several types of electric heating units: (a) electric baseboard, (b) fan-forced wall units, (c) radiant ceiling panel, and (d) four applications of kick-space heaters.

used near the unit, a 3/4-in. (minimum) ventilated spacer strip must be used between the heater and the wall. In such cases, the heater should also be elevated above the floor or rug to allow ventilation to flow from the floor upward over the total heater space.

One complaint received over the years about this type of heater has been wall discoloration directly above the heating units. When this problem occurred, the reason was almost always traced to one or more of the following:

1. High wattage per square foot of heating element.
2. Heavy smoking by occupants.
3. Poor housekeeping.

Radiant ceiling heaters. Radiant ceiling heaters are often used in bathrooms and similar areas so that the entire room does not have to be overheated to meet the need for extra warmth after a bath or shower. They are also used in larger areas, such as a garage or basement, or for spot-warming a person standing at a workbench.

Most of these units are rated from 800 to 1,500 watts (W) and normally operate on 120-volt circuits. As with most electric units, they may be controlled by a remote thermostat, but since they are usually used for supplemental heat, a conventional wall switch is often used. They are quickly and easily mounted on an outlet box in much the same way as conventional lighting fixtures. In fact, where very low wattage is used, ceiling heaters may often be installed by merely replacing the ceiling lighting fixture with a heater.

Radiant heating panels. Radiant heating panels are commonly manufactured in 2-ft by 4-ft sizes and are rated at 500 watts. They may be located on ceilings or walls to provide radiant heat that spreads evenly through the room. Each room may be controlled by its own thermostat. Since this type of heater may be mounted on the ceiling, its use allows complete freedom for room decor, furniture placement, and drapery arrangement. Most are finished in beige to blend in with nearly any room or furniture color.

Units mounted on the ceiling give the best results when located parallel to, and approximately 2 ft from, the outside wall. However, this type of unit may also be mounted on walls.

Electric infrared heaters. Rays from infrared heaters do not heat the air through which they travel. Rather, they heat only persons and certain objects that they strike. Therefore, infrared heaters are designed to deliver heat into controlled areas for the efficient warming of people and surfaces both indoors and outdoors (such as to heat persons on a patio on a chilly night or around the perimeter of an outdoor swimming pool). This type of heater is excellent for heating a person standing at a workbench without heating the entire room, melting snow from steps or porches, sunlike heat over outdoor areas, and similar applications.

Some of the major advantages of infrared heat include:

1. No warm-up period is required. Heat is immediate.
2. Heat rays are confined to the desired areas.
3. They are easy to install, as no ducts, vents, and so on, are required.
4. The infrared quartz lamps provide some light in addition to heat.

When installing this type of heating unit, never mount the heater closer than 24 inches from vertical walls unless the specific heating unit is designed for closer installation. Read the manufacturer's instructions carefully.

Forced-air wall heaters. Forced-air wall heaters are designed to bring quick heat into an area where the sound of a quiet fan will not be disturbing. Some are very noisy. Most of these units are equipped with a built-in thermostat with a sensor mounted in the intake air stream. Some types are available for mounting on high walls or even ceilings, but the additional force required to move the air to a usable area produces even more noise.

Floor insert convection heaters.   Floor insert convection heaters require no wall space, as they fit into the floor. They are best suited for placement beneath conventional or sliding glass doors to form an effective draft barrier. All are equipped with safety devices, such as a thermal cutout to disconnect the heating element automatically in the event that normal operating temperatures are exceeded.

Floor insert convector heaters may be installed in both old and new homes by cutting through the floor, inserting the metal housing and wiring, according to the manufacturer's instructions. A heavy-gauge floor grille then fits over the entire unit.

Electric kick-space heaters.   Modern kitchens contain so many appliances and so much cabinet space for the convenience of the owner that there often is no room to install electric heaters except on the ceiling. Therefore, a kick-space heater was added to the lines of electric heating manufacturers to overcome this problem.

For the most comfort, kick-space heaters should not be installed in such a manner that warm air blows directly on occupant's feet. Ideally, the air discharge should be directed along the outside wall adjacent to normal working areas, not directly under the sink.

Radiant heating cable.   Radiant heating cable provides an enormous heating surface over the ceiling or concrete floor so that the system need not be raised to a high temperature. Rather, gentle warmth radiates downward (in the case of ceiling-mounted cable) or upward (in the case of floor-mounted cable), heating the entire room or area evenly.

There is virtually no maintenance with a radiant heating system, as there are no moving parts and the entire heating system is invisible—except for the thermostat.

Combination heating and cooling units.   One way to have individual control of each room or area in the home, as far as heating and cooling are concerned, is to install through-wall heating and cooling units. Such a system gives the occupants complete control of their environment with a room-by-room choice of either heating or cooling at any time of year at any temperature they desire. Operating costs are lower than for many other systems due to the high efficiency of room-by-room control. Another advantage is that if a unit should fail, the defective chassis can be replaced immediately or taken to a shop for repair without shutting down the remaining units in the home.

When selecting any electric heating units, obtain plenty of literature from suppliers and manufacturers before settling on any one type. In most cases you are going to get what you pay for, but shop around at different suppliers before ordering the equipment.

Delivery of any of these units may take some time, so once the brand, size, and supplier have been selected, place your order well before the unit is actually needed.

Electric furnaces. Electric furnaces are becoming more popular, although they are somewhat surpassed by the all-electric heat pump. Most are very compact, versatile units designed for either wall, ceiling, or closet mounting. The vertical model can be flush mounted in a wall or shelf mounted in a closet; the horizontal design (Fig. 4-2) can be fitted into a ceiling (flush or recessed).

Central heating systems of the electrically energized type distribute heat from a centrally located source by means of circulating air or water. Compact electric boilers can be mounted on the wall of a basement, utility room, or closet with the necessary control and circuit protection, and will furnish hot water to convectors or to embedded pipes. Immersion heaters may be stepped in one at a time to provide heat capacity to match heat loss.

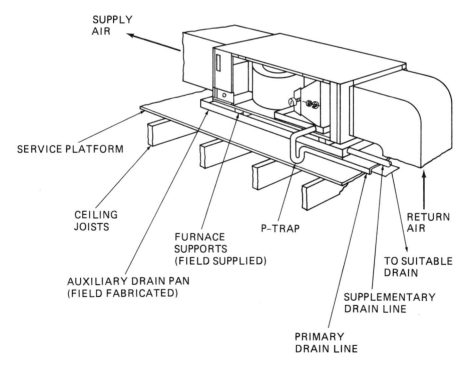

Figure 4-2   Horizontal application of an electric furnace.

The majority of electric furnaces are commonly available in sizes up to 24 kilowatts (kw) for residential use. The larger boilers with proper controls can take advantage of lower off-peak electricity rates, where they prevail, by heating water during off-peak periods, storing it in insulated tanks, and circulating it to convectors or radiators to provide heat as needed.

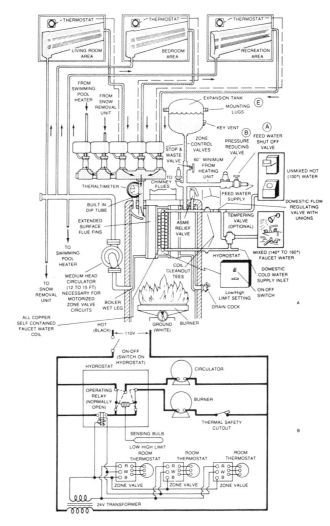

Figure 4-3   A typical hot-water system operating diagram. A wiring diagram is shown at the bottom of the illustration.

HOT-WATER SYSTEMS

A zone hydronic (hot-water) heating system permits selection of different temperatures in each zone of the home. Baseboard heaters located along the outer walls of rooms provide a blanket of warmth from floor to ceiling; the heating unit also supplies domestic hot water simultaneously, through separate circuits. A special attachment coupled to the hot-water unit can be used to melt snow and ice on walkways and driveways in winter, and a similar attachment can be used to heat your swimming pool during the spring and fall seasons.

A typical hot-water system operating diagram is shown in Fig. 4-3, and is explained as follows: When a zone thermostat calls for heat, the appropriate zone valve motor begins to run, opening the valve slowly; when the valve is fully opened, the valve motor stops. At that time, the operating relay in the hydrostat is energized, closing contacts to the burner and the circulator circuits. The high-limit control contacts (a safety device) are normally closed so the burner will now fire and operate. If the boiler water temperature exceeds the high-limit setting, the high-limit contacts will open and the burner will stop, but the circulator will continue to run as long as the thermostat continues to call for heat. If the call for heat continues, the resultant drop in boiler water temperature—below the high-limit setting— will bring the burner back on. Thus, the burner will cycle until the thermostat is satisfied; then both the burner and circulator will shut off.

Hot-water boilers for the home are normally manufactured for use with oil, gas, or electricity. While a zoned hot-water system is comparatively costly to install, the cost is still competitive with the better hot-air systems. The chief disadvantage of hot-water systems is that they don't use ducts. If you wish to install central air conditioning, you must install a complete duct system along with the central unit. Chillers, or refrigerated water, may be run through the same pipes, but such systems are usually too expensive for residential use.

5
Introduction to
Computer Programming

BASIC, COBOL, FORTRAN, Pascal! Do these computer words make any sense to you? If not, never fear. This chapter gives you sufficient basic information to use practically any computer to solve numerous problems confronting anyone working in the HVAC industry.

It is not necessary to understand exactly how a computer operates. Many individuals can instruct a computer to perform and still be quite ignorant of just how it actually does its magic. By the same token, how many people drive cars without having the slightest understanding of how an internal combustion engine works, or how the automatic transmission "shifts" into the required gears at various intervals? All that is required to understand and use the programs contained in this book is that a computer cannot make decisions on its own; it needs instructions. Furthermore, the programmer needs to "talk" in a language that the computer understands. With only this knowledge, and the basic operational instructions that come with each computer, you can begin working with programs immediately. However, a somewhat better understanding of how these programs were originated—along with an overview of a computer system—is in order to put the reader in a better position to use the programs and to modify them to suit various needs.

A set of instructions for a computer is called a program, and is much like a recipe for preparing an exotic dish for the table. The program consists of a series of steps which are to be performed in the order given, and the computer will follow these right to the letter—despite the fact that the instructions may be incorrect, because computers lack the ability to decide what you intended. They can only act upon what you actually instruct them to do.

BASIC is one language that most computers understand. It stands for Beginner's All-Purpose Symbolic Instruction Code, and there is hardly a computer, big or small (Apple, Wang, Atari, IBM, Radio Shack, and so on) which cannot communicate in BASIC.

To make BASIC work, the computer must also have another program or instruction in operation that can interpret the words it reads, and then perform the operations which are desired by the programmer; it's much like having an interpreter in a foreign country. But the computer is not quite as smart as your average human interpreter. It's fast, but by human standards, it is quite stupid. For example, if you tell the computer to "GO TO", it probably will not do anything except print "error" or something to that effect, depending on which computer you are using. Had you typed "GOTO", the computer would immediately know what to do. In other words, in BASIC language, one space out of place can make or change a program completely.

Even though BASIC has been designed to "understand" English, it has a limited vocabulary. For example, BASIC knows what to do when "STOP" is typed on the keyboard, but type "WHOA", "WAIT A MINUTE", or other synonyms for "STOP" and the computer just stares blindly with its mouth open . . . wondering what to do next!

PRELIMINARY PLANNING

To write any computer program, a precise definition of what the program is to accomplish is required. Also, a detailed step-by-step plan of how the program goals will be achieved must be known or worked out, and finally, a knowledge of how the programming statements can be used to complement the step-by-step plan.

1. The precise definition of what the program is to accomplish is the first and most important part of the creative cycle. This must describe exactly what is to be accomplished.

2. Work out a plan (program), in a language that the computer under-stands, to accomplish the goal of the first step.

3. Run the program to test for accuracy.

4. Debug the program to operate properly on your computer.
5. Store or save the program for future use, so that it can be recalled at any convenient time.

One problem that often confronts the HVAC worker is to calculate the area of a round metal duct. When the diameter of a round duct is known, the area may be found by the following equation: $A = 3.14 \times d \times d$. Such a simple calculation can be performed quickly on a pocket calculator, but since this a familiar calculation, it will be used to demonstrate how a computer program is developed.

The exact method of developing a step-by-step computer program will vary from person to person. Some people rely heavily on a technique known as flow charting, while others have an intuitive "feel" for program development and can write programs right off the top of their heads. Actually, it does not matter which method is used provided accurate results are obtained.

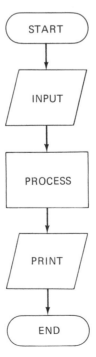

Figure 5-1 The symbols used for the round duct area.

In most cases, when simple programs are to be written, flow charts are seldom used, but even the most experienced programmers will use this technique when a long and complicated program is required. To demonstrate the technique, a flow chart will be used to develop the program on finding the area of a duct.

In general, a flow chart is a set of distinctively shaped symbols that indicates the steps of program execution. The technique of flow charting could take the space of an entire book to describe adequately, but to get the "feel" of things, everything described in this chapter will be kept simple. The symbols used for the round duct area program are as shown in Fig. 5-1.

This is the job that must be accomplished to write the program, and standard programming statements will be used.

WRITING THE PROGRAM

To begin, a REM or REMark Statement is used to identify the program.

10 REM **AREA OF ROUND DUCT**

The next step involves INPUTing the values of the items to be used in the computation. These data will come from the keyboard, and a variable name is needed that will receive the data. So, "D" is used for the diameter. At this point, the program will look something like this:

10 REM **AREA OF ROUND DUCT**
20 INPUT D

Notice that each line of instruction is numbered; this is necessary to give the computer directions. The INPUT is needed from you, so the computer will ask a question on the screen via "?". You then enter the known diameter of the round duct. Since the area of the duct is to be found, the following equation must be entered into the program.

$$A = .7854*D^2$$

In the next line (30), the equation is written and most of the program is now complete. However, to make the program of any value, we want to see the results, so the computer is told to display the results on the screen via the instruction "PRINT". In fact, it is desired to see all the figures: diameter of duct and area of duct. The instructions are given as follows:

50 PRINT D
60 PRINT A
80 STOP

If you have a computer handy at this time, it is suggested that you type in the program on your computer exactly as it is shown. It will only take a minute to type, and to see how it works on your own computer will be helpful.

When this program has been keyed into the computer, all that is necessary is to type "RUN", or the equivalent key. When the "?" appears, enter the diameter of 10 and press RETURN. The computer will make the calculation in a split second and display the answer on the screen as 78.54. Try it on your computer.

Now this program is written in the simplest form possible and is perfectly alright for one-time use. However, if it becomes necessary to go back to the program in the future, chances are you will forget what the computer is asking first. What is the question the computer is asking when the program first appears on the monitor?

The first order of business is to more accurately describe what the computer wants in the input. Then instead of merely typing in "INPUT D", the computer will print exactly what is required for it to complete the calculation; that is,

```
20 INPUT ''DIAMETER OF ROUND DUCT IN INCHES'';D
```

The words in quotes will be displayed on the screen, asking the computer operator exactly what the computer needs to know to complete its work, and will appear as follows:

```
DIAMETER OF ROUND DUCT IN INCHES?
```

Bear in mind, however, that the computer itself is still reading only "D" and therefore the original equation is still valid.

Continuing to the PRINTout portion of the program, the first simple program that was listed had no identification of what the PRINTed data represented, so some identification is in order for a program that will be permanently used for practical applications. Here is one solution:

```
40 PRINT ''THE AREA OF A ROUND AIR DUCT WITH A DIAMETER OF'' ;D; ''INCHES''
        50 PRINT ''IS'' ;A; ''SQUARE INCHES''
```

With these modifications in the original program, the new version will appear.

Now that looks somewhat better, and this program can be stored on a diskette for future use without having to worry about remembering what data have to be fed into it to put it in operation. To save, type in,

SAVE ' 'AREA

The word "AREA" is the name given this program; it's a means of identifying it when recalling the program, although any other name could have been used.

Upon reviewing this new version, perhaps even more improvements can be made. For example, all the lines run together; a space between the input and print lines would make the results look neater. All that is necessary is to type the following:

35 PRINT

Since line 35 was not used in the program (line 30 jumps to line 40), this space is available, or it could have been 31, 32, and so on. The BASIC statement, PRINT, without an argument causes a blank line to be printed on the screen, leaving a space between the input and print lines.

A closer examination of the program will reveal other things which might be improved upon. For example, is it really necessary to have the inputs listed twice on the screen? This might be confusing, and it might be best just to have the results printed once the program has been executed. To do this, instead of typing in PRINT in line 35, let's type

35 CLS

This command informs the computer to clear the screen before printing lines 40 and 50, and in doing so, only the following will appear on the screen when the computer completes its calculations:

THE AREA OF A ROUND AIR DUCT WITH A DIAMETER OF 10 INCHES
IS 78.54 SQUARE INCHES

With a little thought, the inventive budding computer operator should be able to think of many other HVAC calculations that can be performed using this program format. Merely substitute inputs in their appropriate locations, and then key in the required equation on line 30. Granted, this program is extremely short and does not offer much of a challenge. However, nothing is more discouraging to the beginner than to spend several hours typing a long program into the computer and find that it does not function correctly due to a typo or other error. Therefore, this first sample has purposely been kept short so that typos and other errors may quickly be found and corrected, giving the new programmer confidence to proceed to the more challenging programs that follow.

HVAC SYSTEMS COST ANALYSIS AND OTHER AVAILABLE SOFTWARE

The information contained in this section consists of available software for use in HVAC design, analysis, installation, and contracting. Due to the large quantity of software available, only those that have been tried or studied are listed. Most are available for the personal and professional computers most often used in consulting engineers' and contractors' offices.

A brief description of each software package is listed here. For more information, contact the supplier.

4-Point graphics

This graphics design tool is an image editor allowing the user to draw lines, circles, boxes, ellipses, and polygons. It also allows for picture inversion, texturization of regions of a picture, multicolored text and four cursor point modes, with the animation of up to 99 individual segments in any sequence for a smooth continuous movie. [Available from International Microcomputer Software, Inc. (415) 454-7101.]

The executive package

This package is a management tool of more than 40 problem-solving applications. It instructs the manager how to perform everything from risk analysis, interest computation, inventory scheduling, product pricing, and inflation modeling to forecasting corporate growth. [Available from Alpha Software Products (617) 229-2924.]

TK!Solverpack—mechanical engineering

Models in this software package include: two-point supported beam, catilever beam, elastic torsion beam, cylindrical wall heat transfer, thermal effectiveness of fins, fluid flow in pipes, hydraulic system analysis/design, hydrostatic-hatch design, area moment of inertia, Mohr's Circle, helical spring, and natural frequency of vibration in rotational systems. [Available from Wang Laboratories, Inc. (800) TEL-WANG.]

Accountmaster 8/16

Containing six modules, this package provides the retail and wholesale environments with a full general accounting system. The software may be operated as an integrated system or in stand-alone modules. The modules include General Ledger, Accounts Receivable, Accounts Payable, Payroll, Inventory, and Other Entry. [Available from SBSG, Inc.]

Peachtree: job costing

The Job Cost System gives smaller businesspersons a reliable means of entering estimates and cost transactions, as well as tracking costs and profitability on a job-by-job basis. [Available from Wang Laboratories, Inc.]

The boss payroll management

The Boss Payroll System calculates payrolls by salary, hourly wage, piecework, and contract. It also handles the complicated tax calculations for employees working for tips. This payroll module computes and writes checks for up to 33,000 job tickets in a single pay period. It will print on all standard tax forms, W-2s, and 1099s and prepares the quarterly (940, 941) reports, and all state tax forms. This module will interface to the Financial Accounting System, also available from Balcones. [Available from Balcones Computer Corp. (512) 346–1771.]

Peachtree: peachpay payroll

Peachpay Payroll offers a comprehensive range of controls over all aspects of the payroll accounting process. It can be used independently or can be interfaced with the General Ledger, also available from Peachtree. [Available from Wang Laboratories, Inc.]

The boss time billing system

This package is designed for the service-oriented business whose billing and accountability may be divided among many clients/customers. It can generate and print bills for 9,999 client accounts and 9,999 jobs as well as keep track of over 33,000 time tickets for 999 employees. [Available from Balcones Computer Corp.]

Total accounting system

The Total Accounting System is made up of eight general business modules: Total Ledger, Total Receivables, Total Payables, Total Payroll, Total Inventory, Q/Label, Total Utilities, and Total Simple. These modules may be purchased in any combination, and all work stands alone or as an integrated system. [Available from TCS Software, Inc. (713) 977–7505.]

MICS/1 job costing and billing

The MICS Job Costing and Billing System is a comprehensive job costing program specifically designed for the construction industry. It includes a job cost accounting system, extensive job cost reports, a subcontractor and subcontract file, and features accurate billing based on standard AIA documents including change order and extras. [Available from MICS (213) 457–4416.]

Construction management

This package provides for complete job costing capabilities for contractors or firms with job costing needs. It provides the contractor with a complete budget variance report by subdivision, job, or subphase within each job. The system tracks all costs from accounts payable and payroll, providing a percentage-of-job-complete report of any requested job. It graphs all activity by account, and prepares complete financial statements upon demand in any user-definable format and style. Control totals are also displayed at all times to show balance of accounts, journals, and ledgers. [Available from Cyma Corporation (602) 835–8880.]

E-Z Bid II

E-Z Bid II is designed to provide an automated method of producing accurate cost estimates for the small- to medium-sized contractor. It calculates costs based on the most current material/labor prices and prints a formal bid sheet. This package maintains an on-line inventory system to provide for automatic retrieval of unit prices and labor standards as items and quantities are entered. User-defined inventory master standards or industry standards may be maintained. [Available from Z/SOFTWARE (713) 852–3437.]

Residential/commercial services

This package is designed for businesses whose principal source of revenue is derived from contract services. These services are generally performed at regular intervals with the associated fees usually being fixed and repetitive. The package includes an Accounts Receivable module and a General Ledger module. [Available from ADS Software, Inc. (703) 344–6818.]

PC Asynchronous communications

Asynchronous communications software enables the user to emulate a standard teletypewriter or to emulate a Wang 2200 terminal. With the teletypewriter emulation, the use of dial-up or leased lines to retrieve or transfer data from host systems and information services and to communicate interactively with a wide variety of systems is featured. During 2200 terminal emulation, the Wang PC has full access to the 2200 system's applications and devices, including printers, disks, and communications options. [Available from Wang Laboratories, Inc.]

Microlink II

This easy-to-use telephone communications package connects the PC keyboard and screen to information services of time-sharing computers. The program captures information in disk files and will send any type of disk file. [Available from Digital Marketing (415) 938–2880.]

Lotus 1-2-3

Developed by Lotus Development Corp. and usually distributed through the computer manufacturer, this package is an integrated spreadsheet, graphics, and database management program. It is intended for the professional user who is heavily involved in the use of spreadsheets and detailed row/column "what-if" situations.

PC Multiplan

PC Multiplan is an electronic spreadsheet application designed by Microsoft. Targeted as a financial planning and data analysis tool, it can be easily used for capital budgeting, financial analysis, sales force decisions, product planning, and production management. PC Multiplan is designed for the nonprogramming professional. Ease of use and sophistication of commands are of note as well as naming capability, linking ability, and creation of up to eight windows. [Available from Wang Laboratories, Inc.]

PC Data base

The PC Data Base offers the nontechnical user a simple way to structure, group, and access large amounts of data. Data from the database can be merged with PC Word Processing. PC DB is a true relational database supporting multiple views using multiple individual records. Extensive multitiered, on-line inquiry and fast response time are of note. Sorting, on-line reports, and creation of derived fields are supported. [Available from Wang Laboratories, Inc.]

The statistician

This package contains 100 FORTRAN subroutines which are designed to aid the mathematician and scientist in performing mathematical functions. Some of the major sets of subroutines are: matrix storage and operation, correlation and regression, design analysis, discriminate analysis, eigen analysis, time series, linear analysis, and polynominal solutions. [Available from Alpha Computer Service.]

Cardfile

This package stores, retrieves, and displays information that is typically kept in index card files: summaries of articles and books, notes, menus, catalog of books, phonograph records, tapes, and so on. Data are entered through the text editor. It allows 21 lines per file record with three key field/lines. [Available from Digital Marketing (415) 938–2880.]

Peachtree: calendar management

Calendar Management is an effective, convenient scheduling tool. Ideally suited to the needs of a group of busy professionals or executives, it can accommodate as many as 98 individuals. [Available from Wang Laboratories, Inc.]

Marketfax

This sales and marketing software package targets, launches, follows, and streamlines mail merging on word processing functions, and produces management and sales reports on all prospects and clients. MARKETFAX automatically sends follow-up letters and correspondence, and maintains a client history for each letter produced. [Available from Scientific Marketing, Inc. (714) 957–0225.]

Notebook

Notebook is a database management system designed to store and retrieve text. There are few restrictions on the amount of information entered and its format. Space does not have to be saved in each record for information that occasionally appears. Categories may be altered at any time without modifying existing data. [Available from Digital Marketing.]

Cost-acumen

COST-ACUMEN is a cost accounting and project management software package for architects and engineers. It provides accurate and current data about company finances. It monitors a firm's operating costs, expedites invoicing, manages projects, analyzes employee productivity and overhead contribution, spots cost overruns, and more. Fully formatted and user-defined reports are included. [Available from Computer Applications Corp. (901) 458–8630.]

Eagle software: money decisions

Money Decisions is a collection of over 70 time-tested financial problem solvers. These programs provide interactive and comprehensive tools for decision making on loans, business management, investments, forecasting, and statistics. Volume 1 contains 34 routines; Volume II contains 36 routines. Each volume can operate alone or in conjunction with the other set of problem solvers. [Available from Wang Laboratories, Inc.]

Building energy analysis program

This package calculates monthly and annual operating costs on buildings having as many as 1,000 zones and 100 air systems. The program provides for many sophisticated techniques in analyzing the operating costs of a building. All common types of cooling and heating plans are provided as well as all types of air terminal systems. As many as eight energy sources can be matched to as many as nine building energy-use categories. This program provides the engineer with a fast, powerful tool for evaluating all the complex factors involved in analyzing operating costs. [Available from Elite Software Development, Inc. (409) 775–1782.]

Labeltronics system 1000

This program is a comprehensive label production system. It allows shipping and warehouse personnel to easily produce a variety of labels containing special fonts, variable fields, text formats, and bar codes (horizontal or vertical). Label production may occur in either batch or demand modes. The Product 5 version provides these standard capabilities. The Product 6 version includes a logo-printing capability. This special design-print system is delivered with a printer subsystem to drive specific dot matrix printers which produce the corporate logo.

Labeltronics system 2000

This system produces bar coded labels for warehouse stock inventory control. Inventoried stock is assigned a specific bar code which is read by the portable bar code reader. Audit trail data are captured at the stock site and shipment site; in turn, full on-hand quantity and stock deviation reports are produced. The RJS Bar Code Reader is included with the package. It connects to the RS-232 port on the PC for data capture. [Available from Lowell Systems (617) 459–4930.]

6
Residential Heating Calculations

Unlike most other types of occupancies, residences do not require elaborate procedures for heating calculations. In fact, the heat loss for some existing homes is done on the square-foot method; that is, in certain areas of the country, the heating contractors have learned from experience what the average heat loss will be on a square-foot basis. In Virginia, for example, this figure runs from 10 to 12 Btuh per square foot, depending upon the type of construction. However, such calculations can be unsuitable in many circumstances—especially in the hands of designers with little practical experience—and therefore, the following method is recommended for calculating the heat loss for average residential applications.

During cold weather, the home must be kept comfortable by having the inside maintained at a desirable temperature and humidity. Therefore, it is necessary to provide a heat source to meet this requirement.

A good heating system should feature:

1. Adequate, dependable, and trouble-free operation
2. Comfort during cold weather
3. Reasonable installation cost
4. Reasonable annual operating cost
5. Ease of service and maintenance

To meet these goals, certain steps must be taken to determine the best type of system to use, the size of the equipment, and the best fuel. A complete survey of the building's structural conditions must be made, along with the heat-loss calculations, before any of these factors can be determined.

Heat loss is expressed in either Btu per hour or in watts. Both are measures of the rate at which heat is transferred and may be converted from one to the other by the following two formulas:

$$\text{Watts} = \text{Btu}/3.4 \qquad \text{Btu} = \text{watts} \times 3.4$$

In general, there are four steps in determining heat loss through walls, roof, ceiling, windows, and floor.

1. Determine the net area in square feet.
2. Find the proper heat-loss factor from tables.
3. Allow for infiltration.
4. Multiply the area by the factor; the product will be expressed in Btu.

Figure 6-1 shows an example of a heat-loss estimating form that one might use to make heat-loss calculations more quickly and efficiently. Spaces are provided for all the necessary data and calculations and in the proper order to make the calculations routine and simple. All that is required now is to fill in the spaces with correct information and make sure the mathematical calculations are correct. The result is a room-by-room survey showing exactly how much heat will be required to maintain a home at the desired temperature during the months that heat is needed.

The form in Fig. 6-1 requires exact dimensions of windows, doors, ceilings, floors, and the like. While these dimensions are being taken, it is also a good time to make a floor plan of your home. Such a sketch will not only make identification of particular areas easier when the form is being completed, it will also help to lay out the system components.

Floor plans are not made full size, because the size of the drawing would be impractically large. Therefore, the drawing is reduced so that all the distances on the drawing are smaller than the actual dimensions of the home, but all dimensions are reduced in the same proportion. The ratio, or relation between the size of the drawing and the size of the building, is indicated on the drawing (1/8 in. to 1 ft, for example), and the dimensions shown are the actual building dimensions, not the distance that is measured on the drawing.

Architect's scales are available in many different ratios ranging from 1/6 in. = 1 ft to 1-1/2 in. = 1 ft. The scale 1/4 in. = 1 ft is the most common scale for residential drawings. Drawing paper ruled in 1/4-in. squares can also be purchased to simplify the drawing.

HEATING CALCULATION FORM

NAME OF PROJECT OR AREA ....
DESIGN CONDITIONS: Outside Dry Bulb Temperature ....
Inside Dry Bulb Temperature .... Temperature Difference ....

PART 1:   Ceiling Type and Insulation Thickness ....
          Floor Type and Insulation ....
          Type of Windows ....
          Type of Walls and Insulation ....
PART 2:   Infiltration
          area width x area length x ceiling height
          ───
                           60

          (   ) width x (   ) length x (   ) ceiling height
          ───
                           60

                                                         Heat Loss
          = ... x 1.08 x .... T.D. = ...
PART 3:   Heat Loss
Windows: .... sq. ft. x 0.55 x .... T.D. = ...
Walls: .... sq. ft. x 0.13 x .... T.D. = ...
Roof: .... sq. ft. x 0.20 x .... T.D. = ...
Floor: .... sq. ft. x 0.09 x .... T.D. = ...

TOTAL HEAT LOSS IN BTUH   ....
Divide by 3.4 to obtain heat loss in watts   ....

Figure 6-1 One type of heat-loss estimating form for residential construction.

PREPARING THE SKETCH

If the home was designed by an architect, chances are that a complete set of working drawings already exist. If not, check with the architect for copies of the drawings, or the building contractor may have a set that could be used for the heat-loss calculations. If all these sources fail to produce a set, then a complete set of measurements must be made to draw the sketch.

Figure 6-2 is an example of what a drawing should resemble after it is completed. Begin by measuring the outside perimeter of the home, drawing the wall lines, and inserting dimensions. It would be helpful if someone was available to give assistance. Measure and locate all windows and doors on the drawing along with chimneys, carports, and so on. Continue by measuring all inside partitions, doors, and the like, and indicating their locations on the sketch.

It should be noted where there are storm windows and doors; the amount of insulation in the attic, outside walls, and under the floor; the type of roof, floor, and so on. The blank spaces on the calculation form in Fig. 6-1 will serve as a guide as to what information is required for a complete heat-loss estimate. All this information should be obtained before any work is started on the calculations to result in a more accurate estimate and a saving of time.

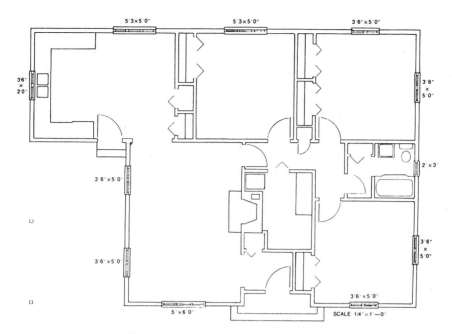

Figure 6-2   Typical residential floor plan.

COMPLETING THE HEAT-LOSS CALCULATIONS

The heat-loss calculation form is based on the design conditions of the home and the area it is located in. Outside design conditions are the extremes of temperature occurring in a specific locality, while the inside design condition is the degree of temperature and humidity that will given optimum comfort.

The outside dry-bulb temperatures for calculating heating loads are shown in Table 6-1. For cities and localities not listed in this table, find a city that is geographically near or closely approximates, the local conditions and use the temperature given. The inside dry-bulb temperature for heating in colder months is 70 to 75 degrees Fahrenheit. Therefore, the temperature difference will be the difference between the inside design temperature (say, 70 degrees) and the outside design conditions for the locality. For example, assume that Washington, DC is the location; after referring to Fig. 6-3, it is found that the outside design condition for winter heating is 0 degrees Fahrenheit. So the temperature difference is 70 degrees (70 − 0 =   70). However, if Miami, FL is the location, the temperature difference would be 35 degrees, since the òutside design temperature for Miami is 35 degrees Fahrenheit.

To demonstrate exactly how to make heat-loss calculations for a given home, the floor plan of the residence in Fig. 6-2 will be used as an example.

TABLE 6-1 High and Low Average Temperatures for Calculating Heating Loads in Various Cities in the United States and Canada.

State & City	Winter DB	Summer DB	Daily Range	Summer WB	Latitude Deg.
ALABAMA					
Anniston	10	95	M	78	35
Birmingham	10	95	M	78	35
Gadsden	10	95	M	78	35
Mobile	20	90	L	80	30
Montgomery	20	95	M	78	30
Tuscaloosa	10	95	M	78	35
ALASKA					
Anchorage	-24	—	M	—	60
Barrow	-48	—	—	—	70
Bethel	-43	—	—	—	60
Cordova	-13	—	M	—	60
Fairbanks	-57	—	—	—	65
Juneau	-5	—	—	—	60
Ketchikan	4	—	—	—	55
Kodiak	4	—	—	—	55
Kotzebue	-46	—	—	—	65
Nome	-36	—	—	—	60
Seward	-4	—	—	—	60
Sitka	2	—	—	—	60
ARIZONA					
Bisbee	30	100	H	72	30
Flagstaff	-5	85	H	61	35
Globe	30	105	H	76	35
Nogales	30	105	H	72	30
Phoenix	35	105	H	76	35
Tucson	30	100	H	72	30
Winslow	-5	95	H	65	35
Yuma	40	110	H	78	35
ARKANSAS					
Bentonville	0	95	M	76	35
Fort Smith	5	95	M	76	35
Hot Springs	10	95	M	78	35
Little Rock	10	95	M	78	35
Pine Bluff	10	95	M	78	35
Texarkana	10	100	M	78	35
CALIFORNIA					
Bakersfield	30	105	H	70	35
El Centro	35	110	H	78	35
Eureka	30	90	M	65	40
Fresno	30	105	H	74	35
Long Beach	35	90	L	70	35
Los Angeles	40	90	M	70	35
Montague	15	95	—	70	40

State & City	Winter DB	Summer DB	Daily Range	Summer WB	Latitude Deg.
IDAHO					
Boise	-10	95	H	65	45
Idaho Falls	-15	90	H	65	45
Lewiston	-10	95	H	65	45
Pocatello	-15	90	H	65	45
Twin Falls	-15	95	H	65	40
ILLINOIS					
Aurora	-10	95	M	75	40
Bloomington	-10	95	M	76	40
Cairo	0	100	M	78	35
Champaign	-10	95	M	77	40
Chicago	-10	95	M	75	40
Danville	-10	95	M	77	40
Decatur	-10	95	M	78	40
Elgin	-15	95	M	76	40
Joliet	-10	95	M	76	40
Moline	-10	95	M	76	40
Peoria	-15	96	M	76	40
Rockford	-15	95	M	76	40
Rock Island	-10	95	M	76	40
Springfield	-10	95	M	77	40
Urbana	-10	95	M	77	40
INDIANA					
Elkhart	-10	95	M	75	40
Evansville	-5	95	M	78	40
Fort Wayne	-5	95	M	75	40
Indianapolis	-10	95	M	76	40
Lafayette	-10	95	M	76	40
South Bend	-10	95	M	75	40
Terre Haute	-5	95	M	78	40
IOWA					
Burlington	-10	95	M	78	40
Cedar Rapids	-15	95	M	78	40
Charles City	-20	95	M	78	45
Clinton	-15	95	M	78	40
Council Bluffs	-10	100	M	78	40
Davenport	-10	95	M	78	40
Des Moines	-15	95	M	78	40
Dubuque	-15	95	M	78	40
Fort Dodge	-15	95	M	78	40
Keokuk	-15	95	M	78	40
Marshalltown	-15	95	M	78	40
Sioux City	-15	95	M	78	40
Waterloo	-15	95	M	78	40
KANSAS					

State & City	Winter DB	Summer DB	Daily Range	Summer WB	Latitude Deg.
MICHIGAN					
Alpena	-10	90	M	75	45
Ann Arbor	-5	90	M	75	45
Big Rapids	-5	90	M	75	45
Cadillac	-10	90	M	75	45
Calumet	-20	80	M	73	45
Detroit	-5	90	M	75	45
Escanaba	-20	85	M	75	45
Flint	-10	90	M	75	45
Grand Haven	-5	90	M	74	45
Grand Rapids	-5	90	M	73	45
Houghton	-20	80	M	75	45
Kalamazoo	-5	90	M	75	45
Lansing	-10	90	M	75	45
Ludington	-5	90	M	75	45
Marquette	-15	80	M	73	45
Muskegon	-5	90	M	74	45
Port Huron	-10	90	M	75	45
Saginaw	-10	90	M	75	45
Sault Ste. Marie	-20	80	M	71	45
MINNESOTA					
Alexandria	-25	85	M	74	45
Duluth	-25	80	M	71	45
Minneapolis	-25	90	M	76	45
Moorhead	-30	95	M	75	45
St. Cloud	-25	90	M	76	45
St. Paul	-25	90	M	75	45
MISSISSIPPI					
Biloxi	25	90	L	80	30
Columbus	10	95	M	78	35
Corinth	5	95	M	78	35
Hattiesburg	20	95	M	80	30
Jackson	15	95	M	78	30
Meridian	15	95	L	79	30
Natchez	15	95	M	78	30
Vicksburg	15	95	L	78	30
MISSOURI					
Columbia	-10	100	M	78	40
Hannibal	-10	95	M	77	40
Kansas City	-10	100	M	76	40
Kirksville	-10	95	M	78	40
St. Joseph	-10	100	M	78	40
St. Louis	-5	95	M	78	40

City					
Red Bluff	15	100	H	72	40
Sacramento	30	100	H	72	40
San Bernardino	30	105	H	72	35
San Diego	45	80	L	68	35
San Francisco	35	80	M	65	35
San Jose	40	90	M	70	35
COLORADO					
Boulder	-15	95	M	64	40
Colorado Springs	-10	95	H	65	40
Denver	-10	95	H	64	40
Durango	-5	95	H	65	35
Fort Collins	-15	95	H	65	40
Grand Junction	-5	95	M	65	40
Leadville	-10	95	H	64	40
Pueblo	-15	95	H	65	40
CONNECTICUT					
Bridgeport	0	85	L	75	40
Hartford	0	90	M	75	40
New Haven	0	85	M	75	40
New London	5	85	L	75	40
Norwalk	0	85	L	75	40
Torrington	0	90	M	75	40
Waterbury	0	90	L	75	40
DELAWARE					
Dover	10	90	M	78	40
Milford	10	90	M	78	40
Wilmington	5	90	M	78	40
DIST. OF COLUMBIA					
Washington	10	90	M	78	40
FLORIDA					
Apalachicola	25	95	L	76	35
Fort Myers	40	95	M	76	35
Gainesville	30	95	M	76	35
Jacksonville	30	95	M	78	30
Key West	55	100	M	76	25
Miami	45	90	L	76	25
Orlando	35	95	M	78	30
Pensacola	35	95	M	76	30
Tallahassee	25	95	L	76	30
Tampa	35	95	M	78	30
GEORGIA					
Athens	10	95	M	76	35
Atlanta	10	95	M	76	35
Augusta	20	100	L	76	35
Brunswick	25	95	M	78	30
Columbus	20	100	M	78	35
Macon	20	95	M	76	35
Rome	10	95	L	76	35
Savannah	25	95	M	76	30
Way Cross	25	95	M	78	30

City					
Iola	-5	100	M	76	40
Leavenworth	-10	100	M	76	40
Salina	-10	100	M	78	35
Topeka	-10	100	M	78	35
Wichita	-5	100	M	75	40
KENTUCKY					
Bowling Green	0	95	M	78	35
Frankfort	0	95	M	78	40
Hopkinsville	0	95	M	78	35
Lexington	0	95	M	78	40
Louisville	0	95	M	78	40
Owensboro	0	95	M	78	40
Shelbyville	0	95	M	78	40
LOUISIANA					
Alexandria	20	95	L	78	30
Baton Rouge	20	95	M	80	30
New Orleans	25	95	L	80	30
Shreveport	15	95	M	78	35
MAINE					
Augusta	-15	85	L	73	45
Bangor	-20	85	L	73	45
Bar Harbor	-10	85	L	73	45
Belfast	-10	85	L	70	45
Eastport	-10	85	L	73	45
Lewiston	-10	85	M	73	45
Millinocket	-15	85	M	73	45
Orono	-20	85	L	73	45
Portland	-10	85	L	73	45
Presque Isle	-20	85	L	73	45
Rumford	-15	85	L	73	45
MARYLAND					
Annapolis	10	90	M	78	40
Baltimore	10	90	M	78	40
Cambridge	10	90	L	78	40
Cumberland	0	90	M	78	40
Frederick	5	90	M	75	40
Frostburg	-5	90	M	75	40
Salisbury	10	90	M	78	40
MASSACHUSETTS					
Amherst	0	90	M	75	40
Boston	0	90	L	74	40
Fall River	0	85	M	75	45
Fitchburg	5	90	M	75	40
Framingham	5	90	L	74	45
Lawrence	5	85	L	75	45
Lowell	5	85	L	75	45
Nantucket	0	85	L	74	45
New Bedford	0	90	L	75	45
Pittsfield	10	85	L	76	45
Plymouth	5	90	M	75	40
Springfield	5	90	L	75	40
Worcester	5	90	L	78	40

City					
Anaconda	-30	85	H	59	45
Billings	-30	90	H	66	45
Butte	-30	85	H	59	45
Great Falls	-40	90	H	63	50
Havre	-40	95	M	70	45
Helena	-30	90	H	63	50
Miles City	-35	95	H	69	45
Missoula	-30	90	H	63	45
NEBRASKA					
Grand Island	-15	100	H	75	40
Hastings	-15	100	M	75	40
Lincoln	-15	95	M	78	40
North Platte	-15	100	H	78	40
Omaha	-15	100	M	73	40
Valentine	-20	95	M	78	45
York	-15	95	M	78	40
NEVADA					
Elko	-10	95	H	63	40
Las Vegas	10	110	H	71	35
Reno	5	95	H	65	40
Tonopah	5	90	M	63	40
Winnemucca	-10	95	H	65	40
NEW HAMPSHIRE					
Berlin	-15	85	H	73	45
Claremont	-15	85	M	73	45
Concord	-15	85	H	73	45
Franklin	-15	85	M	73	45
Hanover	-15	85	M	73	45
Keene	-10	85	L	73	45
Manchester	-10	85	L	74	45
Nashua	-10	85	L	74	45
Portsmouth	-5	85	L	74	45
NEW JERSEY					
Asbury Park	10	90	L	78	40
Atlantic City	10	90	L	78	40
Bayonne	0	90	M	75	40
Belvidere	0	90	L	75	40
Bloomfield	5	90	L	78	40
Bridgeton	0	90	L	78	40
Camden	0	90	L	78	40
East Orange	0	90	L	75	40
Elizabeth	0	90	L	75	40
Jersey City	0	90	L	76	40
Newark	0	90	M	75	40
New Brunswick	0	90	L	75	40
Paterson	0	90	L	76	40
Phillipsburg	0	90	M	78	40
Trenton	0	90	L	78	40

Table Continued on Next Page.

107

State & City	Winter DB	Summer DB	Daily Range	Summer WB	Latitude Deg.
NEW MEXICO					
Albuquerque	10	95	M	65	35
El Morro	0	85	H	65	35
Haton	-5	95	H	65	35
Roswell	5	100	H	71	35
Santa Fe	5	90	M	65	35
Tucumcari	5	95	H	70	35
NEW YORK					
Albany	-10	90	M	74	45
Auburn	-10	90	M	74	45
Binghamton	-5	90	M	72	40
Buffalo	-5	85	M	73	45
Canton	-20	85	M	74	45
Cortland	-10	90	M	73	45
Elmira	-5	90	M	73	45
Glens Falls	-15	90	M	73	45
Ithaca	-5	90	M	74	40
Jamestown	-5	90	M	73	45
Lake Placid	-15	90	M	73	45
New York	-5	90	M	76	40
Niagara Falls	-5	85	M	73	45
Ogdensburg	-20	85	M	73	45
Oneonta	-10	90	M	74	45
Oswego	-5	90	L	75	45
Port Jervis	0	90	M	74	40
Rochester	-5	90	M	74	45
Schenectady	-10	90	M	74	45
Syracuse	-10	90	M	74	45
Watertown	-15	85	M	73	45
NORTH CAROLINA					
Asheville	5	90	M	75	35
Charlotte	15	95	M	78	35
Greensboro	10	90	M	76	35
Hatteras	20	90	L	80	35
New Bern	20	95	M	78	35
Raleigh	15	95	M	78	35
Salisbury	10	95	M	78	35
Wilmington	20	90	M	81	35
Winston-Salem	10	90	M	76	35
NORTH DAKOTA					
Bismarck	-30	95	H	73	45
Devils Lake	-30	90	M	70	50
Dickinson	-30	95	H	70	45
Fargo	-30	95	H	75	45
Grand Forks	-30	90	H	72	50
Jamestown	-30	95	M	73	45
Minot	-35	90	M	71	50
Pembina	-35	90	M	73	50
Williston	-35	90	M	73	50
OREGON					
Arlington	5	95	M	68	45
Baker	-15	90	M	66	45
Eugene	15	90	H	68	45
Medford	20	95	H	68	40
Pendleton	-10	90	H	66	45
Portland	10	85	H	68	45
Roseburg	20	90	H	68	45
Salem	15	90	H	68	45
Warmic	0	90	H	66	45
PENNSYLVANIA					
Altoona	-5	90	M	75	40
Bethlehem	0	90	M	75	40
Coatesville	5	85	M	75	40
Erie	-5	90	M	74	40
Harrisburg	-5	90	M	75	40
New Castle	-5	90	M	78	40
Oil City	-5	90	M	75	40
Philadelphia	0	90	M	78	40
Pittsburgh	-5	90	M	75	40
Reading	0	90	M	75	40
Scranton	0	90	M	74	40
Warren	-10	90	M	75	40
Williamsport	-5	90	M	74	40
York	5	90	M	75	40
RHODE ISLAND					
Block Island	5	85	L	75	40
Bristol	0	90	L	75	40
Kingston	0	85	L	75	40
Pawtucket	0	90	M	75	40
Providence	0	90	M	75	40
SOUTH CAROLINA					
Charleston	20	90	L	80	35
Columbia	20	95	M	78	35
Florence	20	95	M	79	35
Greenville	10	95	M	75	35
Spartanburg	10	95	M	78	35
SOUTH DAKOTA					
Aberdeen	-25	95	M	75	45
Huron	-20	100	H	75	45
Pierre	-20	95	H	70	45
Rapid City	-20	95	H	70	45
Sioux Falls	-20	95	H	73	45
Watertown	-25	95	M	73	45
TENNESSEE					
Chattanooga	10	95	M	76	35
Jackson	5	95	M	78	35
Johnson City	5	95	M	78	35
Knoxville	5	95	M	75	35
Memphis	5	95	M	78	35
UTAH					
Logan	-10	95	H	65	40
Milford	-5	95	H	66	40
Ogden	-5	90	H	65	40
Salt Lake City	0	95	H	65	40
VERMONT					
Bennington	-10	90	M	73	45
Burlington	-15	90	M	73	45
Montpelier	-20	85	M	73	45
Newport	-20	90	M	73	45
Northfield	-15	90	M	73	45
Rutland	-5	90	M	73	45
VIRGINIA					
Cape Henry	15	90	L	78	35
Charlottesville	15	90	M	78	40
Danville	10	90	M	78	35
Lynchburg	10	85	L	76	35
Norfolk	15	90	M	78	35
Petersburg	10	90	M	78	35
Richmond	10	90	M	78	40
Roanoke	5	90	M	76	35
Wytheville	5	90	M	76	35
WASHINGTON					
Aberdeen	20	85	L	64	45
Bellingham	15	80	L	65	50
Everett	20	80	L	65	50
North Head	20	80	L	64	50
Olympia	15	80	M	65	45
Seattle	15	80	M	65	50
Spokane	-15	90	M	64	50
Tacoma	15	80	L	65	46
Tatoosh Island	20	80	M	67	50
Walla Walla	-10	95	M	75	45
Wenatchee	-5	90	H	73	45
Yakima	-5	90	H	72	45
WEST VIRGINIA					
Bluefield	0	95	M	75	35
Charleston	0	90	H	75	40
Elkins	-5	95	H	73	40
Fairmont	0	90	H	76	40
Huntington	0	90	M	76	40
Martinsburg	0	90	M	76	40
Parkersburg	0	90	M	75	40
Wheeling	-5	90	M	75	40

Province & City	Win-ter DB	Sum-mer DB	Daily Range	Sum-mer WB	Lati-tude Deg.
Cincinnati	5	90	M	75	40
Cleveland	-5	90	M	75	40
Columbus	-5	90	M	75	40
Dayton	-5	90	M	75	40
Lima	-5	90	M	75	40
Marion	-5	90	M	75	40
Sandusky	-5	90	M	75	40
Toledo	-5	90	M	75	40
Warren	-5	90	M	75	40
Youngstown	-5	90	M	75	40
OKLAHOMA					
Ardmore	5	100	M	78	35
Bartlesville	-5	100	M	77	35
Guthrie	0	100	H	77	35
Muskogee	0	95	H	79	35
Oklahoma City	0	100	M	77	35
Tulsa	0	100	M	77	35
Waynoka	-5	105	M	75	35
ALBERTA					
Banff	-30	—	M	—	50
Camrose	-35	—	H	—	55
Calgary	-30	90	H	66	50
Cardston	-30	—	H	—	50
Edmonton	-35	90	H	68	55
Grande Prairie	-40	—	H	—	55
Hanna	-35	—	H	—	50
Jasper	-30	—	H	—	50
Lethbridge	-30	—	H	—	50
Lloydminster	-40	—	H	65	55
McMurray	-35	—	H	—	55
Medicine Hat	-40	90	H	—	50
Red Deer	-35	—	H	—	50
Taber	-35	—	H	—	50
Wetaskiwin	-35	—	M	—	55
BRITISH COLUMBIA					
Chilliwack	5	—	M	—	50
Courtenay	10	—	M	—	50
Dawson Creek	-40	—	H	—	55
Estevan Point	15	—	H	—	50
Fort Nelson	-40	—	M	—	60
Hope	0	—	H	—	50
Kamloops	-20	90	M	67	50
Kimberly	-5	—	H	—	50
Lytton	10	—	H	—	50
Nanaimo	10	—	M	—	50
Nelson	-10	—	H	—	50
Penticton	-5	—	H	—	50
Port Alberni	10	—	M	—	50
Prince George	-30	—	H	—	55
Prince Rupert	10	80	L	—	55
Princeton	-15	—	H	—	50
Revelstoke	-25	—	H	—	50
Trail	-10	—	H	—	50
Vancouver	-10	80	L	—	50
Vernon	-15	—	H	—	50
Victoria	15	—	L	67	50
Westview	10	—	M	—	50

Province & City	Win-ter DB	Sum-mer DB	Daily Range	Sum-mer WB	Lati-tude Deg.
TEXAS					
Abilene	5	95	M	74	30
Amarillo	0	95	M	72	35
Austin	15	100	M	78	30
Brownsville	30	95	M	78	25
Corpus Christi	25	95	M	80	30
Dallas	10	95	M	78	30
Del Rio	20	100	M	78	30
El Paso	10	100	M	69	30
Fort Worth	10	95	L	78	30
Galveston	25	95	M	80	30
Houston	20	95	M	80	30
Palestine	10	100	M	78	30
Port Arthur	20	95	M	80	30
San Antonio	20	100	M	78	30
Waco	10	100	M	78	30
LABRADOR					
Goose Bay	-25	—	L	—	55
MANITOBA					
Boissevain	-35	—	H	66	50
Brandon	-30	—	H	68	55
Churchill	-40	—	H	—	50
Dauphin	-35	—	L	—	55
Flin Flon	-40	—	M	—	50
Minnedosa	-35	—	H	—	50
Neepawa	-35	—	M	—	50
La Prairie	-30	—	M	—	50
Swan River	-35	—	M	—	55
The Pas	-40	—	M	71	55
Winnipeg	-30	90	M	—	50
NEW BRUNSWICK					
Bathurst	-10	—	L	—	45
Campbellton	-10	—	M	—	45
Chatham	-15	90	L	76	45
Edmunston	-5	—	M	—	45
Fredericton	-10	90	H	—	45
Moncton	-5	80	L	67	45
Saint John	-15	—	L	—	45
Woodstock	-15	—	M	—	45
NEWFOUNDLAND					
Corner Brook	0	—	L	—	50
Gander	-5	—	M	—	50
Grand Falls	-5	—	L	—	50
St. John's	0	—	L	—	50
NORTHWEST TERRITORIES					
Aklavik	-45	—	L	—	70
Fort Norman	-40	—	L	—	65
Frobisher	-50	—	L	—	
Resolute	-40	—	L	—	60
Yellowknife	-50	—	L	—	
NOVA SCOTIA					
Bridgewater	0	—	L	—	45
Dartmouth	0	—	M	—	45

Province & City	Win-ter DB	Sum-mer DB	Daily Range	Sum-mer WB	Lati-tude Deg.
Ashland	-25	80	M	71	45
Beloit	-15	95	M	78	45
Eau Claire	-20	90	M	75	45
Green Bay	-20	95	M	73	45
La Crosse	-20	90	M	75	45
Madison	-15	90	M	75	45
Milwaukee	-20	90	M	75	45
Oshkosh	-20	90	M	75	45
Sheboygan	-20	90	M	75	45
WYOMING					
Casper	-25	90	H	62	45
Cheyenne	-20	90	H	62	40
Lander	-30	90	H	65	45
Sheridan	-30	90	H	65	45
Yellowstone Park	-35	85	H	62	45
NOVA SCOTIA					
*Halifax C	5	80	L	75	45
*Halifax A	0	80	L	75	45
Kentville	0	—	L	—	45
New Glasgow	0	85	M	67	45
Spring Hill	-5	—	L	—	45
Sydney	5	—	L	—	45
Truro					
Yarmouth					
ONTARIO					
Bancroft	-20	—	M	—	45
Barrie	-10	—	M	—	45
Belleville	-10	—	M	—	45
Brampton	-5	—	M	—	45
Brockville	-15	—	M	—	45
Chatham	0	85	M	70	45
Cobourg	-10	—	M	—	45
Collingwood	-15	—	M	—	45
Cornwall	-15	—	M	—	45
Ear Falls	-30	—	M	—	50
Fort Frances	-25	—	M	—	50
Fort William	-35	—	M	—	45
Galt	-5	—	M	—	45
Geraldton	-30	—	M	—	50
Goderich	-5	—	M	—	45
Guelph	-5	—	M	—	45
Hamilton	-5	—	M	—	45
Haileybury	-25	—	M	—	50
Hanover	-15	—	M	—	45
Huntsville	-15	—	M	—	45
Kapuskasing	-35	—	M	—	50
Kenora	-35	—	M	—	50
Kingston	-10	—	M	—	45
Kirkland Lake	-25	—	M	—	50
Kitchener	-5	—	M	—	45
Lindsay	-15	—	M	—	45
London	-10	—	M	—	45
Moosonee	-35	—	M	—	50

HEATING CALCULATION FORM

NAME OF PROJECT OR AREA .Living Room.......................

DESIGN CONDITIONS: Outside Dry Bulb Temperature .0°..........

Inside Dry Bulb Temperature .70° Temperature Difference .70°F....

PART 1:   Ceiling Type and Insulation Thickness .2"...............

Floor Type and Insulation .Crawl Space 2" Insulation.

Type of Windows ...Single Pane.................

Type of Walls and Insulation ..3½" Insulation.......

PART 2:   Infiltration

$$\frac{\text{area width} \times \text{area length} \times \text{ceiling height}}{60}$$

$$\frac{(13.75) \text{ width} \times (19.25) \text{ length} \times (8) \text{ ceiling height}}{60}$$

Heat Loss

= ..35.29.. x 1.08 x ...70.... T.D. =   2667.70....

PART 3:   Heat Loss

Windows: ....49. sq. ft. x 0.55 x ....70.... T.D. =   1886.5....

Walls: ....215. sq. ft. x 0.13 x ....70.... T.D. =   1956.5....

Roof: 264.68 sq. ft. x 0.20 x ....70.... T.D. =   3705.1....

Floor: 264.68 sq. ft. x 0.09 x ....70.... T.D. =   1668.80...

TOTAL HEAT LOSS IN BTUH   11,884.6....

Divide by 3.4 to obtain heat loss in watts   3,495.5....

Figure 6-3   Completed heat-loss form for the living room of the home in Figure 6-2.

Assuming again that this home is located near Washington, DC, the same design conditions for this area will be used. With the inside and outside design conditions and the drawing of the house floor plan, a complete room-by-room heat-loss calculation can be made. Use a separate form for each room in the house.

Begin by filling in Part 1 (Fig. 6-1) of the living room form. This information includes:

1. Ceiling below ventilated attic: 2 in. of insulation
2. Floor with crawl space: 2 in. of insulation
3. Windows: single pane with drapes
4. Walls and insulation: plasterboard with 7-1/2 in. of insulation

Part 2 of the form covers heat loss as a result of infiltration, or air leaks through cracks in walls around windows and doors. The living room in the example is 13.75 ft wide by 19.25 ft and has an 8-ft ceiling. When these dimensions are inserted in their proper position in the blanks, the formula can be completed:

$$13.75 \times 19.25 \times 8/60 = 35.29$$

Part 3 of the form includes radiant and conductive heat losses through exterior surfaces, the first being the windows. Find the area of all windows in the living room and enter the answer in the appropriate space on the calculation form. The total area of the windows is 49 square feet.

Item 2 in Part 2 of the form is outside walls: one of the living room walls is 19.25 ft in length, while the remaining outside wall is 13.75 ft in length. The ceiling height is 8 ft. The gross outside wall area is:

$$19.25 \text{ ft} + 13.75 \text{ ft} \times 8 \text{ ft} = 264 \text{ square feet}$$

The calculation form calls for the net wall area (gross wall area − window area), so 49 square feet must be subtracted from 264 square feet to obtain the answer of 215 square feet. This figure is entered in the proper space on the form.

The remaining two spaces are for the areas of the floor and ceiling and since these two areas will have the same dimension, the calculations for both can be completed in one step:

$$19.25 \times 13.75 \text{ ft} = 264.68 \text{ square feet (of floor and ceiling)}$$

This completes all the data necessary for the calculation of the heat loss that must be taken from the drawings; the remaining factors are printed on the form.

Begin with the first figure (infiltration), multiply by the infiltration factor (1.08) and the temperature differential (70 degrees) and enter the product in the appropriate space. Continue down the list until heat loss is calculated for all areas. Summing the subtotals, the room heat loss is found to be 11,884.6 Btuh.

This means that 11,884.6 Btuh will be required to keep the inside temperature at 70 degrees if the outside temperature is 0 degrees. If electric heat is being used, the heat loss in Btuh must be converted to watts. This can be done by dividing 11,884.6 by 3.4 and finding that 3495.5 watts of electric heat would be required to do the job.

The completed heat-loss form for the living room is shown in Fig. 6-3. Study this procedure carefully before continuing to the next area.

If a heating unit was being added to just this room and heating the remaining areas with the existing heating system, it could be stopped now. This method of calculating heat loss is good for one small area or an entire home.

The calculations for the kitchen/dining area, bedroom, and bathroom are performed exactly as for the living room, using the proper dimensions. The results of the calculations are shown in Figs. 6-4 through 6-7. The procedure for calculating the utility room is a little different because of the absence of an outside window or outside walls. Omit these two steps when calculating the heat loss for this area; the results are shown in Fig. 6-8.

HEATING CALCULATION FORM

NAME OF PROJECT OR AREA ....Bedroom No.1....

DESIGN CONDITIONS: Outside Dry Bulb Temperature ..0°...

Inside Dry Bulb Temperature .70°.. Temperature Difference ...$70^o F$...

PART 1: Ceiling Type and Insulation Thickness ..$2"$...

Floor Type and Insulation ..$2"$..

Type of Windows .Single Pane.

Type of Walls and Insulation ..$3\frac{1}{2}"$..

PART 2: Infiltration

$$\frac{\text{area width x area length x ceiling height}}{60}$$

$$\frac{(\ 12\ )\text{ width x }(\ 12.5\ )\text{ length x }(\ 8\ )\text{ ceiling height}}{60}$$

		Heat Loss
= ...20... x 1.08 x ...70... T.D. =		1512.0

PART 3: Heat Loss

Windows:	..28.. sq. ft. x 0.55 x ....70.... T.D. =	1078.0
Walls:	.164. sq. ft. x 0.13 x ....70.... T.D. =	1492.4
Roof:	.144. sq. ft. x 0.20 x ....70.... T.D. =	2016.0
Floor:	.144. sq. ft. x 0.09 x ....70.... T.D. =	907.2

TOTAL HEAT LOSS IN BTUH ....7005.6....

Divide by 3.4 to obtain heat loss in watts ....2060.47....

Figure 6-4 Completed heat-loss form for bedroom No. 1.

HEATING CALCULATION FORM

NAME OF PROJECT OR AREA ..Bedroom No. 2..

DESIGN CONDITIONS: Outside Dry Bulb Temperature .0°..

Inside Dry Bulb Temperature .70°.. Temperature Difference ...70°..

PART 1: Ceiling Type and Insulation Thickness .$2"$.

Floor Type and Insulation ..$2"$..

Type of Windows .Single Pane.

Type of Walls and Insulation .$3\frac{1}{2}"$.

PART 2: Infiltration

$$\frac{\text{area width x area length x ceiling height}}{60}$$

$$\frac{(\ 12.25\ )\text{ width x }(\ 15.5\ )\text{ length x }(\ 8\ )\text{ ceiling height}}{60}$$

		Heat Loss
= ...20.41... x 1.08 x ...70... T.D. =		1542.8

PART 3: Heat Loss

Windows:	..28.. sq. ft. x 0.55 x ...70... T.D. =	1078.0
Walls:	.172. sq. ft. x 0.13 x ...70... T.D. =	1565.2
Roof:	.156. sq. ft. x 0.20 x ...70... T.D. =	2184.0
Floor:	.156. sq. ft. x 0.09 x ...70... T.D. =	982.8

TOTAL HEAT LOSS IN BTUH ....7352.8....

Divide by 3.4 to obtain heat loss in watts ....2162.58....

Figure 6-5 Completed heat-loss form for bedroom No. 2.

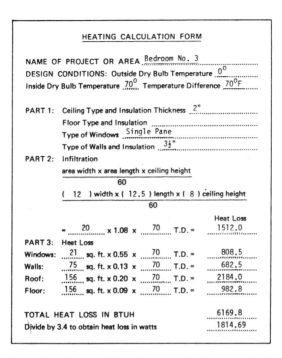

HEATING CALCULATION FORM

NAME OF PROJECT OR AREA _Bedroom No. 3_

DESIGN CONDITIONS: Outside Dry Bulb Temperature _0°_

Inside Dry Bulb Temperature _70°_ Temperature Difference _70°F_

PART 1: Ceiling Type and Insulation Thickness _2"_

Floor Type and Insulation

Type of Windows _Single Pane_

Type of Walls and Insulation _3½"_

PART 2: Infiltration

area width x area length x ceiling height

————————————————
60

(_12_) width x (_12.5_) length x (_8_) ceiling height

————————————————
60

Heat Loss

= _20_ x 1.08 x _70_ T.D. = _1512.0_

PART 3: Heat Loss

Windows: _21_ sq. ft. x 0.55 x _70_ T.D. = _808.5_

Walls: _75_ sq. ft. x 0.13 x _70_ T.D. = _682.5_

Roof: _156_ sq. ft. x 0.20 x _70_ T.D. = _2184.0_

Floor: _156_ sq. ft. x 0.09 x _70_ T.D. = _982.8_

TOTAL HEAT LOSS IN BTUH _6169.8_

Divide by 3.4 to obtain heat loss in watts _1814.69_

Figure 6-6 Completed heat-loss form for bedroom No. 3.

HEATING CALCULATION FORM

NAME OF PROJECT OR AREA _Bath_

DESIGN CONDITIONS: Outside Dry Bulb Temperature _0°_

Inside Dry Bulb Temperature _70°_ Temperature Difference _70°F_

PART 1: Ceiling Type and Insulation Thickness _2"_

Floor Type and Insulation _2"_

Type of Windows _Single Pane_

Type of Walls and Insulation _3 1/2"_

PART 2: Infiltration

area width x area length x ceiling height

————————————————
60

(_6.5_) width x (_8.25_) length x (_8_) ceiling height

————————————————
60

Heat Loss

= _7.14_ x 1.08 x _70_ T.D. = _539.7_

PART 3: Heat Loss

Windows: _4_ sq. ft. x 0.55 x _70_ T.D. = _154.0_

Walls: _48_ sq. ft. x 0.13 x _70_ T.D. = _436.8_

Roof: _52_ sq. ft. x 0.20 x _70_ T.D. = _728.0_

Floor: _52_ sq. ft. x 0.09 x _70_ T.D. = _327.6_

TOTAL HEAT LOSS IN BTUH _2186.1_

Divide by 3.4 to obtain heat loss in watts _642.97_

Figure 6-7 Completed heat-loss form for bathroom.

HEATING CALCULATION FORM

NAME OF PROJECT OR AREA _Utility Room_

DESIGN CONDITIONS: Outside Dry Bulb Temperature _0°_

Inside Dry Bulb Temperature _70°_ Temperature Difference _70°F_

PART 1: Ceiling Type and Insulation Thickness _2"_

Floor Type and Insulation _2"_

Type of Windows _Single Pane_

Type of Walls and Insulation _3 1/2"_

PART 2: Infiltration

area width x area length x ceiling height

————————————————
60

(_5.5_) width x (_9_) length x (_8_) ceiling height

————————————————
60

Heat Loss

= _6.6_ x 1.08 x _____ T.D. = _498.4_

PART 3: Heat Loss

Windows: _____ sq. ft. x 0.55 x _____ T.D. =

Walls: _____ sq. ft. x 0.13 x _____ T.D. =

Roof: _49.5_ sq. ft. x 0.20 x _70_ T.D. = _693.0_

Floor: _49.5_ sq. ft. x 0.09 x _70_ T.D. = _311.5_

TOTAL HEAT LOSS IN BTUH _1502.9_

Divide by 3.4 to obtain heat loss in watts _442.02_

Figure 6-8 Completed heat-loss form for utility room.

The heating equipment selected for these areas must meet or exceed the calculated heat loss, which, in turn, will maintain the required temperature inside the building. If at all possible, heating equipment for any individual room or area should not exceed the calculated loss by more than 10 percent. In duct systems, the duct losses should be calculated before determining the required heat output. A rule of thumb for duct loss is to multiply the calculated heat loss by a factor of 1.15 to 1.25.

SIMPLIFIED COOLING CALCULATIONS

An accurate calculation of how much heat enters a building on a hot summer day is essential for proper air conditioning. This calculation dictates the size of components required to cool the interior. Care and accuracy pay off in savings and comfort later, so always check the math for errors.

The Residential Cooling Load Estimate Form (Fig. 6-9) will be used as a guide to ascertain that all pertinent data are included. The two lines at the top of the form should be filled in first: the top line for identification, and the second to provide a basis for accurate calculation in your geographic location. Refer to Table 6-2 to obtain the outside design conditions required to complete the second line of the form. For example, if the building in question is near Washington, DC, Table 6-2 gives the summer outside temperature as 90° (DB), a medium (M) daily range, and a latitude of 40°. Once these data are entered on the form, the calculations can begin. Use a floor plan of the house in Fig. 6-10 as an example.

WINDOWS

Item 1a on the form deals with the amount of solar heat entering the building through glass surfaces. Begin by determining the number of square feet of window area on each side of the building; that is, north, south, east, and west. For example, the building in Fig. 6-10 has the following glass areas:

North exposure: 70.5 sq ft

South exposure: 88.0 sq ft

East exposure: 41.0 sq ft

West exposure: 42.0 sq ft

When measuring the area of windows, the window area is the area of the wall opening in which the window is installed—not just the glass itself. Once the glass area of all exposures is found, separate the total number of square feet of glass for each side into the total number of square feet of shaded glass and the total number of square feet of unshaded glass.

Customer .... Date .... Address ....
Design Conditions .... Outside temperature .... Daily Range .... Latitude ....

1a Windows—Solar Heat (See back side for example)	Area Sq. ft.	No Shades	Roller Shades	Drapes or Venetian	Ventilated Awning	Outside Shade Screens	
(1) Regular Single glass							
(a) North (or Shaded)		19	14	11	16	4	
(b) Northeast and Northwest		51	37	28	17	12	
(c) East and West		77	57	43	18	18	
(d) Southeast and Southwest		66	48	36	17	9	
(e) South		36	26	20	16	5	
(2) Regular Double glass							
(a) North (or shaded)		17	13	10	11	3	
(b) Northeast and Northwest		45	35	26	12	8	
(c) East and West		67	53	40	12	12	
(d) Southeast and Southwest		57	45	34	12	6	
(e) South		31	25	18	11	3	
(3) Heat Absorbing Double glass							
(a) North (or shaded)		10	8	7	8	2	
(b) Northeast and Northwest		26	22	18	9	7	
(c) East and West		40	33	28	10	10	
(d) Southeast and Southwest		34	28	23	9	5	
(e) South		20	16	13	9	3	

1b Windows—air to air heat gain	Area Sq. ft	Outdoor Design Temperature				
		90	95	100	105	110
(1) all single glass		8	12	16	20	24
(2) all double glass		4	7	9	11	13

2 Walls and Doors	Area Sq ft	Daily Temperature Range									
		Low		Medium				High			
		Outdoor Design Temperature									
a Frame and Veneer on frame		90	95	90	95	100	105	95	100	105	110
(1) No insulation		5.9	7.2	4.8	6.1	7.4	8.7	4.8	6.1	7.4	8.7
(2) less than 1 in. insulation		4.3	5.2	3.5	4.5	5.4	6.4	3.5	4.5	5.4	6.4
(3) 1 to 2 in. insulation		2.9	3.6	2.4	3.1	3.7	4.4	2.4	3.1	3.7	4.4
(4) more than 2 in. insulation		1.8	2.2	1.5	1.9	2.3	2.7	1.5	1.9	2.3	2.7
b Masonry walls 8 in. block or brick											
(1) plastered or plain		7.3	9.7	5.4	7.8	10.2	12.6	5.4	7.8	10.2	12.6
(2) Furred, no insulation		4.6	6.1	3.4	4.9	6.4	7.9	3.4	4.9	6.4	7.9
(3) Furred, less than 1 in. insulation		3.1	4.1	2.3	3.3	4.3	5.3	2.3	3.3	4.3	5.3
(4) Furred, 1 to 2 in. insulation		2.1	2.8	1.6	2.3	3.0	3.7	1.6	2.3	3.0	3.7
(5) Furred, more than 2 in. insulation		1.4	1.8	1.0	1.5	1.9	2.4	1.0	1.5	1.9	2.4
Partitions											
(1) Frame, finished one side only, no insulation		8.4	11.4	6.0	9.0	12.0	15.0	6.0	9.0	12.0	15.0
(2) Frame, finished both sides, no insulation		4.8	6.5	3.4	5.1	6.8	8.5	3 4	5.1	6.8	8.5
(3) Frame, finished both sides, more than 1 in. insulation		2.0	2.7	1.4	2.1	2.8	3.5	1.4	2.1	2.8	3.5
(4) Masonry, finished one side, no insulation		2.6	4.4	1.2	3.0	4.7	6.5	1.2	3.0	4.7	6.5
Wood doors*		11.3	13.8	9.3	11.8	14.3	16.8	9.3	11.8	14.3	16.8

3 Ceilings and Roofs		90	95	90	95	100	105	95	100	105	110
a Ceiling under naturally vented attic or vented flat roof											
(1) Uninsulated — dark		9.9	11.0	9.0	10.1	11.3	12.4	9.0	10.1	11.3	12.4
— light		8.1	9.2	7.1	8.3	9.4	10.6	7.1	8.3	9.4	10.6
(2) Less than 2 in. insulation — dark		4.3	4.8	3.9	4.4	4.9	5.4	3.9	4.4	4.9	5.4
— light		3.5	4.0	3.1	3.6	4.1	4.6	3.1	3.6	4.1	4.6
(3) 2 in. to 4 in. insulation — dark		2.6	2.9	2.3	2.6	2.9	3.2	2.3	2.6	2.9	3.2
— light		2.1	2.4	1.9	2.2	2.5	2.8	1.9	2.2	2.5	2.8
(4) More than 4 in. insulation — dark		1.7	1.9	1.6	1.8	2.0	2.2	1.6	1.8	2.0	2.2
— light		1.4	1.6	1.2	1.4	1.6	1.8	1.2	1.4	1.6	1.8
b Built up roof no ceiling											
(1) Uninsulated — dark		17.2	19.2	15.6	17.6	19.6	21.6	15.6	17.6	19.6	21.6
— light		14.0	16.0	12.4	14.4	16.4	18.4	12.4	14.4	16.4	18.4
(2) 2 in. roof insulation — dark		8.6	9.6	7.8	8.8	9.8	10.8	7.8	8.8	9.8	10.8
— light		7.0	8.0	6.2	7.2	8.2	9.2	6.2	7.2	8.2	9.2
(3) 3 in. roof insulation — dark		6.0	6.7	5.5	6.2	6.9	7.6	5.5	6.2	6.9	7.6
— light		4.9	5.6	4.3	5.0	5.7	6.4	4.3	5.0	5.7	6.4
c Ceilings under unconditioned rooms		2.7	3.6	1.9	2.9	3.8	4.8	1.9	2.9	3.8	4.8

4 Floors		90	95	90	95	100	105	95	100	105	110
a Over unconditioned rooms		3.4	4.6	2.4	3.6	4.8	6.0	2.4	3.6	4.8	6.0
b Over basements, enclosed crawl space, or slab on ground		0	0	0	0	0	0	0	0	0	0
c Over open crawl space		4.8	6.5	3.4	5.1	6.8	8.5	3.4	5.1	6.8	8.5

5 Outside Air		90	95	90	95	100	105	95	100	105	110
a Infiltration, Btuh per sq ft of gross exposed wall area		1.1	1.5	1.1	1.5	1.9	2.2	1.6	1.9	2.2	2.6
b Mech. ventilation Btuh per cfm		16.2	21.6	16.2	21.6	27.0	32.4	21.6	27.0	32.4	37.8

6 People (never less than 3)	Number of occupants x 300 Btuh
7 Kitchen appliance allowances	1200 Btuh
SUB TOTAL	Items 1 thru 7
8 Heat gain to ducts	Subtotal Item 1 thru 7 x factor**
9 Total Estimated Sensible Heat Gain	Total (Items 1 thru 8)
10 Latent heat gain allowance	Item 9 x 0.3
11 Total Estimated Design Heat Gain	Item 9 + Item 10 =

*Consider glass area of doors as windows. **Factor for ducts in attic with 2 in. insulation .10 Factor for ducts in attic with 1 in. insulation .15; For ducts in slab floors, insulated ducts in enclosed crawl space, unconditioned basement or furred spaces use factor of .05.

Figure 6-9 Residential cooling load estimate form.

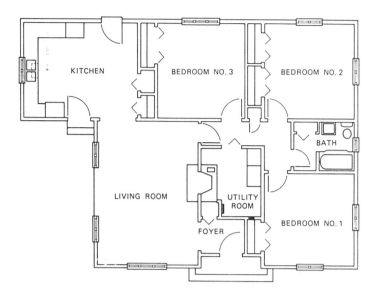

Figure 6-10   Floor plan of a typical residence.

There are many ways a window may be shaded, such as by awnings, tinted glass, or insulating drapes, but in this example, the shading provided by overhanging roofs will be considered. The larger the overhang, the more the walls and windows will be shaded. Also, gable roofs provide overhang shade on two sides as shown in Fig. 6-11; hip roofs provide shade on all four sides (as illustrated in Fig. 6-12). Therefore, for a window under an overhanging roof, figure the glass area as shaded. When no overhang exists, consider it to be unshaded.

The chart in Fig. 6-13 is provided to enable the calculation of heat gain through shaded and unshaded glass areas. All dimensions entered in this

Figure 6-11   Gable roofs provide over-hand shade on only two sides of the building.

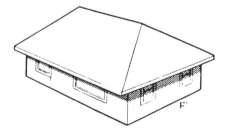

Figure 6-12   Hip roofs provide shade on all four sides of the building.

1.	Direction which wall faces	N	S	E	W
2.	Width of Overhang, ft.	2¹	2¹	˙0	0
3.	Shade-Line Factor	0	2.6	.81	.81
4.	Distance Shade Line Falls below Edge of Overhang, (Line 2) x (Line 3)	0	5.2	0	0
5.	Vertical Distance from Top of Windows to Edge of Overhang, ft.		1.5	1.5	1.5
6.	Distance Shade Line Falls below Top of Windows, (Line 4) - (Line 5), ft.		3.7	˙0	0
7.	Total Area of Shaded Glass, sq. ft.	70.5	13.5	0	0
8.	Total Area Unshaded Glass, sq. ft. (Total Glass Area in Wall) - (Line 7)	0	74.5	41	42

Figure 6-13 Chart for determining heat gain through shaded and unshaded glass areas.

chart should be in feet. If all windows in any one wall are not the same distance below the edge of the overhang or if overhang width varies along a wall, use two or more columns as necessary for that particular wall. Locate the shade line only for those windows in any wall which are shaded by an overhang.

Using Fig. 6-10 as an example, enter the direction each wall faces and then measure the width of the roof overhang (see A of Fig. 6-14) for each wall. These data are entered on line 2 of the chart (Fig. 6-9), under the appropriate direction shown in line 1.

At this point determine the shade line factor—line 3 of the chart. Refer to Table 6-3 and note the latitude of your location; the example house is located near Washington, DC, so its latitutde is 40°. Refer to the following table and circle the latitude that applies.

Figures listed under the latitude of 40°, for example, are the shade-line factors applying to each side of the house. These are entered on line 3 of the

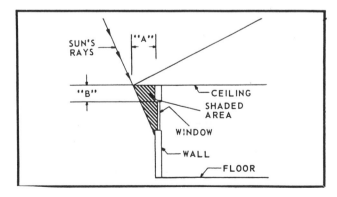

Figure 6-14 Drawing illustrating methods of measuring window opening distances.

TABLE 6-2 Shade-Line Factors.

DIRECTION WINDOW FACES	LATITUDE						
	25°	30°	35°	40°	45°	50°	55°
EAST	0.83	0.83	0.82	0.81	0.80	0.79	0.78
SOUTH	10.10	5.40	3.55	2.60	2.05	1.70	1.32
WEST	0.83	0.83	0.82	0.81	0.80	0.79	0.78

chart and, for the example, are 0, 2.6, 0.81, and 0.81. Note that the north side of the building has a shade-line factor of zero; the north side is considered shaded at all times and does not require a factor.

Now multiply line 2 of the chart in Fig. 6-13 by line 3 and enter the answer on line 4 as shown in the example.

Measure the vertical distance from the top of all window openings to the bottom edge of the roof overhang (shown as B in Fig. 6-14). These measurements are then entered on line 5 of the chart in Fig. 6-13. Subtract the figures on line 5 from line 4 and enter the answers on line 6.

Continue by multiplying the figures on line 6 by the width of the windows on each side of the building. The answer will be the total area of shaded glass and should be entered on line 7 of the chart. The example involves only the south side since the remaining sides have a zero answer. Therefore, by multiplying 3.7 (the figure on line 6) by 9 feet (total width of windows on the south side) we have a total shaded area of 13.5 square feet; this figure is entered on line 7 of the chart. Since the north side is shaded, enter the figures (found earlier) giving the total square feet of window area on this side on the chart also.

Finally, the chart is completed by subtracting line 7 from the corresponding totals of the window areas found earlier.

North exposure: 70.5 sq ft − 70.5 sq ft = 0 sq ft

South exposure: 88.0 sq ft − 13.5 sq ft = 74.5 sq ft

East exposure: 41 sq ft − 0 = 41 sq ft

West exposure: 42 sq ft −0 = 42 sq ft

This gives the total area of unshaded glass and is entered on line 8 of the chart in Fig. 6-13. With this chart completed, refer again to the estimate form in Fig. 6-9 under Item 1a. Here, there are three classifications of glass: regular single glass, regular double glass, and heat-absorbing double glass (tinted glass). Your windows should fall into one of these classifications. Assume that the example has regular double glass (single glazing plus storm windows). Circle (2) under 1a and cross off the other two on the estimate form.

Add up the total areas of shaded and unshaded glass from lines 7 and 8 of the chart in Fig. 6-13 and enter in Fig. 6-9 the total area of shaded glass on line (a); the total area of unshaded glass (east and west) on line (c); and the total area of unshaded glass (south) on line (e). Other shade options are represented by the column headings of Item la of the estimate form and must be considered for a correct estimate of the heat gain. Therefore, choose the treatment applicable to the sample building, circling the factors corresponding with lines (a), (c), and (e). Assume that the example building has drapes throughout, so under drapes or venetian, circle the numbers 10, 40, and 18, respectively. By multiplying the window area figures entered on lines (a), (c), and (e) by the corresponding circled factor, the results are:

$$54 \times 10 = 540.0$$
$$83 \times 40 = 3320.0$$
$$74.5 \times 18 = 1341.0$$

These answers are then entered in the right-hand column at the end of each line before going on to Item 1b: air-to-air heat gain.

Begin this item by adding up the total area of all windows in the home (both shaded and unshaded) and enter the answer in the area sq ft column of the estimate form, Item 1b, line (1) or (2) (whichever applies). Since the example has a total of 241.5 square feet of window area, this figure will be entered in the form under (2)—all double glass. The area in which the building is located has a summer outside design temperature of 90° (DB), so this figure is circled in Item 1b under outdoor design temperature, and the factor 4 beneath it. This factor is then multiplied by the total square feet of window area and the answer entered at the end of the line. The answer is 966.0.

WALLS AND DOORS

The next item (2) on the estimate form is walls and doors, which calculates the amount of heat that enters the building through the outside walls and doors.

First, determine the total number of square feet of all outside walls and then subtract the total square feet of window area from this (since the heat gain through the windows has already been calculated). Using Fig. 6-9 as a reference, follow these steps:

1. Scale the drawings or take actual measurements of the length of each outside wall and total. In the example, this length totals 163.5 feet.
2. Scale or measure the floor-to-ceiling height, which is 8 feet in the example.

3. Multiply the total length (163.5 feet) by the floor-to-ceiling height (8 feet) to obtain a total of 1,308 square feet for the outside walls of the residence.

4. Subtract the total window area (the figure determined earlier and entered in Item 1b, area sq ft column, of the estimate form) from the total square feet of the outside walls. Since the total window area in the example is 241.5 square feet, subtracting this from the total wall area of 1,308 square feet leaves a net wall area of 1,066.5 square feet. This is the figure that will be used to complete Item 2 of the estimate form.

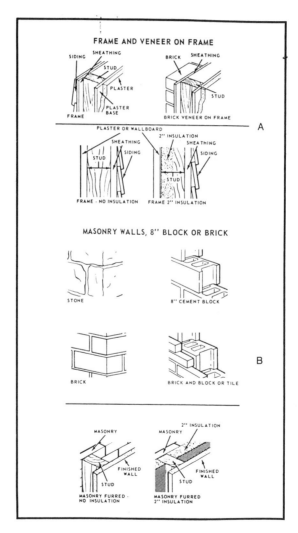

Figure 6-15   Various types of wall construction and insulation.

Below Item 2 of the estimate form are several classifications of wall construction: you must determine which one applies to your walls. To help, the illustrations in Fig. 6-15 show various types of wall construction and insulation. The example has brick veneer on wood framing, so it will fall under classification (a); it also has 3 1/2 in. of insulation in the walls, so it will fall under catagory (4), more than 2 in. insulation.

Next refer to the outside temperature and daily range entered at the top of the estimate form and determine the closest corresponding categories shown in Item 2. Circle the factor beneath it on the line corresponding with the area sq ft figure. Since the building is located in an area with a medium daily range and an outside design temperature of 90°F, circle the 1.5 factor on the estimate form. Then the net square feet of the outside walls (1,066.5) is multiplied by this factor (1.5) and the answer (1,599.75) is entered at the end of the line in the extreme right-hand column.

Below Item 2 of the estimate form there is a classification (c) partitions. This is for use with any partitions in a building that are not outside partitions, but are located adjacent to an area—like a garage—that is separated from the living area and is not cooled. If it does apply, calculate this wall following the same procedure as for outside walls, and enter the figures on the estimate form. This condition does not exist in the example, so this portion of the estimate form will be omitted.

The last classification below Item 2 is (d) wood doors. This pertains to outside doors only. In the example, there are two outside doors which are both 3 feet wide by 6.5 feet high; each, therefore, has an area of 19.5 square feet. The total area of these doors (39 sq ft) is entered on the estimate form, multiplied by the appropriate factor—in the same column as used for outside walls—and the answer is then entered at the end of the line (2d) of the estimate form. The answer for the example is $39 \times 9.3 = 362.7$.

CEILINGS

Going on to Item 3 of the estimate form, notice that three main categories are listed: ceilings under naturally vented attic or vented flat roof, built-up roof with no ceiling, and ceilings under unconditioned rooms. Measure your ceiling areas that apply to one (or more) of these classifications, determine the total square of each, and enter the figures on the appropriate line(s) of the estimate form. Then multiply the area by the applicable factor and enter the answer at the end of the line or lines.

The building in the example has 6 in. of insulation in the ceiling and a light gray roof. Therefore, circle the appropriate factor under (a), classfication (4). Referring to the proper column for the outdoor design conditions, the factor for the example is 1.2. Multiplying this by the total ceiling area

(1,357), the answer is 1,628.4 to be entered at the end of line 4 (light) under classification (3a) on the estimate form.

FLOORS

Item 4, floors, is very similar to the calculations for the ceilings and roofs in Item 3. Again there are three classifications: (a) over unconditioned rooms; (b) over basements, enclosed crawl space, or slab on ground; and (c) over enclosed crawl space. Determine the classification of the floors from the lines, calculate the area in square feet, and enter the answer on the appropriate line(s) of the estimate form. Multiply this area by the applicable factor in the column under the outside design conditions and enter the answer at the end of the line or lines.

The example building has an enclosed crawl space (B under 4), so the factor will be zero—no heat gain through the floor. Therefore, zero will be entered at the end of the line.

Refer to Item 2 of the estimate form (walls and doors) to obtain the total area of the walls and doors; then add the total area of the windows to this figure in order to obtain the gross area of all outside walls. Enter this figure on line (a) under Item 5 (1,308 square feet). Multiply this figure by the applicable factor (1.1) and enter the answer 1,438.8 at the end of line (a).

Mechanical ventilation or exhaust fans used during cooking or bathing must be considered in calculating the air-conditioning system. Check the nameplates of all fans to obtain the cfm rating of each. As a rule of thumb, most kitchen/range exhaust fans will average about 300 cfm, while bath fans will be around 70 cfm. The building in the example has one kitchen fan 300 cfm and a bath fan at 70 cfm for a total of 370 cfm. This figure is entered in the area sq ft column and then multiplied by the applicable factor (16.2) for a total of 5,994, which is entered at the end of line (b) under Item 5. In Item 6 on the form, enter the number of people normally occupying the building, but never enter fewer than three. Assume a number of four; this is multiplied by 300 (Btuh) for an answer of 1,200 to be entered at the end of the line.

Consult the local utility company if there are a lot of appliances operating at once. In this example, use 1,200 at the end of line 7.

Now total Items 1 through 7 to obtain a subtotal of heat gain in the building; the answer will be in Btuh. The example comes out to 19,227.4 Btuh.

If there is concealed heating ductwork (such as is found when ductwork is installed beneath an existing ceiling and a new lowered ceiling is built in to conceal it), multiply the subtotal figure by 0.05 and enter the answer at the end of the line. This condition does not exist in the example so this step has been omitted.

To complete the estimate form, total lines 1 through 8 (19,227.4) and enter this answer on line 9. Then multiply this figure by 0.3 to obtain an allowance for latent or hidden heat. The calculations will be complete when Items 9 and 10 are added and the answer entered on line 11.

The amount of heat entering the building on a summer day when the outside temperature reaches the outdoor design temperature has been determined. Now the selection for the cooling equipment can begin.

If individual room or window air-conditioning units are to be used, the total load will have to be broken down into areas. This is done by determining the number of Btuh per square foot and then installing cooling units equal to the total square feet in the area to be cooled multiplied by the Btuh-per-square-foot factor. For example, the building in the example has a heat gain of 19,804.23 Btuh. This means that 14.59 Btuh of cooling will be required for each square foot. Therefore, if just one section of the building were to be cooled, get the section in square feet and multiply it by 14.59. This gives you the Btuh of cooling for that particular section.

Of course, if a central unit is desired, use one capable of offsetting the heat gain determined on the estimate form. If you're planning to use an add-on air-conditioning system, there are a few other items to look into before deciding upon the equipment to be used. First determine what type of system is now being used and how well it will accommodate the addition of central air conditioning.

Investigate the present heating system and its related ductwork to determine the size of the furnace blower, the number and sizes of the branch ducts, and the type of grilles and register. Also check the electrical system to make certain that there is enough spare capacity to handle the additional load of an air-conditioning system; additional wiring may have to be done before the system is installed.

7
Hot-Water Heating Systems

Hot-water heating systems are frequently used in residential applications for space heating, that is, to heat the entire home. This type of heating system is considered by many to be the most comfortable system available. There are several types of systems, and although some of those mentioned in the following paragraphs have become somewhat outdated, the reader should be familiar with them to enable repairs to be made. Of course, the more modern systems are also covered.

HOT-WATER HEATING

In a gravity-flow heating system, circulation of hot water to the radiators is accomplished by the difference between the weight of water in the supply main and that in the return main. Figure 7-1 illustrates this principle. Water heated in the boiler increases in volume and rises at the same time that the cooler, heavier water in the system moves downward in the return main, causing a constant circulation to be maintained. A steam-heating system operates in much the same way, and such a system is illustrated in Fig. 7-2.

The forced hot-water system employs an electric pump to provide circulation, as shown in Fig. 7-3 (see also Fig. 7-4). In this type of system,

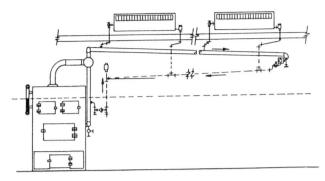

Figure 7-1 Typical gravity-pipe hot-water heating system. Water flow is caused by the difference in weight of the hot water in the supply main and the cooler water in the return main.

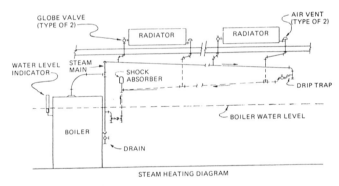

Figure 7-2 System illustrated in Fig. 7-1 as it would appear in a working drawing.

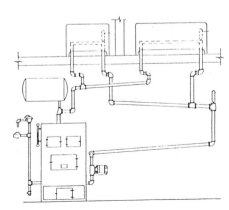

Figure 7-3 Typical two-pipe, forced-circulation, hot-water heating system.

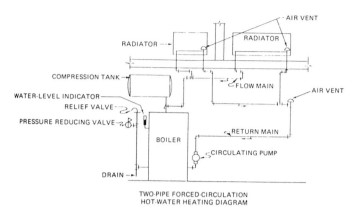

Figure 7-4   System illustrated in Fig. 7-3 as it would appear on a working drawing.

circulation is greatly speeded up so that radiators, water coils, and similar units can be supplied with hot water almost instantly whenever it is needed. Also, a constant temperature can be maintained in the system to compensate for outdoor weather conditions.

BASIC FACTS ABOUT HEATING

A heating system must be designed to replace the heat lost through the roof, walls, and floors of a building and also the heat lost by infiltration of air through cracks around doors and windows. The rate of heat loss is determined by (1) the building construction, (2) the velocity of prevailing winds, and (3) the outdoor temperature.

When the proper calculations are performed, the heat loss of the building can be determined and the required capacity of the heating plant can be chosen.

The accepted measurement of heat is the British thermal unit (Btu): One Btu is the amount of heat required to raise the temperature of one pound of water to one degree Fahrenheit. Nearly all calculations of heat output and heat input are made by the Btu method.

Pressure drop.   Pressure drop is a term that expresses the fact that power is consumed when liquids are moved through pipes, heating units, fittings, and so forth. Pressure drop is caused by the friction created between the inner walls of the conveyor (pipe, for example) and the moving liquid.

Head pressure.   As used in designing the capacity of a circulating pump, head pressure is the maximum pressure drop against which the pump

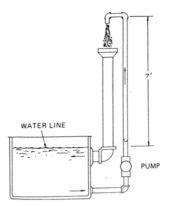

Figure 7-5 Maximum pressure head is the height to which a pump can cause water to flow.

can induce a flow of liquid. If a certain size of booster pump is connected to a tank of water as illustrated in Fig. 7-5, it will pump water to a height of 7 ft. This height, therefore, is the maximum pressure head against which the pump can cause a flow of water.

One- and two-pipe forced hot-water systems. Forced hot-water systems are classified as one-pipe or two-pipe designs. Two-pipe systems are further divided into direct-return and reverse-return layouts.

In the one-pipe system, illustrated in Fig. 7-6, a single main line in one or more circuits is used to circulate water. Branch pipes or risers from this main are equipped with special fittings at their connections to the main line. These fittings introduce the correct amount of resistance needed to assure proper diversion of hot water into the radiator.

In the reverse-return system of a two-pipe system, illustrated in Fig. 7-7, the first radiator of the main line is the last to return, and all radiator circuits are of equal length. Therefore, the problem of proper radiation balance is greatly simplified in this type of system.

In the direct-return system, illustrated in Fig. 7-8, the first radiator taken off the main line is the first radiator to return its load. The last radiator on the line is the last to return. Consequently, the water circuits to the radiators are of unequal length, and maintaining a proper balance of heat distribution can cause serious difficulties at times.

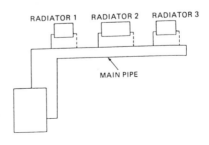

Figure 7-6 One-pipe forced hot-water system.

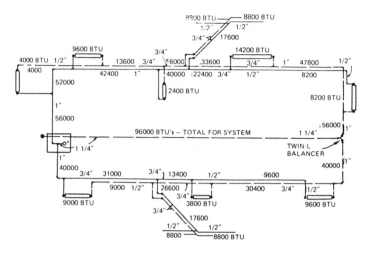

Figure 7-7   Reverse-return two-pipe forced hot-water system.

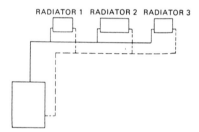

Figure   7-8   Direct-return   two-pipe forced hot-water system.

AIR SUPPLY FOR BOILER ROOMS

All open-flame equipment must be installed in a location in which ventilation facilities permit satisfactory combustion of gas, proper venting, and the maintenance of ambient temperatures at safe limits under normal conditions of use.

The following general rules are based on natural-draft venting and the requirements necessary for proper operation of equipment. They do not take into account the makeup air necessary to supply a building exhaust system. When an exhaust system is installed in a building, provisions should be made for makeup air to prevent negative pressures within the building. These pressures will adversely affect combustion efficiencies of equipment used for heating and water heating.

EQUIPMENT LOCATED IN UNCONFINED SPACES

In unconfined spaces within a building of conventional frame, brick, or stone construction, infiltration will normally provide adequate air to the open-flame equipment. In unconfined space within a building of unusually tight construction, air must be provided from outdoors. A permanent opening having a total free area of not less than 1 in. square per 5,000 Btuh (British thermal units per hour) of total input is required. Ducts that convey this air should have the same cross-sectional area as the free opening, and when rectangular, they should not be less than the cross-sectional area of a 3-in. round duct (7.06 in.^{2}).

EQUIPMENT LOCATED IN CONFINED SPACES

Provisions must be made to supply a means of air circulation when installing equipment in a confined space.

All air from inside the building. The boiler room should be provided with two permanent openings, one near the top of the enclosure and one near the bottom. Each opening should have a free area of not less than 1 in.^{2} per 1,000 Btuh of total input. These openings are connected with the interior areas of the building that, in turn, must have adequate infiltration from the outside.

All air from the outside. The boiler room should have two permanent openings, one in the top and one in the bottom of the enclosure. These openings should communicate directly, or by means of ducts, with the outdoors. When connected directly to the outdoors or when connected by means of vertical ducts, each opening should have a free area of not less than 1 in.^{2} per 4,000 Btuh of total input. If horizontal ducts are used, each opening should have a free area of not less than 1 in.^{2} per 2,000 Btuh of total input. When rectangular, these ducts should not be less than the cross-sectional area of a 3-in. round duct (7.06 in.^{2}).

Louvers and grilles. The free areas do not take into consideration the louvers, grilles, or screens in the openings. Openings equipped with wooden louvers will have 20 to 25 percent free area. Those with metal louvers or grilles will have from 60 to 75 percent free area. Thus the openings will have to be enlarged to compensate for the blocking effect of louvers and grilles.

The examples of heating systems illustrated in Figs. 7-9 through 7-12 were taken from actual working drawings. Each illustration should be

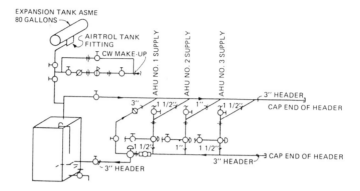

Figure 7-9   Heating system for hot-water coils in air-handling units.

carefully analyzed. The following points are some of the recommended design practices used when planning the layout for residential hot-water heating.

A baseboard radiation system should be installed along the outside walls. The heating elements should be equally distributed under all windows. If the outside walls do not provide sufficient footage for the required radiation, use the inside walls also.

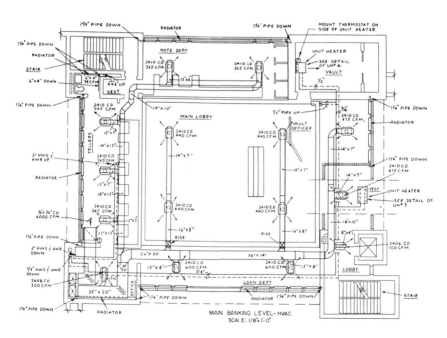

Figure 7-10   Plan view of the HVAC system for the main level of a bank building.

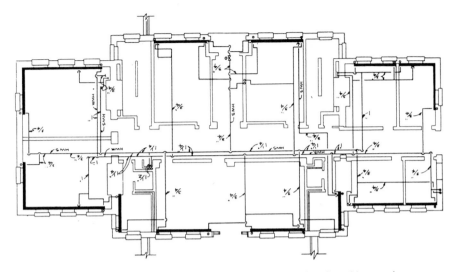

Figure 7-11   Plan view of a heating system for hot-water baseboard heaters in an education building.

To ensure proper heating satisfaction of a nonzoned single-loop system, the water from the boiler should flow in the following sequence:

1. To the bathroom
2. To the kitchen
3. To the living room
4. To the dining room and bedrooms

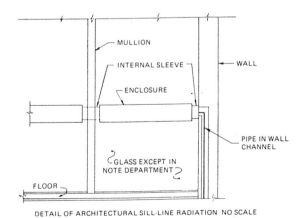

DETAIL OF ARCHITECTURAL SILL-LINE RADIATION NO SCALE

Figure 7-12   Detailed drawing.

This circuiting procedure will result in the most satisfactory heating installation, due to the fact that the hottest water is at the beginning of the loop. The ultimate in heating satisfaction, however, will be obtained by using motorized valves and zoning the system as illustrated in Fig. 7-13. A zoned hydronic (hot-water) heating system permits selection of different temperatures in each zone of the home. Baseboard heaters located along the outer walls of rooms provide a blanket of warmth from floor to ceiling; the heating unit also supplies domestic hot water simultaneously, through separate circuits. A special attachment coupled to the hot-water unit can be used to melt snow and ice on walkways and driveways in winter, and a similar attachment can be used to heat a swimming pool during the spring and fall seasons.

A typical hot-water system operating diagram is shown in Fig. 7-14 and is explained as follows. When a zone thermostat calls for heat, the appropriate zone valve motor begins to run, opening the valve slowly; when the valve is fully opened, the valve motor stops. At that time, the operating relay in the hydrostat is energized, closing contacts to the burner and the circulator circuits. The high-limit control contacts (a safety device) are normally closed so that the burner will now fire and operate. If the boiler water temperature exceeds the high-limit setting, the high-limit contacts will open and the burner will stop, but the circulator will continue to run as long as the thermostat continues to call for heat. If the call for heat continues, the resultant drop in boiler water temperature—below the high-limit setting—will bring the burner back on. Thus, the burner will cycle

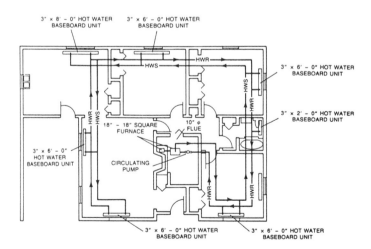

Figure 7-13   Hot-water heating system sketched out on a floor plan.

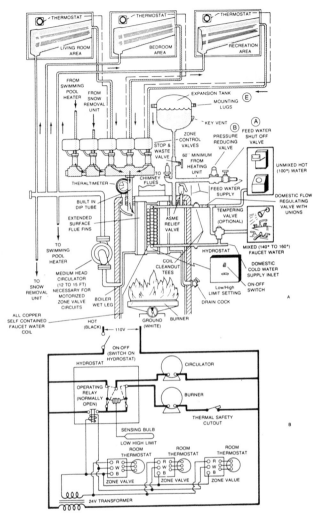

Figure 7-14 (a) Typical hot-water system operating diagram; (b) typical electrical wiring.

until the thermostat is satisfied; then both the burner and circulator will shut off.

Hot-water boilers for the home are normally manufactured for use with oil, gas, or electricity. Although a zoned hot-water system is comparatively costly to install, the cost is still competitive with the better hot-air systems. The chief disadvantage of hot-water systems is that they do not use ducts. If you wish to install central air conditioning, you must install a complete duct system along with the central unit.

HOT-WATER COMBINATION UNITS

Many homes throughout the country utilize older steam or hot-water heating systems which may be in need of repair or replacement. In doing so, the owners may want to consider installing through-wall combination units in place of the radiators. These units are easily installed, and comfort conditioning can then be controlled floor by floor, wing by wing, or room by room. The initial cost of such a system usually is much less than that of a central air-conditioning system offering comparable performance, and the system provides both heating and cooling.

Operating costs for through-wall units are lower than those of many other systems due to the high efficiency of room-by-room control. The living area, for example, can be heated at a temperature of 70°F, while the bedrooms may require only 55°F. Areas that are used only occasionally, such as a guest bedroom or workshop, may be kept at an even lower temperature until occupied. The same principle applies to cooling the areas during warm months. Unlike a central forced-air duct system, through-wall units never need balancing from season to season and if a unit should fail, the defective chassis can be replaced immediately or taken to a shop and repaired.

The main disadvantages of combination heating and cooling units should be considered carefully, however, before making arrangements to go ahead with such a project. First, at each location, you will have a relatively large unit protruding inside your home. There will also be an opening of approximately 15 in. by 54 in. on the outside of your home; this is the grille for air cooling the air-conditioning compressor and for makeup air. Although these openings are usually flush with the outside of the building, the esthetics of a building may be downgraded in certain cases.

Another consideration is the noise that these units make due to the compressor and blower fan. The better units are very quiet, but some are so noisy that you would not want them. Therefore, you should examine several brands closely before making a decision.

The esthetics of through-wall units can be improved somewhat by making certain that the opening is cut to fit the sleeve and louvered grille correctly. Also make sure that the grille fits flush with the outside finished surface. The grilles and trim may then be painted a color to match the finish, making them hardly noticeable. Low shrubs planted in front of the grilles will make them even less conspicuous, but you must provide enough clearance for intake and exhaust air.

INSTALLATION INSTRUCTIONS

Each unit consists of several basic components, the number of which depends on the manufacturer. In most cases these components are all that is necessary for complete installation with the exception of some hand tools and a few miscellaneous items that can usually be purchased locally.

Before starting the installation, review the wall thicknesses and make certain that your measurements are accurate, as they will dictate the method of installing the base unit. Where the walls are thicker than 9-1/4 in., or where built-in radiator enclosures are desired or already provided, usable floor space can be saved and the appearance of the installation enhanced if the base cabinet is partially recessed in the wall. However, if your walls are less than 9-1/4 in. thick, the rear extension may project beyond the outside face of the wall, as shown in Fig. 7-15. Obviously, this is undesirable, and the unit should be made flush with the outside wall by using a filler piece as illustrated in Fig. 7-15. If it is necessary to use a filler strip, add studs between the cabinet and the wall so that the cabinet can be fastened securely.

Start your wall openings following the rough-in dimensions packed with the unit. If you are cutting through wooden studs of an existing building, frame the opening before installing the sleeve through the wall. Most units are designed to fit exactly in a given number of block or brick courses, so if you are installing in a masonry wall, all you will probably need to do is remove the required number of blocks or bricks and insert the sleeve. Once the unit is in place, the equipment itself will provide all the support necessary, so don't worry about angle-iron lintels.

Dimensions for locating the wall opening for typical through-wall heating and cooling units are shown in Fig. 7-16. Figure 7-17 gives useful suggestions for cutting the wall opening and sealing it once the sleeve is in place. The opening should have a neat finish, be weatherproofed, and the bottom of the opening should be pitched toward the outside approximately

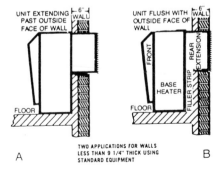

Figure 7-15 (a) On thin walls, the rear extension may project beyond the outside face of the wall, giving an undesirable appearance; (b) the projection is solved by using a filler piece to make the unit flush with the outside wall.

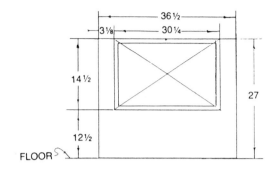

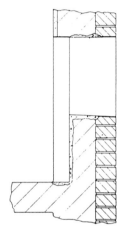

Figure 7-16 Wall section and dimensions for installing a recessed-cabinet unit.

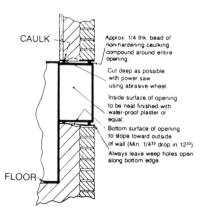

Figure 7-17 Wall sections and dimensions for installing a typical nonrecessed unit. Finishing and cutting instructions also apply to recessed units.

1/4 in. per foot for drainage. At this time you should make preparations for the electrical wiring and, if you are using hot-water heat, for water pipes.

Before installing the base section and rear extension, apply nonhardening caulking compound around the inside of the wall opening as described in Fig. 7-17. Then apply caulking compound around the outside of the base rear extension, to about 1 in. from the rear edge of the cabinet body. Caulk the top and sides only at this time, unless the bottom edge of the masonry is rough. If this is the case, the bottom edge may be caulked also, but be sure to leave two or three 1-in. gaps (weep holes) in the caulking for moisture drainage.

Next, place the base heater rear extension in the wall opening and slide it into the desired location. Shim the bottom of the cabinet, if necessary, to make the rear extension approximately 1.4 in. low (below horizontal) at the end nearest the outside face of the wall. This is important, as it prevents condensed moisture from running toward the inside of the building.

Secure the base unit to the floor and wall using suitable fasteners and check the caulking around the entire rear extension at the outside face of the wall. If the bottom face of the wall has been caulked, check the weep holes to make certain that they have not been clogged by the caulking.

PIPING FOR STEAM OR HOT WATER

By removing two bolts at each end of the coil, the steam or water-heating coil in most through-wall units may be removed in order to make connections. However, the coil should be securely bolted in place and properly pitched before the final pipe connections are made. Either end of the coil may be used as the inlet or the return. The use of 1/2-in.-I.D. (5/8-in.-O.D.) copper tubing is recommended for connecting the heating coil to the pipe.

Once the heating coil has been pitched and bolted securely in place, the pipe connections may be completed as shown in Fig. 7-18. Note that holes are provided in both the back and bottom of the cabinet for heat piping. If the existing piping cannot be arranged to utilize these holes, others may be drilled in the cabinet to suit your particular needs.

For the type of unit shown in Fig. 7-18, you will need two 3/4-in. × 2-1/2 in. black iron nipples (Item 3), one 3/4-in. I.P.S. × 5.8-in. O.D. female copper adapter, and two lengths of 5/8-in. soft copper tubing long enough to reach from the heating coil to the existing piping. A shutoff valve is recommended on the inlet pipe to the coil, mounted as shown in Fig. 7-18 (Item 8). In the case of hot-water piping, be sure to include an air vent (Item 26). Other items will include a 1/2-in. balancing fitting (Item 9) and one 1/2-in. × 1/2-in. × 3/4-in. I.P.S. iron reducing tee. These items are not normally furnished with the units and will have to be purchased at a hardware store or plumbing supply house.

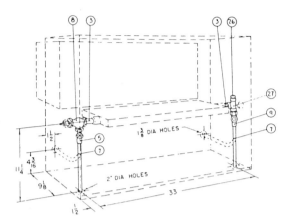

Figure 7-18 Pipe connections for a typical through-wall heating and cooling unit.

With the piping out of the way, slide the blower assembly back into the cabinet extension (if it had to be removed) and reconnect the wires to the thermostat and junction box. However, do not install the mounting plate at this time.

The cooling chassis is now ready to be installed, but this is going to require some help, as it weighs too much for one person to handle. Uncrate the cooling chassis as close as possible to the base unit in which it is to be installed. With your hand, spin the condenser blower wheel to be sure that it has not become loose due to rough handling in shipment. If it has been loosened or the wheels rub against the blower housing, center the setscrew over the flat part of the motor shaft and retighten it.

Slide the cooling chassis all the way into the base section, but be extremely careful not to lift or pull it by any of the copper tubing forming the refrigeration circuit. When properly in place, reinstall the mounting plate.

Before proceeding any further, inspect the base convector rear extension to make sure that it is sealed and insulated properly. If any light shows through, or if there is any way that air might leak between the base section and the wall, caulk and insulate as necessary. This is very important since gaps will allow unconditioned outside air to infiltrate. In addition, in extremely cold weather gaps could cause steam traps or hot-water lines to freeze.

ELECTRICAL WIRING

A separate electrical circuit should be used for each conditioner; each should be provided with a disconnect device at the unit location. The feeder wire and overcurrent protection should be sized in accordance with the National Electrical Code.

Always check the nameplate ratings on the cooling chassis (and on the heating coil if you are using an electric coil). In nearly all cases, the supply voltage will be 240 volts (v), but the amperage rating will vary with the size of the unit. If electric heat is used, the heating element load will be larger than the cooling load; since both operations will never run simultaneously, the wire size and overcurrent protection may be sized for the larger of the two, not for their sum.

For example, if the nameplate rating on your unit is 7.5 amperes (amp) at 230 v for the cooling chassis and you are using hot water for heat, 7.5 amp is the total load. Therefore, the wire would be sized as follows:

$$7.5 \text{ (amperes)} \times 1.25 \text{ (safety factor)} = 9.4 \text{ amp}$$

The wire to use should carry 15 amps. Conventional circuit breakers are not rated smaller than 15 amp, so a 15-amp breaker will be used.

But suppose that the nameplate stated an amperage of 14.9 amp. Again, applying the safety factor, we have $14.9 \times 1.25 = 18.6$ amp. Checking in the table, it is found that No. 12 AWG wire will be used and, in turn, provide an overcurrent device rated at 20 amp.

If an all-electric through-wall unit is used, a typical nameplate rating could state:

Cooling amperes: 7.5

Heating amperes: 12.5

In this case, the wire and overcurrent protection would be sized for the larger of the two loads, the heating load.

Besides the overcurrent protection at the electrical panel, a separate disconnect device at the unit itself will be needed. This can be accomplished in several ways:

1. Have a remote switch in the power line to the unit.
2. Install a double-pole, single-throw (ON-OFF) switch of the proper rating in the cover of the junction box provided.
3. Install a 240-V receptacle in the junction box and attach a plug to the unit's power cord.

In all cases, be absolutely certain to ground the base cabinet to guard against harmful electric shock should a fault occur in the wiring. If armored cable is used for the circuit, the connection to the chassis will also provide a ground, provided that the cable is properly grounded at the breaker panel. If nonmetallic cable with ground wire is used, the bare ground wire should be securely fastened under a screw in the chassis or base section. Most units will have a special grounding screw (painted green) for this purpose.

With the wiring completed, install the filter and the cabinet front. Press the control button marked OFF, and turn on the electric power supply. If using a steam or hot-water heating coil, make sure that the inlet valve is turned off. Then press the button marked COOL, and turn the thermostat knob clockwise to the extreme COOLER position. The compressor will start immediately if the heating coil is cool, and in a few minutes the unit should be discharging cooled air.

The compressor may not start if the room is very cold; it may be necessary to submerge the thermostat bulb in warm water to get the compressor to start. Now turn the thermostat knob to the extreme WARMER position; the compressor should stop unless the room is very warm.

Now test the heating cycle. Press the button marked OFF and wait a few minutes before pressing the one marked HEAT, leaving the thermostat at the extreme WARMER position. The circulating-air fans will run at low speed (for normal heating) if the room is not too hot.

If you install an all-electric model, the heating element will also be energized and warm air will be felt in a few seconds. If the unit uses steam or hot water, you won't feel any significant change in temperature of the air unless the furnace and circulating pumps are operating. But if the lower fan operates, the unit itself is working properly. Press the button marked OFF and all motors should stop. The first unit has now been completed.

Continue this procedure for the remaining units until all are installed. Then paint the outside louvers to match the finish of the building. The inside unit can also be painted to match any room decor, including wood-grain finishes, or you might prefer a wooden enclosure, but be sure to leave an opening for the air discharge and return.

8
Add-on Air-Conditioning Systems

Many HVAC contractors are called upon to convert an existing forced-air heating system to a combination heating/cooling system. In many cases, the entire system is replaced, especially if it is more than 20 years old, and/or in need of repair. However, many existing homes with central forced-air heat—but without air conditioning—can be converted to an excellent heating/cooling system, with automatic controls, for a very reasonable price. In fact, many smaller HVAC contractors are making a very good business of just conversions alone.

The working principle is simple (see Fig. 8-1). A compact cooling coil is installed in the plenum (warm-air outlet) of the furnace and a remote condensing unit is placed outside the home, but as close as possible to the furnace; refrigerant lines connect the condensing unit to the cooling coil. The furnace blower pushes air through the coil and the existing ductwork. In winter, the furnace runs as usual with the condensing unit turned off. The cooling coil has a negligible effect on the volume of heated air coming from the furnace.

Several companies manufacture central air-conditioning systems designed especially for the do-it-yourselfer, with the manufacturers claiming that these kits require little skill and only a few hand tools. However, unless the homeowner has some mechanical ability and has done other projects,

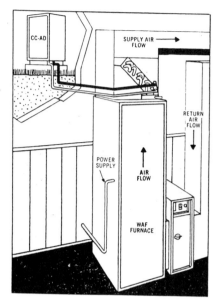

Figure 8-1 Basic components of an add-on cooling system.

many of these do-it-yourself projects have had to be finished by a qualified contractor, often at more expense than if the contractor had done the complete installation initially. In any event, since the cooling coil is designed to fit an existing forced-air furnace, utilizing the existing ductwork, most skilled contractors can finish the complete conversion in a single day.

The length of the refrigerant tubing, type of controls, and, if necessary, a replacement blower for the furnace will affect the total cost. In general, there are two basic steps to adding central air conditioning to the existing forced-air heating system:

1. Analyzing the home's cooling requirements.
2. Selecting and installing the system.

A careful analysis of the home's cooling requirements is an all-important step in selecting the proper size and type of equipment needed for a particular home and forced-air system. It is important because an oversized unit can cause as much dissatisfaction as an undersized unit.

Chapter 6—Residential Heating Calculations—gives step by step procedures necessary for evaluating the home's cooling requirements right down to the completion of the Residential Cooling Load Estimate Form.

Completion of this step will enable the dealer to supply the correct-capacity cooling equipment, exact costs, and detailed instructions for installing the equipment. The kit will look something like the one in Fig. 8-2 and will include two lengths of refrigerant tubing, four baffles, plenum cover,

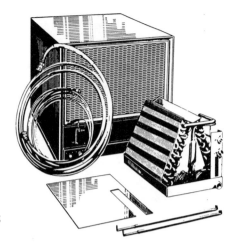

Figure 8-2 The kit will look something like this when it arrives.

coil supports, sealers, cooling coil, condenser/compressor unit, and complete instructions.

MOUNTING THE CONDENSING UNIT

Before ordering the kit, select the exact spot for mounting the condensing unit so the proper length of refrigerant tubing can be ordered.

In general, the condensing unit should be mounted outside the building, as close as possible to the cooling coil inside the furnace plenum, and on solid, level supports such as those shown in Fig. 8-3.

For roof installation, use wooden beams (treated to reduce deterioration) or channel-iron supports. Both should be sized to support the weight of the condensing unit and extended beyond the unit to distribute the load on the roof. And local ironworks can make a support frame once the dimensions of the unit have been provided, or make the frame using bolt-together channel iron available at a local hardware store. When installing such a frame on bonded roofs, check for special installation requirements.

For ground-level installations, use piers or a concrete slab with footers extended below the frost line, wooden beams treated to reduce deterioration, or a channel-iron frame with a suitable base. These are the most common installations and probably the easiest to construct (especially mounting the condensing unit on 4-inch × 4-inch wooden beams).

The condensing unit may also be mounted on a wall of the house, using an angle-iron mounting frame dimensioned to fit the condensing unit and provided with supports for attaching the frame to the building.

If it is necessary to mount the condensing unit more than two feet from the building, make provisions at this time for the electrical and refrigerant

1. Poured or pre-cast leveled concrete slab,
   26'' x 26'' long x approximately 4'' thick.

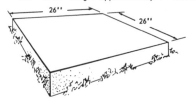

2. Two pre-cast patio blocks approximately
   12'' x 26'' x 4'' thick, leveled.

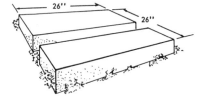

3. Four, 4'' x 8'' x 16'' concrete blocks, set
   and leveled as shown.

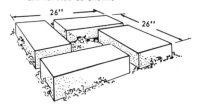

Figure 8-3 Supports on which the condensing unit is mounted.

tubing connections. An electrical conduit will be required for the power supply and a separate conduit for the low-voltage thermostat wiring. However, if the unit is mounted within two feet of the building, the fused disconnect switch can be mounted on the side of the building and the wiring and refrigerant lines can loop directly from the side of the house to the condensing unit.

When locating the condensing unit, clearance must be provided for the air intake and air discharge, refrigerant piping and power connections, and maintenance and servicing access. The recommended minimum clearances can vary from six inches to six feet; check the recommendations of the manufacturer.

INSTALLING THE COOLING COIL

Most cooling coils designed for these kits are charged with a holding charge of refrigerant and sealed at the factory to help simplify the installation. However, always follow the procedure instructions recommended by the manufacturer.

The installer will need only a few hand tools for this job: tin snips, electric drill, screwdriver, knife, hammer, scratch awl, level, drop light, and 1/8-inch drill bits.

Many forced-air heating systems installed within the past 10 to 15 years have provisions in the furnace plenum for adding a cooling system. For instance, one or more of the side panels of the plenum may be secured with sheet-metal screws rather than flanged together. If the existing furnace plenum is constructed in this manner, the installation of the cooling coil will be even easier. Merely remove the sheet-metal screws and lift the panel off; this will give complete access to the inside of the plenum.

If the furnace does not have this provision, an opening will have to be cut in the plenum. Start the hole by striking a screwdriver or cold chisel at an angle against the plenum. Proceed to cut a hole approximately ten inches in diameter to get an inside view of the plenum.

All forced-air furnaces contain duct flanges, but they vary in size from furnace to furnace. Therefore, once the opening is made, insert a drop light and accurately measure the height of the flanges on the furnace. Scribe a horizontal line 1/4 inch higher than the flange on the outside of the plenum. Scribe a second-level line 1/2 inch below the first.

Line up the bottom of the sheet-metal cover that came with the kit with the second-level line just scribed. Center the cover horizontally and mark the location of the holes in the cover on the plenum. Remove the cover and drill the plenum holes with a 1/8-inch drill. Next, hold the cover in position and scribe a line around its perimeter. Remove the cover and scribe a line 1/2 inch inside the perimeter line.

The cut will be made along this inside line so make certain that the cooling coil will fit through the resulting hole. Figure 8-4 shows the opening being cut with tin snips.

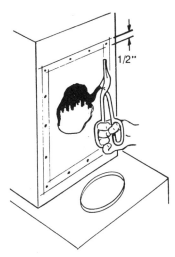

Figure 8-4 Cutting the opening in the furnace plenum with tin snips.

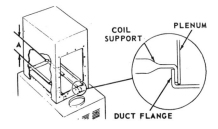

Figure 8-5   Placement of the coil supports.

Place the coil supports that come with most kits inside the opening with the large-diameter tube first. Hook the flanged end of the supports over the furnace flanges as shown in Fig. 8-5. As the end of the support will be located between the duct flange and the plenum wall, be certain that the support end is kept well down as shown in Fig. 8-5.

Some plenums are secured to the duct flange with sheet-metal screws, so don't try to locate the support end over a screw. Distance A in Fig. 8-5 (between the two supports) must be less than the width of the coil it will support.

With the support ends well secured between the duct flange and the plenum, telescope the small-diameter portion of the coil support toward the opposite side of the plenum and insert the flanged end over the duct flange.

Refer to Fig. 8-6 to help you visualize the next steps:

1. Measure depth of plenum (dimension D).

2. As the front of the tubing support bracket of the coil assembly will always be positioned flush with the front of the plenum, it follows that the coil length (L) should be subtracted from the plenum dimension (D) to determine the distance between the back of the coil and the plenum (dimension E).

3. Select one of the wide baffles supplied with most kits and prepare to cut it to fit shaded area B. As the baffle should fit under the condensate tray, add 1-1/2 inches to dimension E and scribe line 1 with an awl as shown in Fig. 8-7.

4. Measure the inside width of the plenum, subtract 3/16 inch for clearance and scribe line 2. The shaded area in Fig. 8-7 should be the correct size to fit area B in Fig. 8-6. Recheck the dimensions to be certain that all measurements are correct; then cut along the scribed lines. Place the baffle in position with the short flange down and against the plenum as shown in Fig. 8-6. If it is impossible to place the short flange down, it may be placed in upright, provided additional care is taken when sealing compound is applied later in the installation.

5. Select the smallest of the remaining baffles. Scribe and cut it in similar fashion to the first baffle to fit in F (Fig. 8-6).

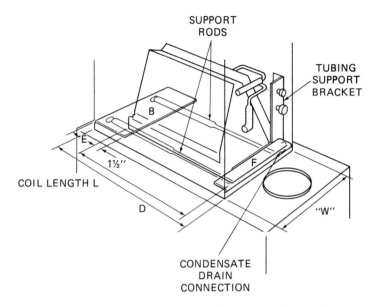

Figure 8-6   Method of positioning the coil supports inside the plenum.

6. Measure the width of the air inlet at the base of the cooling coil, and subtract this figure from the width of the plenum. The result divided by two gives you the width of each of the side baffles (L and R in Fig. 8-8). Their length is, of course, the depth of the plenum (dimension D in Fig. 8-6) minus 1/4 inch or so for ease of fit. The purpose of the end and side baffles is to ensure all air moved by the blower goes through—not around—the coil frame.

7. As shown in Fig. 8-8, place the baffles inside the plenum with the short flange down and against the sides of the plenum. The baffles should be placed in this sequence: first, B; second, F; third, L; and fourth, R.

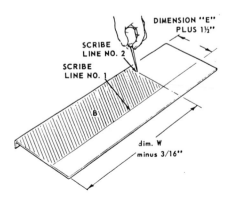

Figure 8-7   Scribing lines on baffles.

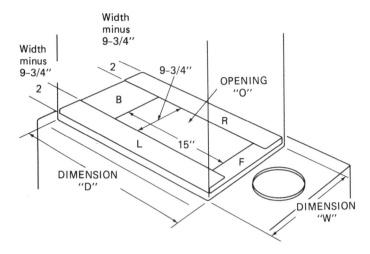

Figure 8-8   Location and dimensions of side baffles in plenum.

8. Opening O in Fig. 8-8, framed by the baffles, should not be smaller than the air inlet to the coil. Furthermore, opening O should be about 1 inch smaller in both width and depth than the overall width and depth of coil used, thus providing a shelf to hold the coil.

9. In the event that baffles L and R do not lie relatively flat on baffles B and F, sheet-metal screws may be used to hold them flat. Place the screws so their heads don't interfere with the coil frame. This procedure will normally be required when there are large plenum areas and, consequently, large overlaps.

10. High-temperature caulking compound should now be placed around the entire perimeter of the plenum and worked or pressed into the area between the baffles and plenum. A second bead of caulking should be placed around the perimeter of the opening. Make certain that the caulking compound has adhered to the baffles; to ensure this, a slight pressure should be applied on top of the bead of caulking with a finger.

To place the coil inside the plenum, grasp the coil by the tubing at point A in Fig. 8-9 and the condensate tray at point B. Always keep the top of the coil near the top of the plenum opening while inserting it; take care that the bottom of the coil doesn't move the bead of caulking out of position.

The front surface of the condensate tray should be flush with the front of the plenum before it is lowered to rest on the caulking strips. After it is gently lowered into place, hold your straight edge or level against the front of the plenum to check it.

Once the coil is in place, try the plenum cover over the opening, matching the holes of the cover with holes in the plenum; the tubing access

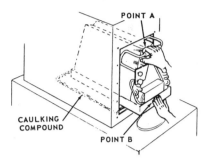

Figure 8-9 Method of inserting coil into plenum.

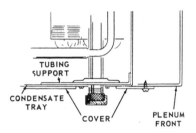

Figure 8-10 Caulk well between the tubing support bracket and cooling-coil cover.

holes on both sides of the cover should now be over the holes in the tubing support bracket. If they aren't, carefully move the coil until they are lined up. When you move the coil, observe the caulking. If the caulking does not seal between the flanges and condensate tray, remove the coil and reposition the caulking. A bead of caulking should also be placed between the tubing support bracket and the cooling coil cover to ensure a good seal (see Fig. 8-10). When an airtight seal has been accomplished, replace the cover, insert and tighten all screws.

At this stage, a 3/4-inch condensate line should be connected to the lowest opening and a J-trap should be fabricated to prevent air leakage through the line. The remainder of the pipe should be pitched at least 1/4 inch per 10 feet to an open floor drain, sump pit, or similar place where the condensate water can be disposed.

INSTALLING THE REFRIGERANT TUBING

Most refrigerant tubing that comes in kits has been specially tempered, evacuated, and partially filled with refrigerant at the factory. A typical kit will consist of:

1. One coil of smaller copper tubing with couplings.
2. One coil of large copper tubing with spring tube bender, insulation, and couplings.

Before attempting to install the refrigerant tubing, inspect it carefully, especially where the couplings are brazed to the ends. If any openings or punctures are detected, have them repaired or replaced.

Once the path of the tubing between the cooling coil and the condensing unit has been determined, the coils may be straightened. A preferred method of uncoiling the tubing is to hold the coil upright, placing one of the ends on a smooth surface (see Fig. 8-11). Hold one end at point A, and proceed to unroll the coil as shown.

Since the cooling coil is usually inside the house and the condensing unit outside, two 2-inch holes must be cut in the wall for the refrigerant lines.

Some bending of the tubing will have to be done, but since the copper tubing has been annealed, it can easily and neatly be formed. The smaller tubing can be formed by hand, the bends made over the thumbs as shown in Fig. 8-12. None of the bends, however, should have a radius smaller than 6 inches.

For the larger tubing, use the tubing bender; this bender is installed on the straight end of the tubing and under any insulation. The bend, with the spring bender covering the area of the bend, should then be made carefully over the knee as shown in Fig. 8-13. In making bends, extreme care must be taken to avoid kinking the tubing, which would make it useless.

Remove the protector plugs from the tubing couplings and the protector caps from the couplings of the condensing unit. Make sure that the rubber seal is inside the male coupling of the outdoor unit; if not, immediately obtain one from the supplier, as it must be used.

Without using wrenches, thread the couplings of the tubing over the respective couplings of the condensing unit. Tighten finger tight. The tubing should now be formed and routed to the cooling coil inside the house. It is recommended that the larger tubing be formed and run first, and the small tubing then run adjacent to it.

Next remove the protective caps from the cooling coil; again make certain that the rubber seal is in place within the fittings. Remove the

Figure 8-11 Preferred method of un-coiling refrigerant tubing.

Figure 8-12 Method of bending the smaller tubing.

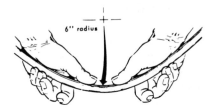

Figure 8-13 Method of bending large
tubing.

protector plugs from the female tubing connection and connect with finger
pressure—no wrenches.

The exact method of connecting the refrigerant tubing to the units will
vary from unit to unit, but the following example will illustrate the basic
process.

Using appropriate wrenches as shown in Fig. 8-14, tighten the
couplings in this sequence:

1. Large tube to inside cooling coil.
2. Small tube to inside cooling coil.
3. Large tube to outdoor unit.
4. Small tube to outdoor unit.

Tighten the couplings until a definite resistance is felt and then tighten
an additional 1/6 to 1/4 of a turn. If a torque wrench is used, the
small-diameter tube should be torqued to between 10 and 12 foot-pounds;
the large tube, 35 to 45 foot-pounds.

Immediately after tightening each coupling, coat the entire coupling
and the brazed joint where the tubing connects to the coupling with a rich
mixture of liquid detergent and water. If leakage is detected between
coupling halves, tighten the coupling nut. If this doesn't work, contact the
dealer or supplier at once.

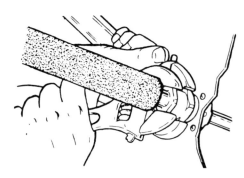

Figure 8-14 Correct use of wrenches to
tighten couplings on refrigerant lines.

INSTALLING THE ELECTRIC WIRING

Follow instructions given in the manufacturer's specifications or instruction manual for installing power and control wiring. Remember that all work must be done in accordance with the National Electrical Code.

Again, different units will have slightly different wiring connections; the wiring diagram in Fig. 8-15 shows a typical hookup.

PRESTARTING CHECKLIST

Before starting the unit, check the following details in order to prevent possible damage.

1. Is there adequate clearance around the condensing unit and its related grilles?
2. Is the electrical wiring in accordance with the wiring diagrams furnished with the system?
3. Are all wiring connections tight?
4. Does the blower turn freely without striking the shroud?
5. Is the thermostat level in a proper location, that is, away from drafts and on an inside wall or partition?
6. Are the filters or filter of adequate size, clean, and in place?
7. Is the ductwork correctly installed, well insulated, and taped?

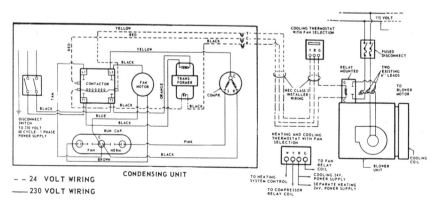

Figure 8-15   Electrical wiring diagram of a typical air-conditioning system.

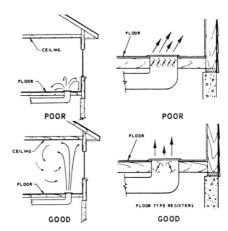

Figure 8-16   All register dampers should be adjusted so that the air projects upward.

START-UP PROCEDURE

To start, first turn the thermostat to its highest setting, and turn on the power at the electric panel or safety switch. Then go from room to room and adjust all registers or diffusers so that the air projects upward as shown in Fig. 8-16. Then move the thermostat indicator to a setting below room temperature, at which time the blower and refrigerant system should operate.

The system may need balancing to provide the greatest volume of air in areas with the greatest exposure; this may be accomplished by a trial-and-error method, using the dampers inside the ductwork for balancing.

Before and after installation, thoroughly read any literature that comes with the unit. Most come with booklets concerning troubleshooting and maintenance of the equipment, so they're worth holding on to.

9
Air-Distribution Ducts

The proper duct design is of prime importance to provide the necessary distribution and return of air in air-conditioning systems. Before such a design can be made, the area to be conditioned may be carefully evaluated to arrive at a satisfactory duct system. The exact approach will vary depending on several factors including the type of building and how it will be used.

In general, duct dimensions (width and height) should be as nearly square as possible for best results, but this is not always practical. The designer should attempt to keep the relationship of width to height to less than 4 to 1, and never more than 8 to 1. Keeping the ductwork to these ratios will help provide the greatest air carrying capacity per square foot of sheet metal, and also will help insure low static friction loss to give minimum operating cost.

The duct in Fig. 9-1 is 36 inches wide by 12 inches high. Using simple mathematics, 36/12 = a duct dimension ratio of 3 to 1.

When planning a duct layout, the design should provide the correct quantity and velocity of air, delivering the air to the various outlets in the most direct path. If there is a sudden change in the direction of air flow, such as in a 90-degree bend, turning vanes should be used as shown in Fig. 9-2.

Where a change in duct dimension is required, the transition should be gradual, and dampers should be installed in each branch for final balancing

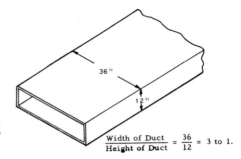

Figure 9-1 A rule-of-thumb for duct design is to keep the ratio of width to height to less than 4 to 1.

$$\frac{\text{Width of Duct}}{\text{Height of Duct}} = \frac{36}{12} = 3 \text{ to } 1.$$

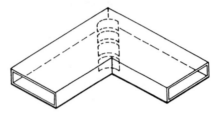

Figure 9-2 Turning vanes are recommended at any abrupt turn in the ductwork.

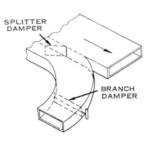

Figure 9-3 Dampers are used in ductwork to balance the system.

of the system. A damper controls the volume of air passing through a duct by changing the cross-section area, as shown in Fig. 9-3.

Motor power to drive the blower increases as the cube of the blower speed,

new hp = orig. hp × new blower speed/orig. blower speed

A study of the preceding relationship shows that ducts must be properly sized for correct motor selection and economical operating costs.

DUCT DESIGN

The HVAC designer will consult the architectural drawings as a reference when designing a suitable HVAC system. Once the heat-loss and heat-gain

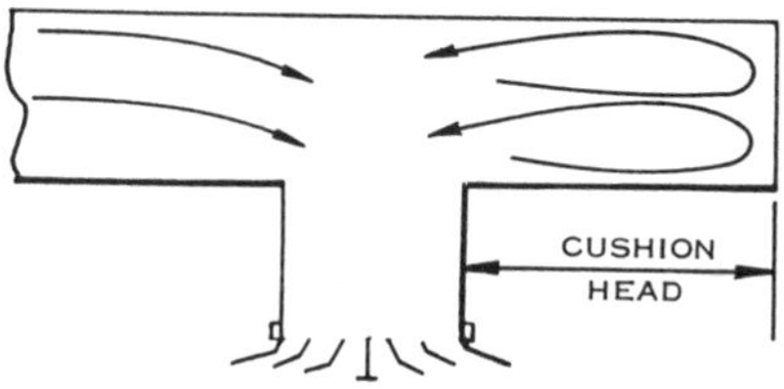

CUSHION HEAD

Figure 9-4 A cushion head is recommended at all duct outlets when the air velocity is above 800 ft. per minute.

calculations have been made, along with gathering other necessary information, the designer will then usually make a sketch of the proposed system. This sketch should show the location of the air-handling units and the duct system. In general, the supply outlets and return intakes should first be arranged for proper air distribution. Dimensions are then selected for the main supply duct, the branch ducts, and the return ducts.

Air-distribution ductwork carries the conditioned air from the fan-coil (blower) unit to the space to be conditioned, and then back to the unit.

Ducts may be selected in a variety of shapes and sizes, but the most conventional are circular, rectangular, or square. The size of the ducts will depend on the quantity and velocity of air to be carried through them.

Tables and other time-saving devices have been compiled to aid in duct sizing. Once the required information has been calculated, the actual sizing of the ductwork is relatively easy, by merely referring to a chart or by using specially designed slide rules. The computer may also be used to good advantage in sizing ductwork for any possible situation. In fact, not only will the computer size the ductwork, but many contractors utilize a computerized system for automatic frabrication.

STATIC PRESSURE

Pressure is exerted by air, as can be readily seen when a tire is inflated. This same pressure is present in ductwork, and since it is not dependent upon air movement, it is called static or stationary pressure. In ductwork, this pressure is exerted against the walls of the duct. An additional pressure is exerted when air is moving; this is called velocity pressure.

FRICTION LOSS

Some of the total pressure in ductwork (static and velocity pressures) is lost due to friction of the air against the sides of the duct. As the air flow increases, so does this friction loss. Conditions that can cause excessive friction loss include:

1. High air velocities.
2. Ducts with small sectional area.
3. Large air flow.
4. Long lengths of ducts.
5. Changes in direction of air flow.
6. Sudden contractions or expansions in air stream.

Recommendations covered in other chapters will help to eliminate excessive friction loss in ductwork systems. Always keep in mind that a good air-distribution system is one that permits quick and satisfactory balancing, and at the same time provides comfort conditions in the room or area.

SIZING DUCTWORK SYSTEMS

For residential and small commercial applications, ductwork is usually sized by charts or duct-sizing slide rules such as the Trane Duct Sizer, and other types usually available from manufacturers of air-conditioning equipment. Two methods are in common use: the static regain method and the equal friction method.

Static regain method. This method requires a velocity reduction at the beginning of each major duct section. This reduction tends to equalize static pressure at the outlets and also results in a regain of enough static pressure to offset friction loss in the ductwork. Done manually, this is a complicated method, requiring many calculations. However, the computer can aid the designer tremendously in solving these tedious calculations very quickly to give the best possible system, especially in systems that have several long duct runs with many outlets. The static regain method is thoroughly explained in the ASHRAE Guide.

Equal friction method. The equal friction method of sizing ductwork is commonly used by many air-conditioning designers, engineers, and contractors. In general, this method establishes an equal friction drop throughout the duct system. The friction drop is based on equal friction for each 100 feet of duct. In use, this sysetm follows a definite sequence which requires the use of a standard friction chart. Again, the computer can be a great help when used in conjunction with proper programs designed for the application.

A typical friction loss chart is shown in Fig. 9-5. Note that four sets of values appear on this chart, each represented by a group of lines, drawn in various positions. To briefly explain how this chart is used, assume a room

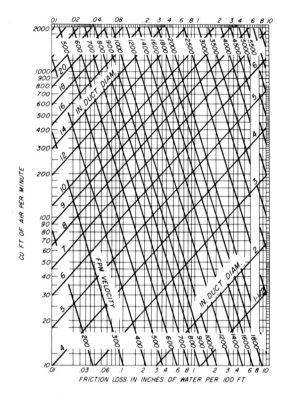

Figure 9-5   Typical friction loss chart.

requiring 70 cfm of air at a velocity of 400 fpm. What size duct should be used to obtain these characteristics?

1. Find 70 cfm on the cfm scale at the left of the chart.
2. Move horizontally to the right, to the 400 fpm line.
3. At the intersection of 70 cfm and 400 fpm, locate the duct diameter line.
4. Read a duct size of slightly less than 6-inch duct diameter. When the duct size is not exact, use the closest standard size.
5. Move downward from this intersection and read about .06-inch water friction loss.

Therefore, the duct size is 6 inches in diameter, with a friction loss of .06 inch of water per 100 feet.

Note that the chart in Fig. 9-6 gives the diameter of round duct. If an equivalent rectangular duct is required, the program in Fig. 9-7 will suffice for most applications. This program, however, is designed to calculate the duct size at a velocity of 800 fpm, which is the normal rate of flow for main

ROUND DUCTS – CAPACITY and FRICTION LOSS

Diameter Inches	Velocity 800 FPM		Velocity 1000 FPM		Velocity 1200 FPM		Velocity 1500 FPM		Velocity 1800 FPM	
	Approx. CFM	Approx. Inches Static Pressure per 100 Equiv. Feet	Approx. CFM	Approx. Inches Static Pressure per 100 Equiv. Feet	Approx. CFM	Approx. Inches Static Pressure per 100 Equiv. Feet	Approx. CFM	Approx. Inches Static Pressure Per 100 Equiv. Feet	Approx. CFM	Approx. Inches Static Pressure per 100 Equiv. Feet
4	70	.330	85	.450	105	.650	130	1.10	155	1.50
5	110	.250	140	.370	160	.530	200	.800	250	1.20
6	155	.195	190	.300	240	.420	300	.630	350	.900
7	220	.160	270	.250	325	.350	400	.520	480	.750
8	280	.140	350	.210	420	.290	520	.440	630	.630
10	430	.105	550	.160	650	.220	810	.340	980	.480
12	625	.083	790	.130	940	.175	1200	.260	1450	.380
14	850	.070	1050	.105	1250	.150	1550	.220	1900	.320
16	1150	.058	1400	.088	1650	.125	2050	.190	2500	.270
18	1400	.051	1750	.078	2050	.110	2700	.160	3100	.240

Figure 9-6 Round duct sizing chart.

Figure 9-7 Rectangular main duct sizing program.

```
10 REM **RECTANGULAR MAIN DUCT-SIZING PROGRAM**
20 PRINT ''THIS PROGRAM CALCULATES THE DUCT SIZE REQUIRED TO DELIVER''
30 PRINT '' A GIVEN VOLUME OF AIR AT A VELOCITY OF 800 FPM. TO RUN, ''
40 PRINT ''ANSWER THE QUESTIONS AS THE COMPUTER ASKED FOR THEM.''
50 PRINT
60 PRINT ''THIS PROGRAM CALCULATES THE DUCT SIZES AT FOUR DIFFERENT''
70 PRINT ''DEPTHS: (1) 6-INCH, (2) 8-INCH, (3) 10-INCH, AND (4) 12-INCH''
80 INPUT ''ENTER THE DEPTH YOU WANT TO USE (1,2,3, OR 4)'';D
91 PRINT
92 PRINT
100 IF D=1 THEN 700
110 IF D=2 THEN 800
120 IF D=3 THEN 900
121 INPUT ''ENTER CFM REQUIREMENT''ep; 130 IF C<241 THEN 500
140 IF C<371 THEN 505
150 IF C<501 THEN 510
160 IF C<631 THEN 515
170 IF C<721 THEN 520
180 IF C<881 THEN 525
190 IF C<10001 THEN 530
200 IF C<1151 THEN 535
210 IF C<1251 THEN 540
220 IF C<1351 THEN 545
230 IF C<1451 THEN 550
240 IF C<1601 THEN 555
250 IF C<1701 THEN 560
260 IF C<1801 THEN 565
270 IF C<1901 THEN 570
280 IF C<2001 THEN 575
290 IF C<2101 THEN 580
300 IF C<2301 THEN 585
310 IF C<2501 THEN 590
```

Figure 9-7 cont'd

```
320 IF C<2801 THEN 595
330 IF C<3101 THEN 600
340 IF C<3401 THEN 605
350 PRINT ''A 12-INCH X'';W;''-INCH DUCT WILL HANDLE''''CFM OF AIR AT A
VELOCITY''
355 PRINT ''OF APPROXIMATELY 800 FPM. THE STATIC PRESSURE IN THIS CASE
WILL BE''
360 PRINT ;SP;''INCHES PER 100 EQUIVALENT FEET OF DUCTWORK.
365 PRINT
370 INPUT ''DO YOU WISH TO MAKE ANOTHER CALCULATION (Y OR N) '';Q$
375 IF Q$=''N'' THEN STOP
380 CLS: GOTO 10
381 PRINT ''A 6-INCH X'';W;''-INCH DUCT WILL HANDLE''''CFM OF AIR AT A
VELOCITY''
382 PRINT ''OF APPROXIMATELY 800 FPM. THE STATIC PRESSURE IN THIS CASE
WILL BE''
383 PRINT ;SP;''INCHES PER 100 EQUIVALENT FEET OF DUCT.
384 GOTO 365
385 PRINT ''AN 8-INCH X'';W;''-INCH DUCT WILL HANDLE''''CFM OF AIR AT A
VELOCITY''
386 PRINT ''OF APPROXIMATELY 800 FPM. THE STATIC PRSSURE IN THIS CASE
WILL BE''
387 PRINT ;SP;''INCHES PER 100 EQUIVALENT FEET OF DUCT.''
388 GOTO 365
389 PRINT ''A 10-INCH X'';W;''-INCH DUCT WILL HANDLE''''CFM OF AIR AT A
VELOCITY''
390 PRINT ''OF APPROXIMATELY 800 FPM. THE STATIC PRESSURE IN THIS CASE
WILL BE''
391 PRINT ;SP;''INCHES PER 100 EQUIVALENT FEET OF DUCT.''
392 GOTO 365
500 LET W=4: LET SP=.15: GOTO 350
505 LET W=6: LET SP=.12: GOTO 350
510 LET W=8: LET SP=.095:GOTO 350
515 LET W=10:LET SP=.081:GOTO 350
520 LET W=12:LET SP=.075:GOTO 350
525 LET W=14:LET SP=6.800001E-02:GOTO 350
530 LET W=16:LET SP=.062:GOTO 350
535 LET W=18:LET SP=.058:GOTO 350
540 LET W=20:LET SP=.055:GOTO 350
545 LET W=22:LET SP=.052:GOTO 350
550 LET W=24:LET SP=.049:GOTO 350
555 LET W=26:LET SP=.048:GOTO 350
560 LET W=28:LET SP=.046:GOTO 350
565 LET W=30:LET SP=.044:GOTO 350
570 LET W=32:LET SP=.042:GOTO 350
575 LET W=34:LET SP=.041:GOTO 350
```

Figure 9-7 cont'd

```
580 LET W=36: LET SP=.039: GOTO 350
585 LET W=40: LET SP=.037: GOTO 350
590 LET W=44: LET SP=.036: GOTO 350
595 LET W=48: LET SP=.033: GOTO 350
600 LET W=54: LET SP=.032: GOTO 350
605 LET W=60: LET SP=.03: GOTO 350
700 INPUT ''ENTER CRM REQUIREMENT'' 'ep; 701 IF C<121 THEN 750
702 IF C<161 THEN 751
703 IF C<201 THEN 752
704 IF C<251 THEN 753
705 IF C<311 THEN 754
706 IF C<361 THEN 755
707 IF C<421 THEN 756
708 IF C<461 THEN 757
709 IF C<531 THEN 758
710 IF C<591 THEN 759
711 IF C<631 THEN 760
712 IF C<681 THEN 761
713 IF C<711 THEN 762
714 IF C<751 THEN 763
715 IF C<801 THEN 764
716 IF C<851 THEN 765
717 IF C<901 THEN 766
718 IF C<941 THEN 767
719 IF C<941 THEN PRINT ''CFM REQUIREMENT TOO LARGE, GO TO DEEPER DUCT
SIZE''
720 GOTO 20
750 LET W=4: LET SP=.25: GOTO 381
751 LET W=5: LET SP=.2: GOTO 381
752 LET W=6: LET SP=.17: GOTO 381
753 LET W=8: LET SP=.15: GOTO 381
754 LET W=10: LET SP=.13: GOTO 381
755 LET W=12: LET SP=.12: GOTO 381
756 LET W=14: LET SP=.11: GOTO 381
757 LET W=16: LET SP=.105: GOTO 381
758 LET W=18: LET SP=9.399999E-02: GOTO 381
759 LET W=20: LET SP=.089: GOTO 381
760 LET W=22: LET SP=.084: GOTO 381
761 LET W=24: LET SP=.08: GOTO 381
762 LET W=26: LET SP=.076: GOTO 381
763 LET W=28: LET SP=.073: GOTO 381
764 LET W=30: LET SP=.071: GOTO 381
765 LET W=32: LET SP=.069: GOTO 381
766 LET W=34: LET SP=.067: GOTO 381
767 LET W=36: LET SP=.065: GOTO 381
800 INPUT ''ENTER CFM REQUIREMENT'' 'ep; 801 IF C<161 THEN 850
```

Figure 9-7 cont'd

```
802  IF C<211 THEN 851
803  IF C<251 THEN 852
804  IF C<341 THEN 853
805  IF C<421 THEN 854
806  IF C<501 THEN 855
807  IF C<581 THEN 856
808  IF C<651 THEN 857
809  IF C<716 THEN 858
810  IF C<791 THEN 859
811  IF C<871 THEN 860
812  IF C<931 THEN 861
813  IF C<1001 THEN 862
814  IF C<1081 THEN 863
815  IF C<1151 THEN 864
816  IF C<1201 THEN 865
817  IF C<1251 THEN 866
818  IF C<1321 THEN 867
819  IF C<1321 THEN PRINT ''CFM RANGE TOO LARGE, GO TO DEEPER SIZE DUCT''
820  GOTO 20
850  LET W=4: LET SP=.19: GOTO 385
851  LET W=5: LET SP=.165: GOTO 385
852  LET W=6: LET SP=.15: GOTO 385
853  LET W=8: LET SP=.13: GOTO 385
854  LET W=10: LET SP=.11: GOTO 385
855  LET W=12: LET SP=.095: GOTO 385
856  LET W=14: LET SP=.089: GOTO 385
857  LET W=16: LET SP=.083: GOTO 385
858  LET W=18: LET SP=.078: GOTO 385
859  LET W=20: LET SP=.073: GOTO 385
860  LET W=22: LET SP=.069: GOTO 385
861  LET W=24: LET SP=.066: GOTO 385
862  LET W=26: LET SP=.063: GOTO 385
863  LET W=28: LET SP=.06: GOTO 385
864  LET W=30: LET SP=.058: GOTO 385
865  LET W=32: LET SP=.056: GOTO 385
866  LET W=34: LET SP=.055: GOTO 385
867  LET W=36: LET SP=.054: GOTO 385
900  INPUT ''ENTER CFM REQUIREMENT''ep; 901  IF C<201 THEN 950
902  IF C<311 THEN 951
903  IF C<421 THEN 952
904  IF C<521 THEN 953
905  IF C<631 THEN 954
906  IF C<731 THEN 955
907  IF C<821 THEN 956
908  IF C<941 THEN 957
909  IF C<1051 THEN 958
```

Figure 9-7 cont'd

```
910  IF C<1151 THEN 959
911  IF C<1251 THEN 960
912  IF C<1351 THEN 961
913  IF C<1426 THEN 962
914  IF C<1501 THEN 963
915  IF C<1576 THEN 964
916  IF C<1651 THEN 965
917  IF C<1726 THEN 966
918  IF C<1901 THEN 967
919  IF C<2101 THEN 968
920  IF C<2251 THEN 969
921  IF C<2401 THEN 970
922  IF C<2801 THEN 971
923  IF C<2801 THEN PRINT ''CFM RANGE TOO GREAT, USE A DEEPER DUCT SIZE''
924  GOTO 20
950  LET W=4: LET SP=.17: GOTO 389
951  LET W=6: LET SP=.13: GOTO 389
952  LET W=8: LET SP=.11: GOTO 389
953  LET W=10: LET SP=.093: GOTO 389
954  LET W=12: LET SP=.081: GOTO 389
955  LET W=14: LET SP=.075: GOTO 389
956  LET W=16: LET SP=.071: GOTO 389
957  LET W=18: LET SP=.064: GOTO 389
958  LET W=20: LET SP=.061: GOTO 389
959  LET W=22: LET SP=.058: GOTO 389
960  LET W=24: LET SP=.055: GOTO 389

961  LET W=26: LET SP=.053: GOTO 389
962  LET W=28: LET SP=.052: GOTO 389
963  LET W=30: LET SP=.049: GOTO 389
964  LET W=32: LET SP=.048: GOTO 389
965  LET W=34: LET SP=.046: GOTO 389
966  LET W=36: LET SP=.044: GOTO 389
967  LET W=40: LET SP=.042: GOTO 389
RUN ''PRNSCRN
968  LET W=44: LET SP=.04: GOTO 389
969  LET W=48: LET SP=.038: GOTO 389
970  LET W=54: LET SP=.036: GOTO 389
971  LET W=60: LET SP=.034: GOTO 389
```

```
RUN ''PRNSCRN
```

ducts. However, the program can be easily modified for other rates of air flow.

If the opposite is desired, that is, obtaining the circular equivalents of rectangular ducts for equal friction and cfm, the short program in Fig. 9-8 may be used, either separately, or incorporated into a master design program by using a loop. A somewhat more complex program is shown in Fig. 9-9.

Figure 9-8 Computer program designed to calculate the circular equivalents of rectangular ducts.

```
10 REM **DUCT SIZING**
20 PRINT ''THIS PROGRAM IS DESIGNED TO CALCULATE THE CIRCULAR EQUIVA-
LENTS''
30 PRINT ''OF RECTANGULAR DUCTS FOR EQUAL FRICTION (INCHES & CM)
40 PRINT
50 INPUT ''ENTER SHORTEST SIDE OF RECTANGULAR DUCT IN
INCHES''                                                    ep; 60 PRINT
70 INPUT ''NOW ENTER THE LONGEST SIDE OF RECTANGULAR DUCT IN INCHES'';L
80 IF S<4.1 THEN 200
90 IF S<5.1 THEN 300
100 IF S<6.1 THEN 400
110 IF S<7.1 THEN 500
111 IF S<8.100001 THEN 600
112 IF S<9.100001 THEN 700
113 IF S<10.1 THEN 800
114 IF S<11.1 THEN 900
115 IF S<12.1 THEN 1000
116 IF 2<13.1 THEN 1100
117 IF S<14.1 THEN 1200
118 IF S<15.1 THEN 1300
119 IF S<16.1 THEN 1400
120 IF S<17.1 THEN 1500
121 IF S<18.1 THEN 1600
122 IF S<19.1 THEN 1700
123 IF S<20.1 THEN 1800
124 IF S<21.1 THEN 1900
125 IF S<22.1 THEN 2000
126 IF S<23.1 THEN 2100
127 IF S<24.1 THEN 2200
137 CLS
138 PRINT ''THE CIRCULAR EQUIVALENT OF A RECTANGULAR DUCTS'';L;''INCHES
WIDE BY''
140 IF S<10.1 THEN 800
148 PRINT                     '' INCHES DEEP IS'''' INCHES IN DIAMETER.''
158 CLS
159 PRINT ''THE CIRCULAR EQUIVALENT OF A RECTANGULAR DUCTS'';L;''INCHES
WIDE BY''
```

Figure 9-8 cont'd

```
160 PRINT                    ''INCHES DEEP IS'†''' INCHES IN DIAMETER.''
161 PRINT
162 INPUT ''DO YOU WISH TO MAKE ANOTHER CALCULATION (Y OR n)''; A$
163 IF A$=''Y'' THEN GOTO 20
164 STOP
200 IF L<8.100001 THEN C=6.1: GOTO 158221
202 IF L<10.1 THEN C=6.8: GOTO 158
203 IF L<11.1 THEN C=7.1: GOTO 158
204 IF L<12.1 THEN C=7.4: GOTO 158
205 IF L<13.1 THEN C=7.6: GOTO 158
206 IF L<14.1 THEN C=7.9; GOTO 158
207 IF L<15.1 THEN C=8.2: GOTO 158
208 IF L<16.1 THEN C=8.399999: GOT
209 IF L<17.1 THEN C=8.600001: GOTO 158
210 IF L<18.1 THEN C=8.899999: GOTO 158
211 IF L<19.1 THEN C=9.100001: GOTO 158
212 IF L<20.1 THEN C=9.3: GOTO 158
213 IF L<22.1 THEN C=9.7: GOTO 158
214 IF L<24.1 THEN C=10!: GOTO 158
215 IF L<26.1 THEN C=10.4: GOTO 158
216 IF L<28.1 THEN C=10.8: GOTO 158
217 IF L<30.1 THEN C=11!: GOTO 158
218 IF L<32.1 THEN C=11.3: GOTO 158
219 IF L<34.1 THEN C=11.6: GOTO 158
220 IF L<36.1 THEN C=11.9: GOTO 158
221 IF L<38.1 THEN C=12.2: GOTO 158
222 IF L<40.1 THEN C=12.5: GOTO 158
223 IF L<42.1 THEN C=12.7: GOTO 158
224 IF L<44.1 THEN C=13!: GOTO 158
225 IF L<46.1 THEN C=13.3: GOTO 158
226 IF L<48.1 THEN C=13.5: GOTO 158
227 IF L<50.1 THEN C=13.7: GOTO 158
228 IF L<52.1 THEN C=13.9: GOTO 158
229 IF L<54.1 THEN C=14.1: GOTO 158
230 IF L<56.1 THEN C=14.3: GOTO 158
231 IF L<58.1 THEN C=14.6: GOTO 158
232 IF L<60.1 THEN C=14.7: GOTO 158
233 IF L<62.1 THEN C=15!: GOTO 158
234 IF L<64.1 THEN C=15.1: GOTO 158
235 IF L<66.1 THEN C=15.3: GOTO 158
240 IF L<12.1 THEN C=7.4: GOTO 158
250 IF L<13.1 THEN C=7.6: GOTO 158
260 IF L<14.1 THEN C=7.9: GOTO 158
270 IF L<15.1 THEN C=8.2: GOTO 158
280 IF L<16.1 THEN C=8.399999: GOTO 158
290 IF L<17.1 THEN C=8.600001: GOTO 158
300 GOTO 158
310 PRINT                     ''INCHES DEEP IS'†''' INCHES IN DIAMETER.''
```

Figure 9-9 Mathematical program for obtaining circular equivalents of rectangular duct.

```
10 REM **MATHEMATICAL PROGRAM FOR OBTAINING CIRCULAR EQUIVALENTS OF**
20 REM **RECTANGULAR DUCT FOR EQUAL FRICTION (INCHES AND CM)**
30 INPUT ''ENTER WIDTH OF RECTANGULAR DUCT IN INCHES'';W
40 PRINT
50 INPUT ''ENTER DEPTH OF RECTANGULAR DUCT IN INCHES'';D
60 A=W*D
70 PRINT
80 PRINT ''AREA OF RECTANGULAR DUCT IS''''SQ. INCHES.''
90 R=SQR(A/3.14
100 C=2*R
110 PRINT ''THE EQUIVALENT ROUND DUCT IS''''INCHES.''
120 STOP
```

```
Ok
RUN
ENTER WIDTH OF RECTANGULAR DUCT IN INCHES? 24

ENTER DEPTH OF RECTANGULAR DUCT IN INCHES? 8

AREA OF RECTANGULAR DUCT IS 192 SQ. INCHES.
THE EQUIVALENT ROUND DUCT IS 15.63925 INCHES.
Break in 120
Ok
RUN ''PRNSCRN
```

A chart giving the capacity and friction loss of rectangular ducts is shown in Fig. 9-10. The capacity and friction loss of round ducts are shown in Fig. 9-11, and a chart giving friction loss of rectangular elbows may be found in Fig. 9-12. The designer will find all of these helpful in his or her daily work. These charts could also be good practice in designing your own special programs for use in HVAC applications.

Supply-air outlets are a major part of any air-distribution system because they provide a means of distributing properly controlled air to a room or area. For proper air distribution, the supply outlets must:

1. Be the right quantities in the correct location.
2. Be the correct type and size to deliver the correct air volume and velocity, and also to obtain proper air motion and temperature equalization.

RECTANGULAR DUCTS – CAPACITY and FRICTION LOSS

Velocity 800 FPM

Size Inches	8" CFM	Friction Loss*	10" CFM	Friction Loss*	12" CFM	Friction Loss*	14" CFM	Friction Loss*	16" CFM	Friction Loss*	18" CFM	Friction Loss*	20" CFM	Friction Loss*	22" CFM	Friction Loss*	24" CFM	Friction Loss*	30" CFM	Friction Loss*	36" CFM	Friction Loss*
4	160	.190	200	.170	240	.150	280	.140	300	.130	340	.120	370	.120	390	.110	430	.105	510	.092	—	—
6	250	.150	310	.130	370	.120	420	.110	460	.105	530	.094	590	.089	630	.084	710	.087	800	.071	940	.065
8	340	.130	—	—	—	—	—	—	—	—	—	—	—	—	—	—	—	—	—	—	—	—
10	420	.110	520	.093	—	—	—	—	—	—	—	—	—	—	—	—	—	—	—	—	—	—
12	500	.095	630	.081	720	.075	—	—	—	—	—	—	—	—	—	—	—	—	—	—	—	—
14	580	.089	730	.075	880	.068	1000	.063	—	—	—	—	—	—	—	—	—	—	—	—	—	—
16	650	.083	820	.071	1000	.062	1150	.057	1350	.053	—	—	—	—	—	—	—	—	—	—	—	—
18	715	.078	940	.064	1150	.058	1300	.054	1500	.050	1750	.045	—	—	—	—	—	—	—	—	—	—
20	790	.073	1050	.061	1250	.055	1450	.050	1650	.046	1900	.042	2000	.040	—	—	—	—	—	—	—	—
22	870	.069	1150	.058	1350	.052	1550	.048	1800	.044	2100	.040	2300	.038	2650	.035	—	—	—	—	—	—
24	930	.066	1250	.055	1450	.049	1700	.045	2000	.041	2300	.038	2500	.036	2850	.034	3100	.032	—	—	—	—
26	1000	.063	1350	.053	1600	.048	1850	.042	2100	.039	2500	.036	2750	.034	3000	.033	3400	.030	4000	.027	4800	.024
28	1080	.060	1425	.052	1700	.045	2000	.040	2200	.038	2700	.034	2900	.033	3250	.031	3600	.029	4300	.025	5200	.023
30	1150	.058	1500	.049	1800	.044	2100	.039	2450	.036	2900	.033	3100	.032	3400	.030	3800	.028	4700	.024	5500	.022
32	1200	.056	1575	.048	1900	.042	2200	.038	2600	.035	3100	.032	3300	.030	3700	.029	4000	.027	4900	.023	6000	.021
34	1250	.055	1650	.046	2000	.041	2300	.037	2750	.034	3200	.031	3600	.029	3850	.028	4300	.026	5200	.023	6400	.020
36	1320	.054	1725	.044	2100	.039	2500	.036	2900	.033	3400	.030	3700	.028	4000	.027	4500	.025	5500	.022	6800	.020
40	1510	.048	1900	.042	2300	.037	2800	.034	3150	.031	3800	.028	4000	.027	4700	.025	5000	.024	6100	.021	7400	.019
44	1650	.046	2100	.040	2500	.036	3000	.032	3500	.029	4000	.027	4400	.025	4900	.024	5400	.022	6700	.020	8000	.018
48	1800	.044	2250	.038	2800	.033	3200	.030	3800	.028	4400	.025	4800	.024	5200	.023	6000	.021	7500	.019	9000	.017
54	1950	.042	2400	.036	3100	.032	3600	.029	4100	.027	4900	.024	5300	.023	5800	.022	6500	.020	8200	.018	10000	.016
60	2100	.039	2800	.034	3400	.030	3900	.028	4600	.025	5000	.022	5700	.022	6300	.020	7100	.019	9000	.017	11500	.015
66	—	—	—	—	—	—	3600	.028	4700	.026	5400	.024	5900	.021	7100	.019	8000	.017	9800	.016	12500	.014
72	—	—	—	—	—	—	4000	.027	4700	.027	5400	.025	6400	.023	6800	.019	8100	.017	10500	.015	13000	.013
78	—	—	—	—	—	—	5000	.023	5800	.022	6800	.019	7200	.019	8100	.017	9100	.016	11000	.014	14000	.013
84	—	—	—	—	—	—	5400	.022	6200	.021	7300	.018	7800	.018	8600	.017	10000	.016	12000	.013	15000	.012

*Friction loss value is per 100 equivalent feet.

Figure 9-10   A rectangular duct sizing chart.

An improperly designed system can cause drafts, stuffiness, temperature stratification, high velocities in occupied zones, fluctuating velocities, improper air movement creating warm or cool spots, and in general, an uncomfortable system.

Outlets should be sized to project the air so that the velocity and temperature reach an acceptable level before entering the occupied zone. Recommended velocity is approximately 20 to 50 fpm; the lower value (20 fpm) is acceptable for cooling while the higher is acceptable for heating.

Dia Size in Inches	Recommended (600 FPM)		Maximum (900 FPM)	
	Approx CFM	Approx Inches-Static Pressure Drop Per 100 Equivalent Feet	Approx CFM	Approx Inches-Static Pressure Drop Per 100 Equivalent Feet
4	52	.20	80	.40
5	82	.15	125	.31
6	118	.12	180	.25
7	160	.095	240	.20
8	210	.080	320	.17
9	270	.070	400	.15
10	323	.060	490	.15
12	470	.050	700	.105

Figure 9-11   Chart giving capacity and friction loss of round duct.

2 Vane   1 Vane

Duct Dimensions	R/B=.5	R/B=1.0	R/B=1.5	R/B=.5	R/B=1.0	R/B=1.5	No Vanes	Single Thickness Vanes	Double Thickness Vanes	R/B=.5	R/B=1.0	R/B=1.5	R/B=.5	R/B=1.0 1.5
										(1 Vane)			(2 Vane)	
							Equivalent Length of Straight Duct Feet							
84 × 36	204	69	15	210	56	26	294	60	30	60	24	21	45	21
84 × 30	180	40	13	182	55	25	260	50	25	50	20	18	38	18
84 × 24	168	32	11	175	53	25	216	40	20	40	16	14	30	14
84 × 18	153	25	9	151	48	24	165	30	15	30	12	11	23	11
72 × 36	186	39	15	198	62	23	282	60	30	60	24	21	45	21
72 × 30	162	35	13	174	55	23	242	50	25	50	20	18	38	18
72 × 24	158	30	11	162	47	23	210	40	20	40	16	14	30	14
72 × 18	135	25	9	144	43	21	165	30	15	30	12	11	23	11
60 × 36	174	36	14	180	45	20	264	60	30	60	24	21	45	21
60 × 30	154	32	12	165	43	20	235	50	25	50	20	18	38	18
60 × 24	148	26	10	145	40	20	200	40	20	40	16	14	30	14
60 × 18	123	24	7	130	38	19	162	30	15	30	12	11	23	11
48 × 36	144	34	13	156	38	16	250	60	30	60	24	21	45	21
48 × 30	140	30	12	144	37	16	215	50	25	50	20	18	38	18
48 × 24	136	26	10	136	35	16	188	40	20	40	16	14	30	14
48 × 18	111	20	8	112	32	15	153	30	15	30	12	11	23	11
48 × 12	90	17	6	96	29	14	110	20	10	20	8	7	15	7

Size														
36 x 36	135	31	12	135	32	13	225	60	30	60	24	21	45	21
36 x 30	120	28	11	120	30	13	197	50	25	50	20	18	38	18
36 x 24	114	24	10	108	28	12	170	40	20	40	16	14	30	14
36 x 18	100	20	8	102	26	12	141	30	15	30	12	11	23	11
36 x 12	79	15	6	71	23	12	105	20	10	20	8	7	15	7
36 x 8	67	12	5	69	21	10	79	14	7	14	6	5	10	5
30 x 30	112	27	11	110	26	11	188	50	25	50	20	18	38	18
30 x 24	98	23	10	102	24	11	162	40	20	40	16	14	30	14
30 x 18	90	20	8	90	22	10	141	30	15	30	12	11	23	11
30 x 12	74	15	6	75	20	10	100	20	10	20	8	7	15	7
30 x 8	60	11	5	62	19	9	73	14	7	14	6	5	10	5
24 x 24	90	21	9	90	21	9	150	40	20	40	16	14	30	14
24 x 18	78	18	7	76	19	8	125	30	15	30	12	11	23	11
24 x 12	68	13	5	68	18	8	94	20	10	20	8	7	15	7
24 x 8	52	10	4	54	16	8	70	14	7	14	6	5	10	5
24 x 6	45	8	4	48	14	7	55	10	5	10	4	4	8	4
18 x 18	67	16	7	67	16	7	112	30	15	30	12	11	23	11
18 x 12	57	12	5	54	15	5	85	20	10	20	8	7	15	7
18 x 8	48	9	3	46	13	3	65	14	7	14	6	5	10	5
18 x 6	40	8	3	40	12	3	51	10	5	10	4	4	8	4
16 x 16	59	14	6	60	14	6	100	27	14	27	11	9	20	9
16 x 14	53	13	5	53	13	6	91	23	12	23	9	8	18	8
16 x 12	48	12	5	51	13	6	83	20	10	20	8	7	15	7
16 x 10	45	10	4	50	12	5	72	17	9	17	7	6	13	6
16 x 8	42	9	3	44	12	5	63	14	7	14	5	5	10	5
16 x 6	35	7	3	36	11	5	51	10	5	10	4	4	8	4
14 x 14	53	12	5	53	12	5	88	23	12	23	9	8	18	8
14 x 12	47	11	5	46	11	5	77	20	10	20	8	7	15	7
14 x 10	42	10	4	45	10	5	70	17	9	17	7	6	13	6
14 x 8	39	8	3	41	9	4	60	14	7	14	5	5	10	5
14 x 6	35	7	3	35	9	3	49	10	5	10	4	4	8	4
12 x 12	45	11	4	45	11	4	75	20	10	20	8	7	15	7
12 x 10	42	10	4	39	10	3	66	17	9	17	7	6	13	6
12 x 8	38	8	3	36	9	3	57	14	7	14	5	5	10	5
12 x 6	34	7	3	34	9	3	47	10	5	10	4	4	8	4
10 x 10	38	9	4	37	9	4	63	17	9	17	7	6	13	6
10 x 8	34	8	3	33	8	4	54	14	7	14	5	5	10	5
10 x 6	28	6	2	29	7	3	44	10	5	10	4	4	8	4
8 x 8	30	7	3	30	7	3	50	14	7	14	5	5	10	5
8 x 6	25	6	2	25	6	2	41	10	5	10	4	4	8	4

Figure 9-12 Friction loss of rectangular elbows.

OUTLET SELECTION

There are three basic types of supply outlets:

1. Grilles and registers.
2. Wall, baseboard, and floor diffusers.
3. Ceiling diffusers.

Grille.   The grille is a covering for any opening through which air passes. Typical grilles are shown in Fig. 9-13; one has vertical bars while the other has horizontal bars, for either single or double deflection.

Register.   A register is a covering for any opening through which air passes and has a built-in damper for controlling the air passing through it. A fixed-louver register is a nonadjustable register in which the air pattern is factory set. An adjustable-louver register is a register with adjustable bars for directing the air in several different patterns.

Ceiling diffuser.   The ceiling diffuser is a square, oval, circular, or semicircular facing device that covers the supply-air opening of a room or area. Most diffusers are ceiling mounted and are adjustable for air flow direction and rate. Diffusers may also be wall, baseboard, and floor mounted.

LOCATION OF SUPPLY-AIR OUTLETS

Supply-air outlets in an area to be conditioned must be located so that sufficient air is supplied to establish and maintain comfort conditions within the area; that is, a uniform air pattern that is free from hot or cold drafts.

Grilles, for example, when located on the high inside wall are excellent for cooling, but poor for heating. However, satisfactory operation may be had if the return is located low on an outside wall.

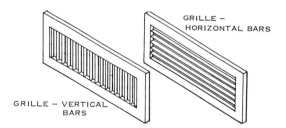

Figure 9-13   Typical grilles; one with vertical bars and the other with horizontal bars.

When located on a low inside wall, fair conditions may be had while cooling and good heating air distribution will result.

When locating a grille on the high inside wall, a single deflection grille should be placed near the ceiling so that velocity drops below 50 fpm before falling into the occupied zone. The length of throw is usually considered to be three fourths the distance between the outlet and the opposite wall. See Fig. 9-14 for air patterns from grilles.

A double deflection grille just above the occupied zone will deflect air toward the ceiling and permits longer travel for temperature equalization before falling into the occupied zone. This does not, however, appreciably increase the length of throw.

When selecting grilles, cfm capacity and length of throw must be considered. The recommended terminal velocity is 50 fpm.

Figure 9-15 gives the nominal values for straight bar setting. In any size, the free area varies with the manufacturer and with each bar deflection setting. For actual applications, consult the manufacturer's catalog for final selection.

Diffusers (Fig. 9-16) are normally located on the outside wall floor or else on low-wall mountings. These locations provide good cooling and excellent heating capabilities as they blanket the outside wall with condi-

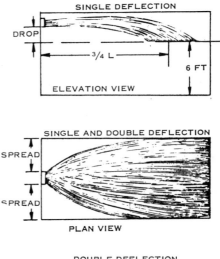

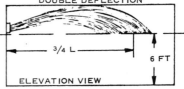

Figure 9-14 Various air patterns obtained with different types of air outlets.

Size Inches	Free Area Square Inches	500 FPM		750 FPM		1000 FPM		1250 FPM		1500 FPM	
		CFM	Throw Feet	CFM	Throw Feet	CFM	Throw Feet	CFM	Throw Feet	CFM	Throw Feet
8 × 4	17	61	9.5	92	14.5	122	19.0	148	23.0	177	27.5
8 × 6	28	97	12.0	146	18.0	195	24.0	243	30.0	292	36.5
10 × 4	22	76	11.0	115	17.0	153	22.5	191	28.0	229	33.5
10 × 6	37	130	14.5	193	21.5	257	28.5	321	35.5	385	42.5
10 × 8	51	177	16.5	266	25.0	354	33.5	443	45.0	531	50.5
12 × 4	27	94	12.0	141	18.0	187	23.5	234	29.5	281	35.5
12 × 6	45	156	15.5	234	23.5	312	31.5	391	39.5	468	47.0
12 × 8	63	218	20.0	328	30.0	437	40.0	547	50.0	657	60.0
14 × 4	32	110	13.0	168	19.5	222	26.0	278	32.5	333	39.0
14 × 6	53	184	17.0	276	25.5	368	34.0	460	42.5	552	51.0
14 × 8	74	257	20.5	386	30.5	514	41.0	642	51.0	770	61.5
16 × 4	38	132	14.5	198	21.5	264	28.5	330	36.0	395	43.0
16 × 6	60	208	18.0	312	27.0	417	36.0	522	45.0	625	54.0
16 × 8	81	280	20.5	422	31.0	562	41.5	703	52.0	845	62.5
18 × 4	43	149	15.0	224	23.0	298	30.5	373	38.0	448	46.0
18 × 6	67	232	19.0	348	23.5	465	38.0	582	47.5	698	57.0
18 × 8	92	320	22.5	480	33.5	640	45.0	800	56.0	960	67.5
20 × 4	48	166	16.0	250	24.0	333	32.0	417	40.5	500	48.5
20 × 6	75	260	20.0	390	30.0	520	40.0	650	50.0	780	60.0
20 × 8	102	354	23.5	531	35.0	708	47.0	885	58.5	1100	72.5
24 × 4	55	191	17.0	287	25.5	382	33.5	478	42.0	573	50.5
24 × 6	90	312	22.0	469	33.0	625	44.0	780	55.0	940	66.0
24 × 8	126	438	26.5	666	40.5	875	53.0	1100	66.5	1310	79.5
30 × 4	70	243	19.0	364	28.5	485	38.0	610	48.0	730	57.5
30 × 6	114	396	25.0	594	37.5	792	50.0	990	62.5	1190	74.5
30 × 8	160	555	29.0	835	45.0	1110	59.5	1390	74.5	1670	89.5
36 × 4	87	302	22.0	453	32.5	604	43.5	755	54.5	905	65.0
36 × 6	137	476	27.0	714	40.5	953	54.5	1190	68.0	1425	81.5
36 × 8	184	638	31.0	958	47.0	1280	58.0	1600	78.5	1920	94.0

Based on single deflection straight bar setting

Figure 9-15   Capacity and throw chart for supply grilles and registers.

tioned air and stop cold air before it enters the room, thus preventing drafts in the heating operation. They absorb heat at the source in the cooling mode.

Diffuers should also be selected for cfm capacity and length of throw. Consult the manufacturer's catalog for specifications before making your selection.

A few types of ceiling diffusers are shown in Fig. 9-17. Note that full-round, half-round, and square shapes are represented here. These types of supply-air outlets have limited use for combination heating and cooling applications. This type of air outlet normally provides poor air distribution in the heating mode, and is therefore not recommended except for use where mild winter climates prevail.

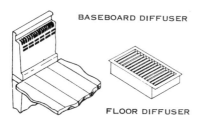

BASEBOARD DIFFUSER

FLOOR DIFFUSER

Figure 9-16   Diffusers designed for low-wall mounting.

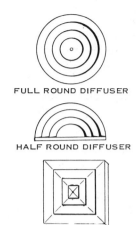

FULL ROUND DIFFUSER

HALF ROUND DIFFUSER

Figure 9-17   Three types of ceiling diffusers in common use.

Full-round and square types of ceiling diffusers should be installed in the center of square rooms or areas. When it is not practical to locate these in the exact center, satisfactory operation will result if longer throw does not exceed the shorter throw by more than 50 percent.

If structural conditions prevent the use of round diffusers, half-round diffusers may be located in the ceiling adjacent to the sidewall.

SELECTION CONSIDERATIONS

The location and types of supply-air outlets are determined by the engineer or designer after considering the following:

1. The size and shape of the room or area to be conditioned.
2. The decor of the area.
3. The furniture placement within the area, if known.
4. The ceiling, wall, and floor finish of the area to be conditioned.
5. The required budget.
6. Whether the system is designed for heating, cooling, or both. If both, the one that is used the most during the year should be given the greater consideration.
7. The total air quantity required for the area under consideration.
8. The total load and draft conditions of the area.
9. The diffusion or spread pattern required with the space to be conditioned.
10. The level of noise allowed in the space to be conditioned.

From the preceding list, supply-air outlets should be located according to the shape, size, usage, and load concentration of the area, and according to whether the system is used in a cooling or heating application or both. During the design process, the steps are as follows:

1. Study the architectural drawings and specifications, making the required calculations to determine the size, shape, and use of each room or area.
2. Select the outlet type and locate the outlets according to the requirements and conditions in the area under consideration.

RETURN-AIR INLETS

Return-air inlets provide a means of returning the conditioned air to its original source so that it can be reconditioned. In most cases, these inlets should be located in a position opposite that of the supply-air outlets. For example, when the supply outlet is located on an inside wall or ceiling diffuser, locate the return inlet low on the outside wall. When the supply outlet is located on an outside wall, locate the return inlet either high or low on the inside wall.

Recessed, floor-mounted return-air inlets are not recommended for use in commercial buildings because they are likely to become "dirt catchers."

In some buildings, return-air inlets can be located in a central area. However, in buildings where all the supply air cannot return to one central inlet, the return-air inlets and their related ductwork must be located in several areas.

The common types of return-air inlets include grilles and registers, and when choosing either for an application, they should be selected for cfm capacity and face velocity. In general, 500 fpm is the recommended velocity in an occupied zone, while 800 fpm is acceptable above an occupied zone. Figure 9-18 provides nominal ratings for various sizes of return grilles and registers. However, in actual design, the manufacturer's catalog must be consulted for exact ratings.

DUCTWORK FABRICATION

Ductwork for residential HVAC systems has, traditionally, been constructed of sheet metal, and the practice continues today. However, in recent years, fiberglass ducts have been used extensively for residential and small commercial air-distribution systems. When properly installed and supported, fiberglass ductwork can be highly recommended for many applications.

CFM	Free Area Sq in	Side Wall Return Grilles	Floor Grilles		
60- 140	40	10 x 6	4 x 14		
140- 170	48	12 x 6	4 x 18 or 6 x 10		
170- 190	55	10 x 8	4 x 18 or 6 x 12		
190- 235	67	12 x 8	6 x 14		
235- 260	74	18 x 6	6 x 16 or 8 x 14		
260- 370	106	12 x 12		8 x 20	
370- 560	162	18 x 12		8 x 30	
560- 760	218	24 x 12	10 x 30 or 12 x 24		
760- 870	252	18 x 18	12 x 30		
870- 960	276	30 x 12	12 x 30		
960-1170	340	24 x 18			
1170-1470	423	30 x 18	18 x 30		14 x 30
1470-1580	455	24 x 24		20 x 30	
1580-1770	510	36 x 18			22 x 30
1770-1990	572	30 x 24	24 x 30		
1990-2400	690	36 x 24	24 x 36		
2400-3020	870	36 x 30		30 x 36	

Figure 9-18 Grille and register sizing chart.

Many existing buildings without air conditioning are heated with steam or hot water and use pipes rather than ductwork for the circulation of heat. While it is somewhat more difficult (and expensive) to install air conditioning in these places than in ones with ductwork, there are still several practical ways to get the job done.

Through-wall heating and cooling units can be installed using the existing piping. Or you could install a self-contained air-conditioning unit as shown in Figs. 9-19 and 9-20 with a new duct system, entirely independent from the existing heating system. When many people think of ductwork,

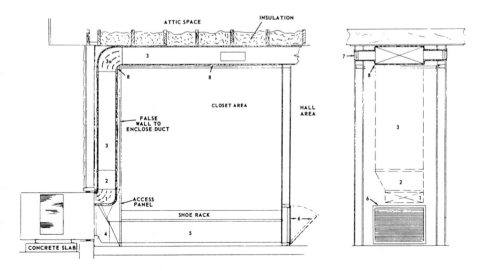

Figure 9-19 Combination heating and cooling unit mounted on concrete slab, projecting through the house wall.

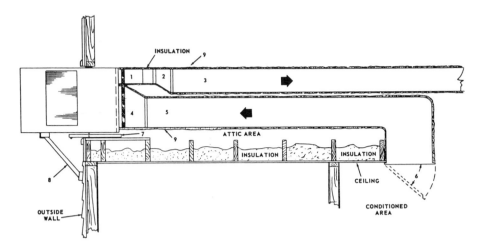

Figure 9-20 Combination heating and cooling unit mounted through the wall in attic area.

they have visions of spot welders, sheet-metal brakes, and other expensive tools running into thousands of dollars. This is not the case with fiberglass ducts: they're within the capabilities of nearly every HVAC shop.

Unlike ductwork constructed from sheet metal, fiberglass duct requires only a few common hand tools for assembly and installation. They include a sharp knife, a hammer, pliers, a heat-seal tool, butt-joint tools, and a staple gun.

Furthermore, a conventional sheet-metal system requires consideration of thermal efficiency, acoustical efficiency and vapor resistance as well as air delivery. All these features must be engineered and installed in a step-by-step process. Not so with fiberglass duct! It's an air conveyor which has insulation, sound absorber, and vapor barrier built in. By incorporating these custom-engineered system requirements into a single product, fiberglass ductwork not only reduces the time, money, and effort required to design and install ducts, but also assures that the system will have minimum loss, noise, and condensation.

ROUND DUCT

Prefabricated round duct is quickly and easily installed with standard sheet-metal fittings, a knife, heat-seal iron, factory-supplied templates, and sealing tape. The sheet-metal fittings assure proper alignment and provide reinforcement at the joints, which are also secured with pressure-sensitive aluminum tape and heat sealed. This assures continuation of the vapor barrier and strong, airtight joints. Should a puncture occur in the vapor barrier, it can easily be mended by applying tape over the damaged area.

RECTANGULAR DUCT

Rectangular fiberglass duct is easy to use; even the largest sections can be positioned easily due to their light weight and resilience. Sheet-metal connectors are not required for joining rectangular duct sections unless the duct span exceeds the maximum allowable span for a specific thickness of duct board at a given pressure. However, rectangular duct runs do require suspension on 6-foot (maximum) centers unless the duct can be supported by structural members.

COMBINED DUCT INSTALLATIONS

Round duct take-offs from rectangular duct are easily accomplished with fiberglass duct. A round sheet-metal fitting the same diameter as the round duct take-off is secured to the rectangular trunk. The round take-off is then slipped over the metal fitting and pushed tightly against the rectangular trunk, taped around the curvature of the connection, and heat sealed.

PLANNING THE INSTALLATION

Begin by making a careful analysis of the building's present and future cooling requirements. This shows the size of unit that is required and helps to determine the size of ducts needed to serve various areas.

See other chapters in this book on duct sizing to obtain the correct cross-sectional area. Try to find a floor plan of the building, but if this is not possible, take measurements and sketch one. Include all windows, doors, lighting fixtures, large beams, and any other obstruction that might interfere with the running of the ductwork. With the sketch and a copy of the cooling calculations, lay out the ductwork by size and routing.

Another possible advisor is the manufacturer of the cooling unit or the factory representative. Make copies of the sketch and cooling calculations and mail them to the manufacturer. Be sure to indicate the exact location of the self-contained cooling unit; that is, on the ground (Fig. 9-19), through the wall (Fig. 9-20), and so on. Tell them you are planning to add an air-conditioning system to the building—utilizing their equipment—and would appreciate their laying out the ductwork.

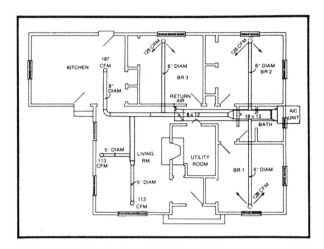

Figure 9-21   Floor plan of residence with ductwork laid out.

Regardless of who designs the duct system, the final layout should appear something like Fig. 9-21. This drawing includes all windows, doors, wall partitions, the location of the self-contained cooling unit, the routing of ductwork, the location of grilles and diffusers, and the size of each. The drawing should be drawn to scale, and it might even include a section through the building to help you visualize the system better.

When dimensions appear on rectangular duct, say, 24 in. × 16 in., the first dimension always means the width of the duct, and the second dimension is the depth of the duct. Dimensions given for round duct, like 8 in. diameter, means the inside diameter of the duct.

Select supply-air outlets carefully; they are a critical part of any air-distribution system. The ideal supply-air outlet will deflect or diffuse the air silently, adjust to change the air-flow rate, and be able to throw the conditioned air no less than three quarters of the distance from the outlet to the opposite wall. Outlets are located according to the shape, size, and heat load of the area.

Air-conditioning systems also require grilles and ducts to return air to the cooling unit. While the location of a return is not as critical as that of a supply outlet, it should be located on the size of the room opposite to the supply. With this information, and using Fig. 9-21 as a guide, the materials can be ordered and installation can begin.

Assume that the self-contained air-conditioning unit has been installed in the attic of the building according to the manufacturer's instructions, wiring has been performed in accordance with the National Electrical Code, and everything is ready for the ductwork.

FABRICATING FIBERGLASS DUCT

The section of ductwork closest to the unit (Fig. 9-21) is rectangular (18 inches wide by 12 inches deep) and will be fabricated from a flat fiberglass duct board. First determine the width of the board required. Board width is equal to twice the interior duct width (2 × 18 or 36 inches in this case) plus twice the interior height (2 × 12 or 24 inches), plus an allowance for grooving. The table in Fig. 9-22 may be used for quick selection of board width. The figures have been precalculated and include the amount of material needed for the duct section plus groove allowances.

THICKNESS		HEIGHT																						
1½"			6	7	8	9	10	11	12	13	14	15	16	17	18	19	20	21	22	23	24	25	26	27
	1"	6	7	8	9	10	11	12	13	14	15	16	17	18	19	20	21	22	23	24	25	26	27	28
WIDTH																								
	6	32	34	36	38	40	42	44	46	48	50	52	54	56	58	60	62	64	66	68	70	72	74	76
6	7	34	36	38	40	42	44	46	48	50	52	54	56	58	60	62	64	66	68	70	72	74	76	78
7	8	36	38	40	42	44	46	48	50	52	54	56	58	60	62	64	66	68	70	72	74	76	78	80
8	9	38	40	42	44	46	48	50	52	54	56	58	60	62	64	66	68	70	72	74	76	78	80	82
9	10	40	42	44	46	48	50	52	54	56	58	60	62	64	66	68	70	72	74	76	78	80	82	84
10	11	42	44	46	48	50	52	54	56	58	60	62	64	66	68	70	72	74	76	78	80	82	84	86
11	12	44	46	48	50	52	54	56	58	60	62	64	66	68	70	72	74	76	78	80	82	84	86	88
12	13	46	48	50	52	54	56	58	60	62	64	66	68	70	72	74	76	78	80	82	84	86	88	90
13	14	48	50	52	54	56	58	60	62	64	66	68	70	72	74	76	78	80	82	84	86	88	90	92
14	15	50	52	54	56	58	60	62	64	66	68	70	72	74	76	78	80	82	84	86	88	90	92	94
15	16	52	54	56	58	60	62	64	66	68	70	72	74	76	78	80	82	84	86	88	90	92	94	96
16	17	54	56	58	60	62	64	66	68	70	72	74	76	78	80	82	84	86	88	90	92	94	96	98
17	18	56	58	60	62	64	66	68	70	72	74	76	78	80	82	84	86	88	90	92	94	96	98	100
18	19	58	60	62	64	66	68	70	72	74	76	78	80	82	84	86	88	90	92	94	96	98	100	102
19	20	60	62	64	66	68	70	72	74	76	78	80	82	84	86	88	90	92	94	96	98	100	102	104
20	21	62	64	66	68	70	72	74	76	78	80	82	84	86	88	90	92	94	96	98	100	102	104	106
21	22	64	66	68	70	72	74	76	78	80	82	84	86	88	90	92	94	96	98	100	102	104	106	108
22	23	66	68	70	72	74	76	78	80	82	84	86	88	90	92	94	96	98	100	102	104	106	108	110
23	24	68	70	72	74	76	78	80	82	84	86	88	90	92	94	96	98	100	102	104	106	108	110	112
24	25	70	72	74	76	78	80	82	84	86	88	90	92	94	96	98	100	102	104	106	108	110	112	114
25	26	72	74	76	78	80	82	84	86	88	90	92	94	96	98	100	102	104	106	108	110	112	114	116
26	27	74	76	78	80	82	84	86	88	90	92	94	96	98	100	102	104	106	108	110	112	114	116	118
27	28	76	78	80	82	84	86	88	90	92	94	96	98	100	102	104	106	108	110	112	114	116	118	120
28	29	78	80	82	84	86	88	90	92	94	96	98	100	102	104	106	108	110	112	114	116	118	120	
29	30	80	82	84	86	88	90	92	94	96	98	100	102	104	106	108	110	112	114	116	118	120		
30	31	82	84	86	88	90	92	94	96	98	100	102	104	106	108	110	112	114	116	118	120			
31	32	84	86	88	90	92	94	96	98	100	102	104	106	108	110	112	114	116	118	120				
32	33	86	88	90	92	94	96	98	100	102	104	106	108	110	112	114	116	118	120					
33	34	88	90	92	94	96	98	100	102	104	106	108	110	112	114	116	118	120						
34	35	90	92	94	96	98	100	102	104	106	108	110	112	114	116	118	120							
35	36	92	94	96	98	100	102	104	106	108	110	112	114	116	118	120								
36	37	94	96	98	100	102	104	106	108	110	112	114	116	118	120									
37	38	96	98	100	102	104	106	108	110	112	114	116	118	120										
38	39	98	100	102	104	106	108	110	112	114	116	118	120											
39	40	100	102	104	106	108	110	112	114	116	118	120												
40	41	102	104	106	108	110	112	114	116	118	120													
41	42	104	106	108	110	112	114	116	118	120														
42	43	106	108	110	112	114	116	118	120															
43	44	108	110	112	114	116	118	120																
44	45	110	112	114	116	118	120																	
45	46	112	114	116	118	120																		
46	47	114	116	118	120																			
47	48	116	118	120																				
48	49	118	120																					
49	50	120																						

Figure 9-22 Board width selection chart.

The left-hand column lists inside duct width in inches, and the figures across the top are inside duct height. Figures are given for both 1-inch and 1-1/2-inch board thicknesses.

To use the chart, find the duct width in the proper thickness column on the left. Then find the duct height in the proper thickness column across the top. Read across and down to the point of intersection, which is the board width necessary.

To illustrate the use of this chart for the 18-in. × 12-in. duct, locate the 18-in. width figure in the 1-in. (board thickness) column on the left. Locate the 12-in. height figure in the 1-in. height row at the top of the chart. Then read across from 18 in. and down from 12 in. to the point of intersection. The board width is 68 inches. Ducts up to 10 feet in length can be fabricated from flat board, providing the total width of the board required does not exceed 70 inches. We will need a fiberglass board 68 inches wide by 10 feet long.

Begin fabrication by marking the board with four measurements as shown in Fig. 9-23. Measure from left to right, using the formula provided on the work sheet in Fig. 9-23; the three "V" grooves are all made with a red grooving tool (for this brand of fiberglass board). Place the tool with its left

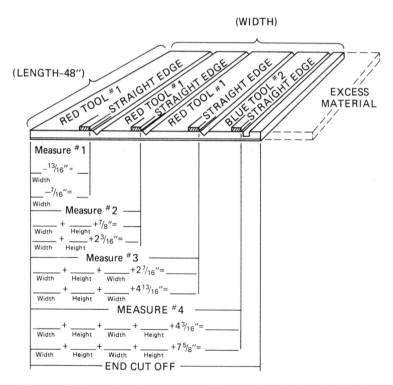

Figure 9-23 Method and measurements for grooving fiberglass duct board.

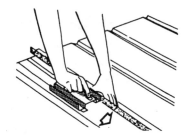

Figure 9-24 Grooving board with blue
end-cutting tool.

Figure 9-25 Cutting insulation material
from the board.

edge at each mark and cut along a straight line using a straightedge as a
guide. The groove will appear off to the right of the mark rather than on the
mark. Push, don't pull, the tool firmly and evenly to prevent the tool from
riding out of the groove or gouging.

When the three "V" grooves have been cut with the red tool, cut the
fourth and final groove in the board with the blue tool, pushing in the
direction of the arrow in Fig. 9-24, along the mark indicated in Fig. 9-23.
The tool will not completely cut through both insulation and jacket.

If a board exactly the right width has been selected, there will be no
excess board to remove. Using a utility knife, cut the insulation material
from the aluminum jacket by sliding the knife the length of the board
between the jacket and the insulation as shown in Fig. 9-25. Cut back only to
the first end cutoff groove (approximately two inches).

Since the blue tool does not cut completely through the insulation, it is
necessary to separate the insulation strip from the side of the last groove
with a utility knife—be careful not to cut through the jacket. After removing
this excess insulation strip, scrape the adhesive side of the aluminum tab
clean with the blade of the knife. (See Fig. 9-26.)

Another piece of duct will connect to this first section, so some
provision for connecting them is necessary. Use a shiplap connection, made
as follows:

1. Use the black butt-joint tool and cut along the edge of the board
   perpendicular to the grooving cuts. The tool must be pushed, rather
   than pulled, along the edge of the board to insure a correct cut as
   shown in Fig. 9-27.
2. Next prepare the male shiplap by turning the board over; this is formed
   on the opposite end of the board from the female shiplap described
   previously. With the aluminum jacket facing up, insert the utility knife
   between jacket and insulation and separate the insulation from the
   jacket for five to six inches from the end of the board. See Fig. 9-28.

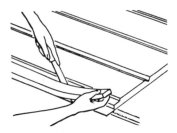

Figure 9-26 Trimming insulation from the fiberglass strip.

Figure 9-27 Cutting the female shiplap joint.

3. Again using the black butt-joint tool, make the shiplap cut. Hold the aluminum jacket back far enough to allow freedom of movement in pushing the tool along the edge of the board as shown in Fig. 9-29.
4. Remove the thin remaining tab of insulation from the left edge of the board to insure a snug fit when the board is formed into shape (see Fig. 9-30). The material will tear easily with your fingers. Allow the aluminum jacket to bend back into normal position along the edge of the board.

Now the duct board is ready to look like a piece of rectangular duct. Hold the duct so that the overlapping staple tab will fold over the top section as indicated in Fig. 9-31, and draw it into shape using one of the sections as the base of the duct. Now hold this folded duct section against your body and draw the edges tightly together with the staple tab overlapping the top section. Beginning from the center of the duct, staple this tab (with staples two inches apart and one inch from the edge of the tab) along the full length of the duct section as shown in Fig. 9-32. Apply aluminum tape to the joint (Fig. 9-33), making certain that both staples and tab are thoroughly covered. Rub the tape down smoothly along the entire joint to form a neat, tight seal.

Figure 9-28 Preparing the board for the male shiplap.

Figure 9-29 Cutting the male shiplap.

Figure 9-30 Removing the corner tab from the fiberglass board.

Figure 9-31 Folding duct sections together.

The first section of the rectangular ductwork is now complete and may be put in place. If all duct sections were the same size as the first section, it would be necessary only to repeat the procedure given for this first section and tape the sections together. However, in the layout in Fig. 9-21, notice that the second section is only 8 inches wide instead of 18 inches. The height is the same—12 inches.

Whenever it becomes necessary to decrease either the height or width of a size of duct, a two-piece transition is constructed. A transition can decrease either the height or width of a duct section, but not both. When it does become necessary to decrease both height and width, two separate transitions are utilized.

Using the formulas given in Fig. 9-34 and a tape measure or rule, mark the board with three measurements as shown, measuring from the left edge of the board. Place the correctly colored tool with its left edge at each mark and cut along a straightedge. Again, the groove will appear to the right of the measurement mark, rather than at the mark. Push, don't pull, the tool firmly and evenly to prevent it from riding out of the groove or gouging the material. The cut at the third measurement is omitted when the board is the exact size required.

After grooving the board and removing any excess, prepare the small end of the transition by calculating trim dimensions for the opposite end of

Figure 9-32 Stapling the connecting tab of duct.

Figure 9-33 Applying tape.

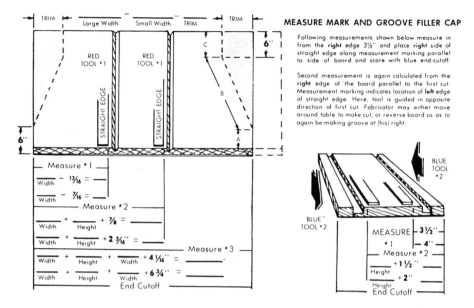

Figure 9-34 Method of laying out a transition duct.

the board, measuring in from each edge of the board the required distance. Using a utility knife, cut through the insulation and jacket to remove trim as directed. When the total of measurements A, B, and C exceeds 48 inches, either distance A or C may be varied to reach a total of 48 inches.

Once the proper cuts have been made, fold the section of the transition with the opening toward your body and the leading edge flush with the work table or floor. Then, starting at the large end, place the filler cap in position so the grooves are aligned with the duct section. Fold the staple tab down flush and begin stapling. Then cut the stapling tab where the filler cap angles in and out to prevent wrinkling. Complete the stapling procedure on both sides, apply tap to the joints and rub them down, then heat seal with a heat tool over the entire tape surface, making sure the heat-seal application is uniform and thorough. These steps are illustrated in Figs. 9-35 through 9-38.

The remaining rectangular ductwork is installed just like these pieces; that is, fabricate regular pieces of duct as described in Figs. 9-23 through 9-33, providing transitions wherever the duct changes size.

The round branches are connected to the rectangular duct sections by using a round sheet-metal fitting the same diameter as the interior diameter of the round fiberglass duct. This fitting may be fabricated from standard sheet-metal pipe by snipping back one end with sheet-metal cutters to form the connecting tabs. At 90°, 180°, 270°, and 360°, cut deeper tabs for fitting against the outside of the duct as shown in Fig. 9-39. To cut the opening in

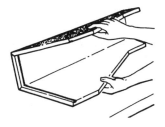

Figure 9-35   Folding transition duct.

Figure 9-36   Installing the filler cap.

Figure 9-37   Sealing the joint.

Figure 9-38   Heat treating the tape and joint for a better seal.

Figure 9-39   Installing fitting into rectangular duct for round duct take-off.

Figure 9-40   Inserting round duct over fitting.

rectangular duct, use the fitting as a template, scribing the size of the cutout in the trunk duct. Fold the four long tabs up; insert the fitting so the tabs rest flush against the duct.

Complete the connection by sliding the round duct section over the metal sleeve so that it butts tightly against the rectangular duct section. Apply tape around the curvature of the connection, rub the tape down smoothly, and apply heat as described previously (see Fig. 9-40).

Straight line connections are made in the round duct by using approved sheet-metal sleeve connectors to provide reinforcement and alignment, as shown in Fig. 9-41. Slide the round duct sections over the metal sleeve, butt tightly together, apply pressure-sensitive tape, rub smooth, and heat seal.

Elbows are constructed in round ducts by using standard sheet-metal elbows and two duct sections cut at a 45° angle. Use a template (usually provided with the round duct sections) and knife, or miter box and saw, to cut a 45° angle in the section, as shown in Fig. 9-42. Insert the sheet-metal elbow (Fig. 9-43), making certain it is correctly aligned, and butt the ends of the sections tightly together over the elbow. Apply tape to the joint, rub down, and heat seal, as shown in Fig. 9-44.

When joining two sections of round duct of different diameters, use a standard sheet-metal ruder as an internal reinforcement and alignment sleeve. Cut six "V" notches in the end of the larger duct section (Fig. 9-45) approximately one inch wide and equal in length to the tapered face of the metal reducer. Slip the reducer in the larger section of the duct until the tabs can be folded down against the tapered face and secure with pressure-sensitive tape around the circumference of the duct; also cover the "V" notches with tape as shown in Fig. 9-46. Slip the smaller section of the duct

Figure 9-41 Method of joining two straight pieces of round fiberglass duct.

Figure 9-42 Cutting a 45° angle in round duct.

Figure 9-43 Joining two 45° sections of duct.

Figure 9-44 Taping the joint.

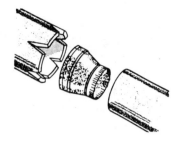

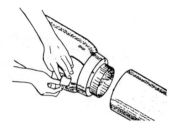

Figure 9-45 Method of reducing round ductwork by inserting sheet-metal reducer into ducts.

Figure 9-46 Taping "V" notches in larger duct.

Figure 9-47 Method of taping round duct reductions.

Figure 9-48 Taping round duct to diffuser.

over the reducer until it is butted tightly against the larger section, tape the joint securely, rub down the tape, and heat seal (see Fig. 9-47).

Supply run-outs may be installed on round ducts in a manner similar to those installed on rectangular ducts. Templates are also provided for this application.

Round duct is slipped onto round diffuser adapters and securely fastened to the sheet metal with two layers of tape. The tape should be applied so that one layer is on the sheet metal and one is on the duct, and overlapping each other by at least one inch, as shown in Fig. 9-48.

A standard sheet-metal pipe damper is easily adapted for use in round duct runs; dampers are highly recommended at each branch take-off for balancing the air supply to each area. Modification merely consists of installing an extended control arm so it will extend beyond the outer surface of the duct. Butt the two sections of duct together as shown in Fig. 9-49, and tape the joint securely with two layers of tape. Puncture the tape so the control arm may protrude before sealing the joint and installing the control handle.

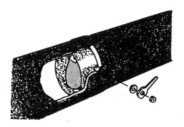

Figure 9-49 Method of installing a damper in a round section of fiberglass duct.

The return-air ductwork of the system in Fig. 9-21 requires the fabrication of an intake box over the return grille in the hallway of the residence. This box may be fabricated from flat duct board formed into rectangular sections with flush ends rather than shiplaps, capped at one end.

First measure the connecting collar to find the inside dimensions of the box or boot. Determine the stretchout dimensions in order to select the proper size of board, then measure and groove the board in the same manner as a one-piece duct section, omitting the shiplap at the end. Trim the section to the proper height and secure this section to the intake or outlet components with sheet-metal screws and washers. Drill pilot holes through the duct and register collar on 6-inch centers.

Next determine the size of the opening required for connecting the branch duct and make this cutout. If a round duct is to be connected, it will be necessary to install the metal connecting sleeve before capping the box. With the duct connection out of the way, the only remaining step is to fabricate and install an end cap on the box.

Measure the interior dimensions of the duct section to be capped, then select an adequate size duct board and mark these dimensions off on the insulation side, allowing an additional 2-1/2 inches on each side for the staple tab. Measure in one inch from the inside duct dimension marks and use a straightedge to make the cut.

Use the blue end cutoff tool to cut the stapled tabs. Prepare the tabs as described previously, removing the insulation from the board and scraping the jacket clean. Make a diagonal cut in each of the four corners to allow for folds in the staple tab.

Finally, install the end cap in the opening and attach by stapling the tabs on each side of the duct; be certain to pull the tabs tight before stapling to assure an airtight closure. Apply tape and rub it thoroughly, then heat seal.

SUSPENDING RECTANGULAR DUCT

Rectangular fiberglass duct requires suspension in 8-foot centers (maximum) for ducts up to 24-foot span; ducts spanning over 24 feet must be suspended at joints on 4-foot centers. However, suspension may be eliminated if the building structural members provide adequate support within the given limitations. Any of the following suspension systems are satisfactory for this purpose.

1. *Strap and Pad System:* Suspend duct on 3/4-inch metal strap. Use 90° metal corner pads on duct corners to prevent jacket puncture (see Fig. 9-50).
2. *Strap and Channel Method:* Fig. 9-51 shows the ductwork suspended in a 3/4-inch metal strap, which is in turn suspended from the framing and attached to a channel-iron member which passes under the duct.
3. *Strap and Rail System:* Suspend the duct on angle iron using 3/4-inch flat metal crossties spaced every three feet along the railing as shown in Fig. 9-52. Metal straps approximately 3/4 inch wide suspended from the roof, ceiling, or framing support the angles. Use sheet-metal screws for fastening the strap and rail members together.
4. *Strap and Angle System:* Suspend the duct on 3/4-inch metal strap hung from the building framing and attach angle iron passing under the duct as shown in Fig. 9-53.

Figure 9-50 Strap and pad suspension system for mounting rectangular duct.

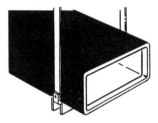

Figure 9-51 Strap and channel method of mounting rectangular duct.

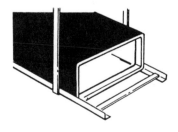

Figure 9-52 Strap and rail system for mounting rectangular duct.

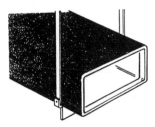

Figure 9-53 Strap and angle system for mounting rectangular duct.

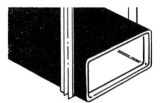

Figure 9-54 T-bar saddle method for mounting rectangular duct.

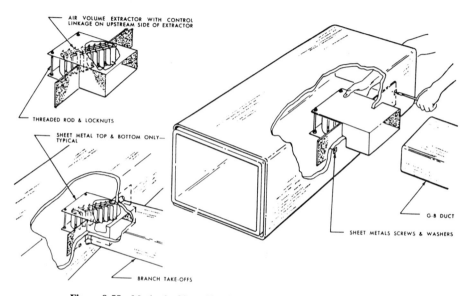

AIR VOLUME EXTRACTOR WITH CONTROL LINKAGE ON UPSTREAM SIDE OF EXTRACTOR

THREADED ROD & LOCKNUTS

SHEET METAL TOP & BOTTOM ONLY— TYPICAL

G-B DUCT

SHEET METALS SCREWS & WASHERS

BRANCH TAKE-OFFS

Figure 9-55 Method of installing branch take-off from rectangular duct.

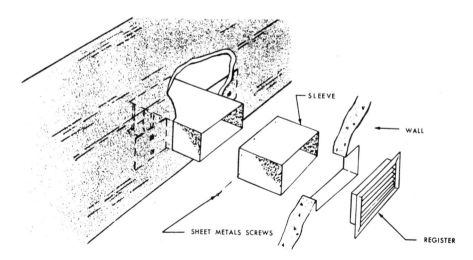

SLEEVE

WALL

SHEET METALS SCREWS

REGISTER

Figure 9-56 Method of installing wall registers from rectangular duct.

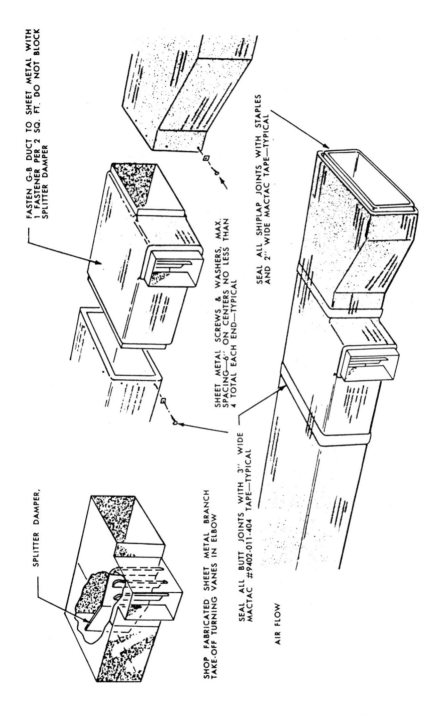

FASTEN G.B DUCT TO SHEET METAL WITH
1 FASTENER PER 2 SQ. FT. DO NOT BLOCK
SPLITTER DAMPER

SEAL ALL SHIPLAP JOINTS WITH STAPLES
AND 2" WIDE MACTAC TAPE—TYPICAL

SHEET METAL SCREWS & WASHERS, MAX.
SPACING—6" ON CENTERS NO LESS THAN
4 TOTAL EACH END—TYPICAL

SPLITTER DAMPER,

SHOP FABRICATED SHEET METAL BRANCH
TAKE-OFF TURNING VANES IN ELBOW

SEAL ALL BUTT JOINTS WITH 3" WIDE
MACTAC #9402-011-404 TAPE—TYPICAL

AIR FLOW

Figure 9-57 Various uses of sheet-metal branch take-off from rectangular duct.

191

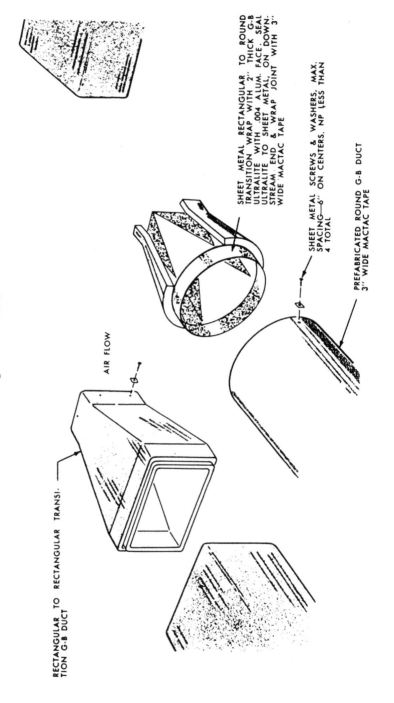

Figure 9-57 cont'd

RECTANGULAR TO RECTANGULAR TRANSI-
TION G-B DUCT

AIR FLOW

SHEET METAL RECTANGULAR TO ROUND
TRANSITION WRAP WITH 2" THICK G-B
ULTRALITE WITH .004 ALUM. FACE. SEAL
ULTRALITE TO SHEET METAL, ON DOWN-
STREAM END & WRAP JOINT WITH 3"
WIDE MACTAC TAPE

SHEET METAL SCREWS & WASHERS, MAX.
SPACING—6" ON CENTERS. NP LESS THAN
4 TOTAL

PREFABRICATED ROUND G-B DUCT
3" WIDE MACTAC TAPE

5. *T-Bar Saddle Method:* Suspend duct on standard stock T-bar (1-1/4 in. × 3/4 in. × 1-1/4 in.) as shown in Fig. 9-54. Trim back the 3/4-inch dimension or "T" and break it to 90° to form the T-bar saddle.

BRANCH TAKE-OFFS

In some cases it may be desirable to use air volume extractors constructed of sheet metal when making a branch take-off from the main duct or plenum. Figure 9-55 shows the installation of such an extractor in a duct take-off, while Fig. 9-56 shows the same extractor used in the installation of a wall register.

There are many other sheet-metal fittings available for various purposes in a duct system. A few of the branch take-off applications are shown in Fig. 9-57. Check with your local supplier of sheet-metal ductwork for help in planning and making up these various shapes.

Each manufacturer of fiberglass ducts may have a slightly different method of fabricating the system, but the procedures given in this chapter are typical. The main difference is nomenclature; one manufacturer may call a grooving tool a "Blue Tool," while another may call it the "No. 2 Tool," and so on. The installation of fiberglass duct—especially the rectangular type—may seem very complicated at first glance. However, once one is tried, with the initial mistakes out of the way and the first section of duct made up, then the installation is easy.

Sheet-metal ductwork is still probably the type most used in residential construction. However, the tools and techniques required to fabricate sheet-metal ductwork cover too wide an area to be included in this book. Separate books on this subject are available, and should be studied.

With the exception of the plenum located at the air-handling unit, many prefabricated sheet-metal duct sections may be purchased in practically any size. Branch take-offs, as well as boots and other components, may be purchased from HVAC distributors.

10
Installing High-Velocity Systems

High-velocity heating/cooling systems are easily adapted to fit existing shops because they are so compact. Their use avoids much of the costly, time-consuming cutting and patching often necessary with conventional air-handling systems. So, if central air conditioning is being added which has no ductwork, or if a completely new comfort system is being installed, the high-velocity system with its 3-1/2-inch-diameter air ducts and 2-inch air outlets may be just the answer.

There are several such systems on the market today, but Dunham-Bush, Inc. of Harrisonburg, VA makes the Space-Pak kit described herein.

THE SYSTEM COMPONENTS

Figure 10-1 shows the basic components of a high-velocity heating and cooling system. Taking the individual items from left to right, they are:

1. *Return-air Assembly:* A centrally located opening for this assembly's grille is probably the only major cutting required to install the system. An optional air cleaner is available which electrostatically removes dust particles from the air to keep the building clean.

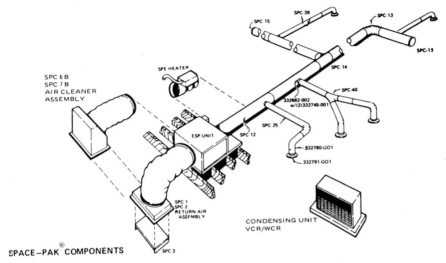

Figure 10-1   Components of a high-velocity heating and cooling system.

2. *Blower Coil Unit:* Attic or basement installation of a high-velocity blower unit is compact and neat. Most kits include a spring-mounted, rubber-isolated blower and electric motor plus an expansion valve, condensate overflow control, and an extra deep cooling coil that removes up to 30 percent more humidity from the air than shallow ones. Sizes are available from 17,000 to over 50,000 Btuh. A prefabricated seven-foot length of 14-inch or 18-inch flexible return-air duct connects the return assembly to the blower (ESP) unit.

3. *Condensing Unit:* The condensing unit is the only piece of outside equipment needed. The twin blowers housed in an aluminum cabinet can be mounted as described previously; that is, rooftop, through the wall, or on a concrete slab. The two-speed motor runs at low speed during normal operation for quietness, then automatically switches to high speed when the outside temperature is about 90°F. The quick-connect refrigerant lines (see Fig. 10-2) connect the condensing unit to the blower coil unit and can be installed in minutes.

4. *Duct Heater:* The optional electric heating system can be added in increments from 5 to 25 kilowatts or from 17,000 to 85,000 Btuh. The heating system is installed in the main plenum duct just downstream of the blower coil.

5. *Plenum Duct:* Seven-inch sound-absorbing fiberglass duct is used for the plenum. An aluminum vapor barrier on the outside of the plenum controls moisture; the flexible two-inch supply ducts are easily cut into the supply plenum.

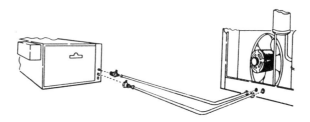

Figure 10-2   Method of connecting refrigerant lines from condensing unit to fan coil unit.

6. *Supply-air Ducts:* Preinsulated flexible supply ducts quickly connect to the main plenum duct; two parts join with a twist of the wrist, giving an airtight seal for good air delivery. The small 3-1/2-inch ducts are easily run between studs and around obstacles, requiring less cutting and patching than conventional forced-air systems. An assortment of factory-made fittings (shown in Fig. 10-1) help speed the installation.

7. *Supply-air Outlet Plate:* The tiny two-inch opening will heat and cool the average room; it can be located in an out-of-the-way corner in ceiling or floor so that it is hardly noticeable. Adjustable dampers built into each outlet permit you to control the air flow according to the season or the number of people in the area.

8. *Controls:* Besides a conventional thermostat and control panel, the controls include: a factory-installed antifrost control which automatically shuts off the compressor if icing of the cooling coil occurs, and a mercury float switch to prevent condensate overflow.

SYSTEM DESIGN

As with any system, proper sizing of a high-velocity system requires accurate calculation of heat gain and loss. Check the index to find the chapters giving the information necessary to perform these calculations.

System layout is a different story; only personnel trained in the design and application of high-velocity systems should attempt to lay one out. The calculations required are complicated and critical, and the numerous design considerations include the thermal load on, and the length of duct run to, each area.

Furnish the manufacturer's engineer with the floor plan and heat-loss and heat-gain calculations and he or she will lay out the system completely, locating duct runs, return and supply fixtures, and all other system hardware at little or no cost.

Once the system is laid out to suit the needs of the building, the small preinsulated ducts and easily connected components make it possible to

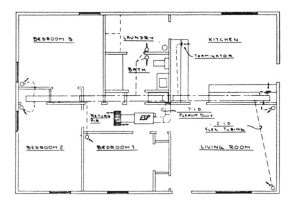

Figure 10-3   Floor plan showing the high-velocity duct system laid out.

install the entire system in one day. Figure 10-3 shows a floor plan with the high-velocity system laid out.

BASIC INSTALLATION PROCEDURES

Many installers begin by locating the return-air grille centrally in the building. Attic or basement location of the blower unit is typical; if there is no other access to the attic, the unit may be inserted through the opening cut for the return-air grille.

When mounting the blower unit in the attic, it is recommended that vibration isolators be installed between the equipment and the house structure as shown in Fig. 10-4. With the unit in place, run the flexible return duct from the blower unit to the return-air opening, making sure that this duct has a 90° turn in it with an inside radius of 6 inches or more. This is to prevent excessive noise in the return assembly. Insert the filter grille and snap the connecting bands in place for a neat installation.

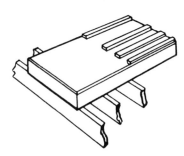

Figure 10-4   A vibration isolator separates the blower unit from the house structure.

Figure 10-5 Boxing in the plenum in a corner.

The plenum duct can be placed in practically any location that will be accessible for the attachment of the supply tubing. Your layout will show exactly how to run this duct, but the plenum is normally located in the attic or basement. In some two-story or split-level homes it may be advantageous to run plenum to both levels, rather than make the smaller supply branches too long.

When boxing is necessary, as between floors or along the ceiling, the small size of the plenum makes it an easy job (see Figs 10-5 and 10-6).

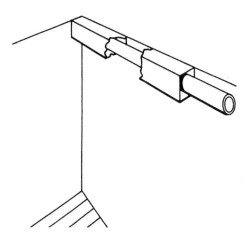

Figure 10-6 Boxing in the plenum along the ceiling edge.

The 2-inch-inside-diameter (3½-inch-outside diameter) tubing conveys the conditioned air from the plenum to the air outlet or teriminator. When installing this and any other ductwork, care should be taken to prevent sharp bends. The minimum radius for a tubing bend is 6 inches.

In two-story or split-level buildings, supply tubing may be run from one story to another inside the walls without much difficulty. In older buildings, however, hidden obstructions in the stud spaces can cause problems. In such cases it may be better to run the supply tubing from the attic down through second-story closets to the first floor (as shown in Fig. 10-7) or box the tubing in a corner (as shown in Fig. 10-8).

A critical factor in minimizing drafts with a high-velocity system is the location of the air outlets or terminators. In general, they should be out of the normal traffic patterns. This will prevent discharge air from blowing directly on the occupants.

Outlets should be located in the ceiling or floor with the center of the terminator 5 inches from the wall (or 5 inches from both walls in the case of a corner). They should never be located directly above shelves or large pieces of furniture. Neither should you attempt to install terminators for horizontal discharge in wall partitions. The resulting sharp bend would probably be very noisy.

If you're installing the system for cooling only, the best location for the outlets is in the floor (Fig. 10-9) or ceiling (Fig. 10-10). Horizontal discharge for cooling is acceptable but is sometimes more difficult to install. Two excellent applications for horizontal discharge are the soffit above cabinets (Fig. 10-11) and the top portion of a closet (Fig. 10-7).

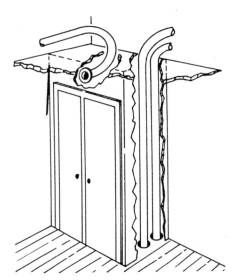

Figure 10-7 Second-floor closets can be used to conceal tubing connecting the first floor and an attic unit.

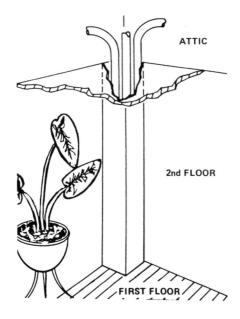

Figure 10-8 Air-supply tubing from attic to first floor boxed in at corner of the room.

All comments regarding the location of outlets for cooling apply to heating also, with one exception. Horizontal air flow should be avoided wherever possible because it does not maintain as narrow a floor-to-ceiling temperature differential as do floor and ceiling outlets.

An adjustable damper is supplied with each air outlet to balance the system. System balance for the heating function may differ from that for

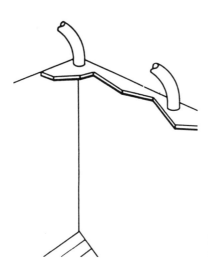

Figure 10-9 One location of ceiling outlets.

Figure 10-10 Proper location of a floor
outlet in a corner.

cooling. In fact, a particular room may require more outlets for one season
than for the other. If a given room requires three terminators for heating and
only two for cooling, install three terminators, close the damper on one
during the cooling season and open it during the heating season. However,
you should remember that an open damper will still reduce the output of that
duct by 10 percent, and when completely closed, it will reduce the output by
only 80 percent.

With the blower coil, main plenum, branch ducts, and air outlets
installed, the only remaining items are the condensing unit, the power

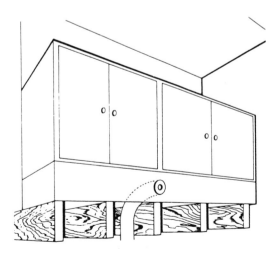

Figure 10-11 Method used to terminate supply tubing in a kitchen soffit.

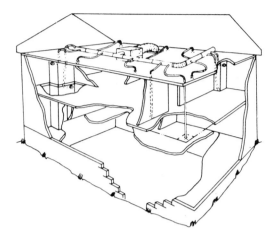

Figure 10-12   One way to install a high-velocity duct system in a two-story building.

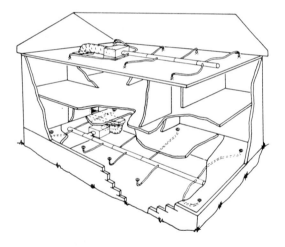

Figure 10-13   Another method of conditioning a two-story building: two independent systems.

wiring, and the controls. The condensing unit is mounted outside on concrete pads or other supports. The refrigerant tubing and electrical wiring are also installed.

Installations in a single-story building (shown in Fig. 10-3) are normally the quickest and simplest. Two-story applications require a little more planning and installation time, and are usually handled in one of two manners:

1. One blower unit and a plenum is installed in the attic of the building. (Most often supply tubing is run from the plenum to ceiling-mounted second-story outlets and down through the second-story walls to the first-story outlets, as shown in Fig. 10-12.
2. The second most common way to handle two-story buildings is to install two separate systems (Fig. 10-13). One is placed in the attic to handle the second story using ceiling-mounted outlets and air return. The other system is placed in the basement or crawl space, with its duct system suspended from the floor joists and supplying floor outlets.

The two-system approach is well suited to buildings with obstructions which would prevent in-wall duct routing. It usually enables a quick, trouble-free installation with an absolute minimum of cutting, patching, and duct runs, and results in a zoned system with independent control of first- and second-floor climates.

11
Electric Heating Units

In general, there are no less than two basic methods of heating with electricity: a central electric furnace or heat pump used in conjunction with ductwork or water piping, or individual units in each room or area. Both methods have their advantages and disadvantages. For example, when individual units are used, each room may be controlled separately, which can save on the cost of fuel and also have the convenience of controlling the temperature to a more comfortable level; that is, the living room, for example, can be heated to, say, 70 degrees F, while the bedrooms can be kept at a lower temperature of perhaps 60 degrees, or whatever is comfortable. Also, rooms or areas not in use can be turned off completely, or else the temperature lowered to just above freezing to protect water pipes and other items critical to low temperatures.

Individual baseboard heaters are usually less expensive to purchase and install than a central system. Forced-air cooling cannot be installed without installing a complete ductwork system and other necessary items. There are, however, individual, through-wall units that operate both in heating and cooling modes and can be provided for each individual room or area. However, these units are relatively expensive—often costing more than a central system if many rooms or units are involved.

204

Heat pumps and electric furnaces operate much the same as oil-fired and gas-fired forced-air furnaces, with the exception that clean electric heat is used instead of burning gas or oil. The remainder of the system is almost identical in that ductwork is provided to transmit the heated air to the area, and also to provide a path for the cooler return air. A fan or blower is used to force the air through the ductwork, and automatic controls are provided to obtain the desired temperatures and overall results of the system.

When an electric heating system is installed in an existing building where other types of heat had been used, the only major modification necessary, in most cases, is enlarging the electric service. Many residents have only a 60-ampere main electric service, or seldom more than 100 amperes if the home is of average size. When electric heat is installed, a 200-ampere electric service is normally considered to be minimum.

Embedded heat cable is another popular form of electric heating. In this type of system, heating cables are concealed in either the ceiling or concrete floor and are controlled with a wall thermostat for each area, providing individual room or area heating control. Such cables may also be used outdoors to melt snow on driveways or walks, or to prevent snow and ice build-up on roofs.

Other types of heaters designed for individual rooms or areas are heat panels, which usually consist of a 4-ft × 8-ft section of flat panel with resistance-heating wires inside. These panels may be wall or ceiling mounted and controlled by a wall thermostat.

Wall- or ceiling-mounted infrared heaters are popular in bathrooms, as are wall-mounted fan-forced heaters. The latter type has a fan motor which circulates the heated air throughout the area. Then there are kick-space heaters for mounting in the kick-space of kitchen cabinets, and a host of other types of electric units.

INSTALLING COMBINATION HEATING AND COOLING UNITS

The desired result, as far as heating and cooling the home is concerned, is ultimate comfort at low cost. When installing units in an existing structure, problems mount up, but there are still may ways to achieve this goal. One method is by using through-wall combination heating and cooling units in various areas of the house. Such a system gives the occupants complete control of their environment with a room-by-room choice of either heating or cooling at any time of the year, at any temperature they desire. Chapter 9 describes in detail how these units are installed.

INSTALLING RADIANT HEATING CABLE

Radiant ceiling heat is acknowledged to be one of the greatest advances in structural heating since the Franklin stove, or so say the manufacturers, and thousands of homeowners all over the country have chosen this type of heat for their homes.

The enormous heating surface precludes the necessity of raising air temperatures to a high degree. Rather, gentle warmth flows downward (or upward in the case of cable embedded in concrete floors) from the surfaces, heating the entire room or area evenly, and usually leaving no cold spots or drafts.

There is no maintenance with a radiant heating system as there are no moving parts, nothing to get clogged up, nothing to clean, oil, or grease, and nothing to wear out.

The installation of this system is within reach of even the smallest HVAC contractors. The most difficult part of the entire project is the layout of the system; that is, how far apart to string the cable on the ceiling or in a concrete slab.

An ideal application of electric radiant heating cable would be during the renovation of an area within an existing residence, where the ceiling plaster is beginning to crack and this ceiling will be recovered with drywall or other type of plaster board. Or, perhaps the basement floor needs repair and three inches of additional concrete will be poured over the existing floor. These are ideal locations to install radiant heating cable.

INSTALLATION IN PLASTER CEILINGS

To determine the spacing of the cable on a given ceiling, deduct one foot from the room length and one foot from the room width and multiply this new length by the new width, which will give the usuable ceiling area in square feet. Multiply the square feet of the ceiling by 12 to get the ceiling area in inches before dividing by the length of the heating cable. The result will be the number of inches apart to space the cable.

For example, assume that a room 14 × 12 ft has a calculated heat loss of 2,000 watts. Therefore, (14 ft − 1 ft) (12 ft − 1 ft) × 12 in. = 13 × 11 × 12 = 1,716. We then look in manufacturers' tables and see that a 2,000-watt heating cable is 728 feet in length. Dividing the usable area (1,716 sq in.) by this length (728), we find that the cable should be spaced 2.3 inches apart.

The drawing in Fig. 11-1 shows a typical heating cable installation as suggested by one manufacturer. However, nearly every brand of heating cable will be installed in exactly the same way, and the procedure is as follows:

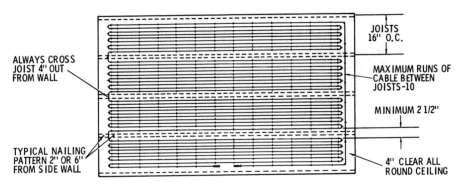

Figure 11-1   Typical layout of ceiling heat cable.

1. Nail outlet box on inside wall approximately 5 ft above the finished floor for your thermostat location.
2. Drill two holes in wall plate above this junction box location.
3. Drill two holes through ceiling lath above thermostat junction box location.
4. Put the spool of heat cable on a nail, screwdriver, or any type of shaft you have at hand for unwinding the cable from the spool.
5. Cover the accessible end of the 8-ft nonheating lead wire with nonmetallic loom. Loom should be long enough so at least 2 inches will go on ceiling surface and reach to the thermostat outlet box, but leave 6 inches of lead wire inside of this junction box for viewing the identification tags. Never, for any reason, remove those tags. Also do not cut or shorten the nonheating leads.
6. Run the accessible end (loom and all) of your cable through one of the holes in the ceiling, down the wall, through the plate, into the thermostat outlet or junction box.
7. Pull slack out of your nonheating leads and staple securely to the ceiling. Any excess nonheating lead should be covered with plaster the same as the heat cable. Do not staple or bend the cable.
8. Your next step will be to mark the ceiling. First mark a line all the way around the room 6 inches away from each wall; this accounts for the one foot you deducted from the width and length. A chalk line is best for this. Now take a yardstick, often given to regular customers at the local hardware store, and notch it for your calculated spacing. Run the cable along the ceiling 6 inches out from the wall to an outside wall, where you attach it in parallel spacing. In this example the spacing is 2½ inches. Always keep the cable at least 2 inches from metal corner lath, or other metal reinforcing.

9. When you are down to the return lead wire, you are back to the starting wall. Cover this lead with the same length of loom as you did the starting lead. Then staple this return lead securely to the ceiling, run through the other hole in the ceiling, down the wall and into the thermostat outlet box.

10. Connect the thermostat, which should be fed by a circuit of proper wire size according to the current, in amperes, drawn by the heating cable. Divide the wattage by the rated voltage. Your answer will be the load in amperes. Then use the following table to size your wire.

AMPS	TYPE TW WIRE
15 or lower	10 AWG
15–20	8 AWG
20–30	6 AWG
30–50	4 AWG

Always make certain that the heating cable is connected to the proper voltage. A 120-volt cable connected to a 240-volt circuit will melt the cable, while a 240-volt heating cable connected to 120 volts will produce only 25 percent of the rated wattage of the cable.

INSTALLING CONCRETE CABLE

The heat loss is calculated in the same manner as for any other area. For best results, the heating cable should never be spaced less than 2½ inches apart when installing in concrete floor except around outside walls, which may be spaced on 1½-inch minimum centers for the first 2 feet out from the wall. The concrete thickness above the cable should be from ½ to 1 inch.

The spacing of the cable is found exactly as previously shown for the spacing of the cable on the ceiling, and then the installation procedure is as follows:

1. Secure junction box on an inside wall approximately 5 ft from the finished floor to house the thermostat.

2. Install a piece of rigid conduit from the switch or thermostat junction box to house the nonheating leads, between the concrete slab and the switch or thermostat outlet box.

3. Approximately 6 inches of the lower end of the conduit should be embedded in the concrete and a smooth porcelain bushing should be on this end of the conduit to protect the nonheating leads where they leave the conduit.

4. Place the spool of heating cable on a nail, screwdriver, or other shaft you have at hand for unwinding the cable from the spool.

5. Run the accessible end of the 8-ft nonheating lead through the conduit to the thermostat junction box, leaving 6 inches extending out of the box. Never remove the identification tags or shorten the nonheating leads. They should be embedded in the concrete the same as the heating portion of the cable.

6. Run the cable along the floor 6 inches out from the wall to the outside or exposed wall, fastening the cable to the floor either with staples or masking tape.

7. The cable usually is spaced 1½ inches apart for the first 2 feet around the exposed wall and never less than 2½ inches apart for the remaining area.

8. Run the return nonheating lead wire through the conduit to the thermostat junction box in the same manner as the starting nonheating lead was run in Item 5.

In general, the concrete slab should be prepared by applying a vapor barrier of 4 to 6 inches of gravel. Then pour 4 inches of vermiculite or other insulating concrete over the gravel after the outside edges of the slab have been insulated, in accordance with good building practice. The heating cable is then installed as described previously.

At this time, the homeowner should inspect and test the cable before the final layer of concrete is installed, because once the concrete is poured, it's an expensive matter to repair. First, visually inspect the cable for any possible damage to the insulation during the application. Then, with a suitable ohmmeter, check for continuity and capacity of the cable. Concealed breaks may be found by leaving an ohmmeter connected to the cable, and then brushing the cable lightly with the bristles of a broom. Any erratic movement of the meter dial will indicate a fault.

During the pouring of the final coat of concrete, it is recommended that the ohmmeter be left connected to the heating cable leads to detect any possible damage to the cable during the pouring of the finish layer of ordinary concrete (do not use insulating concrete). If an ohmmeter is not available at the time, a 100-watt lamp may be connected in series with the cable to immediately detect any damage during the installation of the concrete. The lamp will glow as long as the circuit is complete and no damage occurs. However, if a break does occur, the lamp will go out and the break can be repaired before the concrete hardens.

Repairs to a broken cable are made by stripping the ends of the broken cable and rejoining the ends with a No. 14 AWG pressure-type connector provided and approved for this purpose. The splice must then be insulated with thermoplastic tape to a thickness equal to the insulation of the cable.

Use any thermoplastic tape listed by the Underwriters' Laboratories as suitable for temperature of 176°F.

Once the finish layer of concrete sets, asphalt tile, linoleum tile, or linoleum can be laid on the concrete in the normal manner.

Besides the heating of one's home, electric heating cable also has many other uses for homeowners. It can be embedded in concrete or asphalt surfaces for the removal of ice and snow, provide water pipes exposed to cold weather with freeze protection, for roof and gutter deicing, and for heating soil in your hotbed or window box—keeping the temperature at a constant 70°F. The cost of heat cable is relatively inexpensive and the installation goes fast.

12
Wiring for Heating, Ventilating, and Air Conditioning

There are many different electrical power supplies that will be encountered while working with HVAC systems, but for residential use, the 120/240-volt, single-phase, three-wire service will be the most common. This type of electric service is used primarily for light and power, including single-phase motors up to about 7-1/2 hp.

Electric power is normally distributed at high voltages for economy; that is, the higher the voltage, the smaller the wire size necessary to carry the same amount of power. The power company uses transformers at the generators to step up the voltage for cross-country distribution, and then transformers are again used at substations or at the point of utilization to step the voltage down to the amount required for usage. Most power is generated in three phases with one of the phases used to obtain single-phase service.

From a practical standpoint, those involved with HVAC systems need only be concerned with the power supply on the secondary (usage) side of the transformer, as this determines the characteristic of the power supply for use in the building or on the premises.

There are two general arrangements of transformers and secondaries in common use. The first arrangement is the sectional form, in which a unit of load, such as one city street or city block, is served by a fixed length of secondary, with the transformer located in the middle. The second arrangement is the continuous form where the secondary is installed in one long continuous run, with transformers spaced along it at the most suitable points. As the load grows or shifts, the transformers spaced along it can be moved or rearranged, if desired. In sectional arrangement, such a load can be accommodated only by changing to a larger transformer or installing an additional unit in the same section.

One of the greatest advantages of the secondary bank is that the starting currents of motors are divided between transformers, reducing voltage drop and also diminishing the resulting lamp flicker at the various outlets.

Power companies all over the United States and Canada are now trying to incorporate networks into their secondary power system, especially in areas where a high degree of service reliability is necessary. Around cities and industrial applications, most secondary circuits are three phase—either 120/280 volt or 480/208 volt Y-connected. Usually, two to four primary feeders are run into the area, and transformers are connected alternately to them. The feeders are interconnected in a grid, or network, so that should any feeder go out of service, the load is still carried by the remaining feeders.

The primary feeders supplying networks are run from substations at the usual primary voltage for the system, such as 4,160, 4,800, 6,900, or 13,200 volts. Higher voltages are practical if the loads are large enough to warrant them.

TRANSFORMERS

The main purpose of a power transformer is to obtain a voltage supply which is different from the main voltage available. A transformer's capacity is rated in kva (kilovolt-amperes), and must be designed for the frequency (Hz) of the system involved.

To obtain a certain voltage when the available supply is other than the voltage required, either a step-up or step-down transformer may be used, depending on the circumstance. Each type is interchangeable; that is, primary and secondary windings may be reversed.

When selecting transformers, determine the supply line voltage, load voltage requirement, and the load amperage requirement. Then consult manufacturers' catalogs and/or manufacturers' representatives for a specific selection.

At times it may be necessary to obtain a relatively small voltage correction when dealing with motors and motor controls. For example, a motor rated for 240 volts may be connected to a 208-volt power supply. To obtain this additional voltage, a buck-and-boost transformer may be used. In this case, it will be used to boost the voltage. If the reverse is true (a 208-volt motor used on a 240-volt supply), the transformer would be used to buck (lower) the voltage.

In general, a buck-and-boost transformer is a four-winding isolated transformer designed so that the independent windings may be interconnected to function as an autotransformer. Connected in this manner, all power for the load must pass through the transformer windings. Then, by proper interconnection of the windings, the output voltage may be increased or decreased from the input voltage, depending on the ratio between the primary and secondary windings.

Connected as an autotransformer, the largest part of the power goes directly to the load with only the part that is bucking or boosting being involved in transformation. If, for example, only 10 percent of the voltage must undergo transformation, the autotransformer rating is increased approximately ten times the normal rating of the corresponding isolated transformer.

An approximate transformer size can be determined by multiplying the volts (buck or boost) times the load amps. This can only be an approximation due to the wide requirement for voltage change and the amperage used. It is possible for this method to exceed the transformer rating.

CONTROL CIRCUIT TRANSFORMERS

Low-voltage, control circuit transformers (class 2) are used extensively in control circuits to obtain a lower voltage than is available from the power supply. For example, many control circuits operate at 24 volts, and normally 120 volts is the lowest voltage rating used in any electrical system for building construction. Therefore, a transformer is used to reduce the 120-volt circuit to the required 24 volts. In selecting such a transformer, class 2 low-voltage control systems are limited to transformers with a maximum output capacity of 75 VA (watts). If a control transformer is overlooked for a great length of time, the transformer will fail. Therefore, systems which require the addition of controls should be checked to assure the rating of the transformer will not be exceeded. A typical control circuit shows the load of the holding coil, which totals 22 VA. Since a 45-VA transformer is used (45 − 22), 23 VA is available for additional field-installed controls.

ELECTRICAL LINE CURRENT CAPACITY

Electrical conductors must be sized according to the National Electrical Code and also good wiring practices. Besides the information given in various tables as to the allowable amperes that will safely flow through any given wire size, the wire or conductor should also be sized to limit the voltage drop to a maximum of 2 percent in any electrical circuit. This insures efficient operation of both controls and equipment.

Even when sizing wire for low-voltage (24-volt) systems, the voltage drop should be limited to 3 percent because excessive voltage drop causes:

1. Failure of control coil to activate.
2. Control contact chatter.
3. Erratic operation of controls.
4. Control coil burnout.
5. Contact burnout.

A table that may be used to size low-voltage wire is shown in Fig. 12-1. To use, assume a load of 35 VA with a 50-foot run for a 24-volt control circuit. Referring to the table, scan the 50-foot column. Note that No. 18 AWG wire will carry 29 VA and No. 16 wire will carry 43 VA, while still maintaining a maximum of 3 percent voltage drop. In this case, No. 16 wire should be used.

When the length of wire is other than listed in the table, the capacity may be determined by the following equation:

$$\text{VA capacity} = \frac{\text{Length of circuit (from table)}}{\text{Length of circuit (actual)}} \times \text{VA (from table)}$$

The 3 percent voltage-drop limitation is imposed to assure proper operation when the power supply is below the rated voltage. For example, if the rated 240-volt supply is 10 percent low (216 volts), the transformer does not produce 24 volts but only 21.6 volts. When normal voltage drop is taken from this 21.6 volts, it approaches the lower operating limit of most controls. If it is assured that the primary voltage to the transformer will always be at rated value or above, the control circuit will operate satisfactorily with more than 3 percent voltage drop.

AWG	Length of Circuit, One Way (ft)											
Wire Size	25	50	75	100	125	150	175	200	225	250	275	300
20	29	14	10	7.2	5.8	4.8	4.1	3.6	3.2	2.9	2.6	2.4
18	58	29	19	14	11	9.6	8.2	7.2	6.4	5.8	5.2	4.8
16	86	43	29	22	17	14	12	11	9.6	8.7	7.8	7.2
14	133	67	44	33	27	22	19	17	15	13	12	11

Figure 12-1   Table showing length of circuit, one way (ft).

In most installations, there are several lines which connect the transformer to the control circuit. One line usually carries the full load of the control circuit from the hot side of the transformer to one control with the return, perhaps through several lines of the various other controls. Therefore, the line from the hot side of the transformer is the most critical regarding voltage drop and VA capacity and must be properly sized.

When low-voltage lines are installed, it is suggested that one extra line be run for emergency purposes. This can be substituted for any one of the existing lines which may be defective. Also, it is possible to parallel this extra line with the existing line carrying the full load of the control circuit if the length of run affects control operation caused by voltage drop. In many cases this will reduce the voltage drop and permit satisfactory operation.

CONTROL RELAY

In general, the purpose of a control relay is to energize or deenergize an electrical circuit to obtain a specific operation of a component. It may be used to control a motor, heater, solenoid valve, or another relay.

In selecting a control relay, determine the voltage to be applied to the coil. Then determine the voltage and current characteristics of the load to be controlled by the contacts and whether load is resistive or inductive. Determine the coil VA rating (this is especially important on low-voltage systems), and then consult a manufacturer's catalog to select a relay to meet the requirements.

TEMPERATURE CONTROLS

Low-voltage thermostats which provide many different combinations of control are available in the following configurations:

1. One- or two-stage cooling.
2. One- or two-stage heating.
3. Manual or automatic changeover between cooling and heating.
4. Constant or automatic fan operation.

Any of the just listed operations may be incorporated into a single thermostat.

13
HVAC Controls

Modern comfort-conditioning systems provide one of the most enjoyable conveniences for every type of building where people are present. To be of any use, however, every HVAC must be controlled—if only to start and stop it.

HVAC controls cover a wide range of types and sizes from a simple toggle switch to energize a fan motor to complex systems utilizing such components as relays, timers, switches, push buttons, and the like. The common function, however, is the same in every case: to control some operation of the HVAC system. These operations include, but are not limited to, the following:

- Starting and stopping the fan-coil unit.
- Energizing auxiliary electric heating elements.
- Blocking out the heating mode when cooling is called for.
- Sensing the condition of the room or area, and acting accordingly.
- Protecting the system.

Motor starters are frequently employed in HVAC systems, since motors are used to run fans, compressors, and the like. Strictly speaking, a motor starter is the simplest form of controller and is capable of starting and stopping the motor and providing it with overload protection.

216

MANUAL STARTERS

A manual starter is a controller whose contact mechanism is operated by a mechanical linkage from a toggle handle or push button, which in turn is operated by hand. A thermal unit and direct-acting overload mechanism provide motor running overload protection. Basically, a manual starter is merely an on–off switch with overload relays.

Manual starters are used mostly on small fans, blowers, pumps, and compressors. They are lowest in cost of all motor controls, have a simple mechanism, and provide quiet operation with no ac magnet hum. The contacts, however, remain closed and the lever stays in the ON position in the event of a power failure—causing the motor to restart automatically when the power returns. Therefore, low-voltage protection and low-voltage release are not possible with these manually operated starters. However, this action is an advantage when the starter is applied to fans or blowers that should run continuously.

Fractional-horsepower manual starters are designed to control and provide overload protection for motors of 1 horsepower (hp) or less on 120- and 240-volt aingle-phase circuits. They are available in single- and two-pole versions and are operated by a toggle handle on the front. When a serious overload occurs, the thermal unit "trips" to open the starter contacts, disconnecting the motor from the line. The contacts cannot be reclosed until the overload relay has been reset by moving the handle to the full OFF position, after allowing about two minutes for the thermal unit to cool. The open-type starter will fit into a standard outlet box and can be used with a standard flush plate. The compact construction of this type of device makes it possible to mount it directly on the driven fan-coil unit or compressor where available space is limited.

Manual motor-starting switches provide on–off control of single-phase or three-phase ac motors where overload protection is not required or is provided separately. Two- or three-pole switches are available with ratings up to 10 hp, 600 v, three phase. The continuous current rating is 30 amp at 250 v maximum and 20 amp at 600 v maximum. The toggle operation of the manual switch is similar to the fractional-horsepower starter. Typical applications of the switch include pumps, fans, and other electrical machinery having separate motor protection. They are particularly suited to switch nonmotor loads, such as auxiliary resistance heaters in heat-pump systems.

The integral-horsepower manual starter is available in two- and three-pole versions to control single-phase motors up to 5 hp and polyphase motors up to 10 hp, respectively.

Two-pole starters have one overload relay, and three-pole starters usually have three overload relays. When an overload relay trips, the starter mechanism unlatches, opening the contacts to stop the motor. The contacts cannot be reclosed until the starter mechanism has been reset by pressing the stop button or moving the handle to the reset position, after allowing time for the thermal unit to cool.

Integral-horsepower starters with low-voltage protection prevent automatic start-up of motors after a power loss. This is accomplished with a continuous-duty solenoid, which is energized whenever the line-side voltage is present. If the line voltage is lost or disconnected, the solenoid deenergizes, opening the starter contacts. The contacts will not automatically close when the voltage is restored to the line. To close the contacts, the device must be reset manually. This manual starter will not function unless the line terminals are energized. This is a safety feature that can protect personnel or equipment from damage and is used wherever standards require low-voltage protection.

MAGNETIC CONTROLLERS

Magnetic controllers use electromagnetic energy for closing switches. The electromagnet consists of a coil of wire placed on an iron core. When current flows through the coil, the iron of the magnet becomes magnetized, attracting an iron bar called the armature. An interruption of the current flow through the coil of wire causes the armature to drop out due to the presence of an air gap in the magnetic circuit.

Line-voltage magnetic motor starters are electromechanical devices that provide a safe, convenient, and economical means of starting and stopping motors for fan-coil units and compressors, and have the advantage of being controlled remotely. The great bulk of motor controllers sold are of this type. Therefore, the operating principles and applications of magnet motor controllers should be fully understood.

In the construction of a magnetic controller, the armature is mechanically connected to a set of contacts, so that when the armature moves to its closed position, the contacts also close. When the coil has been energized and the armature has moved to the closed position, the controller is said to be "picked up" and the armature "seated" or "sealed in." Some of the magnet and armature assemblies in current use are as follows:

1. *Clapper type:* In this type, the armature is hinged. As it pivots to seal in, the movable contacts close against the stationary contacts.
2. *Vertical action:* The action is a straight-line motion, with the armature and contacts being guided so that they move in a vertical plane.
3. *Horizontal action:* Both armature and contacts move in a straight line through a horizontal plane.
4. *Bell crank:* A bell-crank lever transforms the vertical action of the armature into a horizontal contact motion. The shock of armature

pickup is not transmitted to the contacts, resulting in minimum contact bounce and longer contact life.

The magnetic circuit of a controller consists of the magnet assembly, the coil, and the armature. It is so named from a comparison with an electrical circuit. The coil and the current flowing in it cause magnetic flux to be set up through the iron in a manner similar to a voltage causing current to flow through a system of conductors. The changing magnetic flux produced by alternating current results in a temperature rise in the magnetic circuit. The heating effect is reduced by laminating the magnet assembly and armature. By placing a coil of many turns or wire around a soft-iron core, the magnetic flux set up by the energized coil tends to be concentrated; therefore, the magnetic field effect is strengthened. Since the iron core is the path of least resistance to the flow of the magnetic lines of force, magnetic attraction will concentrate according to the shape of the magnet.

The magnetic assembly is the stationary part of the magnetic circuit. The coil is supported by and surrounds part of the magnet assembly in order to induce magnetic flux into the magnetic circuit.

The armature is the moving part of the magnetic circuit. When it has been attracted into its seal-in position, it completes the magnetic circuit. To provide maximum pull and to help ensure quietness, the faces of the armature and the magnet assembly are ground to a very close tolerance.

When a controller's armature has been sealed in, it is held closely against the magnet assembly. However, a small gap is always deliberately left in the iron magnet circuit. When the coil becomes deenergized, some magnetic flux always remains—and if it were .not for the gap in the iron circuit, the residual magnetism might be sufficient to hold the armature in the sealed-in position.

The shaded-pole principle is used to provide a time delay in the decay of flux in dc coils, but is used more frequently to prevent chatter and wear in the moving parts of ac magnets. A shading coil is a single turn of conducting material mounted in the face of the magnet assembly or armature. The alternating main magnetic flux induces current in the shading coil, and these currents set up auxiliary magnetic flux which is out of phase from the main flux. The auxiliary flux produces a magnetic pull out of phase from the pull due to the main flux, and this keeps the armature sealed in when the main flux fails to zero. Without the shading coil, the armature would tend to open each time the main flux goes through zero cycle. Excessive noise, wear on magnet faces, and heat would result.

Figure 13-1 shows an exaggerated view of a pole face with a copper band or short-circuited coil of low resistance connected around a portion of the pole tip. When the flux is increasing in the pole from left to right, the induced current in the coil is in a clockwise direction.

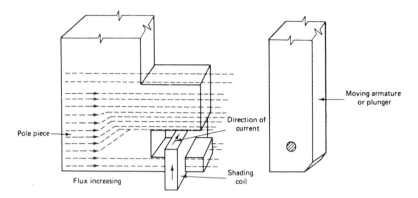

Figure 13-1   Section of a magnetic pole face with current moving in a clockwise direction.

The magnetomotive force produced by the coil opposes the direction of the flux of the main field. Therefore, the flux density in the shaded portion of the iron will be considerably less, and the flux density in the unshaded portion of the iron will be more than would be the case without the shading coil.

Figure 13-2 shows the pole with the flux still moving from left to right, but decreasing in value. Now the current in the coil is in a counterclockwise direction. The magnetomotive force produced by the coil is in the same direction as the main unshaded portion but less than it would be without the shading coil. Consequently, if the electric circuit of a coil is opened, the current decreases rapidly to zero, but the flux decreases much more slowly due to the action of the shading coil.

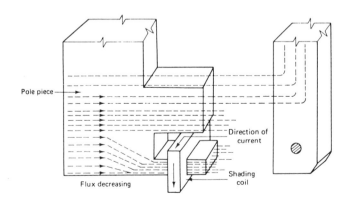

Figure 13-2   Section of a magnetic pole face with the current moving in the shading coil in a counterclockwise direction.

OVERLOAD PROTECTION

Overload protection for an electric motor is necessary to prevent burnout and to ensure maximum operating life. Electric motors will, if permitted, operate at an output of more than rated capacity. Conditions of motor overload may be caused by an overload on driven machinery, such as fans or compressors; by low-line voltage; or by an open line in a polyphase system, which results in single-phase operation. Under any condition of overload, a motor draws excessive current that causes overheating. Since motor winding insulation deteriorates when subjected to overheating, there are established limits on motor operating temperatures. To protect a motor from overheating, overload relays are employed on a motor control to limit the amount of current drawn. This is overload protection, or running protection.

The ideal overload protection for a motor is an element with current-sensing properties similar to the heating curve of the motor, as shown in Fig. 13-3, which would act to open the motor circuit when full-load current is exceeded. The operation of the protective device should be such that the motor is allowed to carry harmless overloads but is quickly removed from the line when an overload has persisted too long.

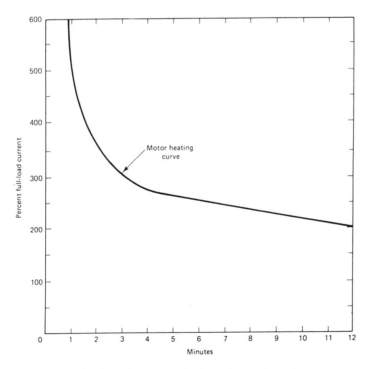

Figure 13-3 The ideal overload protection is one in which sensing properties are very similar to the heating curve of the motor.

Fuses are not designed to provide overload protection. Their basic function is to protect against short circuits (overcurrent protection). Motors draw a high inrush current when starting and conventional single-element fuses have no way of distinguishing between this temporary and harmless inrush current and a damaging overload. Such fuses, chosen on the basis of motor full-load current, would "blow" every time the motor is started. On the other hand, if a fuse were chosen large enough to pass the starting or inrush current, it would not protect the motor against small, harmful overloads that might occur later. Dual-element or time-delay fuses can provide motor overload protection but suffer the disadvantage of being nonrenewable and must be replaced.

The overload relay is the heart of motor protection. It has inverse-trip-time characteristics, permitting it to hold in during the accelerating period (when inrush current is drawn), yet providing protection on small overloads above the full-load current when the motor is running. Unlike dual-element fuses, overload relays are renewable and can withstand repeated trip and reset cycles without need of replacement. Overload relays cannot, however, take the place of overcurrent protective equipment.

The overload relay consists of a current-sensing unit connected in the line to the motor, plus a mechanism, actuated by the sensing unit, which serves, directly or indirectly, to break the circuit. In a manual starter, an overload trips a mechanical latch, causing the starter contacts to open and disconnect the motor from the line. In magnetic starters, an overload opens a set of contacts within the overload relay itself. These contacts are wired in series with the starter coil in the control circuit of the magnetic starter. Breaking the coil circuit causes the starter contacts to open, disconnecting the motor from the line.

Overload relays can be classified as being either thermal or magnetic. Magnetic overload relays react only to current excesses and are not affected by temperature. As the name implies, thermal overload relays relay on the rising temperatures caused by the overload current to trip the overload mechanism. Thermal overload relays can be further subdivided into two types: melting alloy and bimetallic.

The melting-alloy assembly of heat element (overload relay) and solder pot is shown in Fig. 13-4. Excessive overload motor current passes through the heater element, thereby melting a eutectic alloy solder pot. The ratchet wheel will then be allowed to turn in the molten pool, and a tripping action of the starter control circuit results, stopping the motor. A cooling-off period is required to allow the solder pot to "freeze" before the overload relay assembly can be reset and motor service restored.

Melting-alloy thermal units are interchangeable and of one-piece construction, which ensures a constant relationship between the heater element and solder pot and allows factory calibration, making them virtually tamperproof in the field. These important features are not possible with any

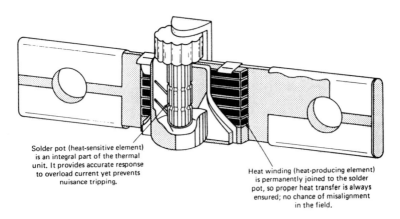

Solder pot (heat-sensitive element) is an integral part of the thermal unit. It provides accurate response to overload current yet prevents nuisance tripping.

Heat winding (heat-producing element) is permanently joined to the solder pot, so proper heat transfer is always ensured; no chance of misalignment in the field.

Figure 13-4 Melting-alloy type thermal overload relay.

other type of overload relay construction. A wide selection of these interchangeable thermal units is available to give exact overload protection of any full-load current to a motor.

Bimetallic overload relays are designed specifically for two general types of application. The automatic reset feature is of decided advantage when devices are mounted in locations not easily accessible for manual operation, and these relays can easily be adjusted to trip within a range of 85 percent to 115 percent of the normal trip rating of the heater unit. This feature is useful when the recommended heater size might result in unnecessary tripping but the next larger size would not give adequate protection. Ambient temperatures affect overload relays, operating on the principle of heat.

Ambient-compensated bimetallic overload relays are designed for one particular situation: when the motor is at a constant temperature and the controller is located separately in a varying temperature. In this case, if a standard thermal overload relay were used, it would not trip consistently at the same level of motor current if the controller temperature changed. This thermal overload relay is always affected by the surrounding temperature. To compensate for temperature variations, the controller may see that an ambient-compensated overload relay is applied. Its trip point is not affected by temperature, and it performs consistently at the same value of current.

Melting-alloy and bimetallic overload relays are designed to approximate the heat actually generated in the motor. As the motor temperature increases, so does the temperature of the thermal unit. The motor and relay heating curves (Fig. 13-5) show this relationship. From this graph, it should be evident that no matter how high the current is drawn, the overload relay will provide protection, yet the relay will not trip unnecessarily.

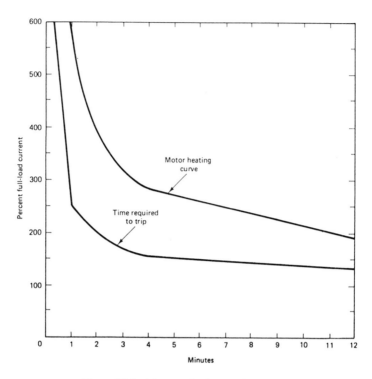

Figure 13-5 Motor and relay heating curve.

When selecting thermal overload relays, the following must be considered:

1. Motor full-load current.
2. Type of motor.
3. Difference in ambient temperature between motor and controller.

Motors of the same horsepower rating and speed do not all have the same full-load current; also refer to the motor nameplate to obtain the full-load amperes for a particular motor. Do not use a published table. Thermal unit selection tables are published on the basis of continuous-duty motors with a 1.15 service factor, operating under normal conditions. The tables are shown in manufacturers' catalogs and also appear on the inside of the door or cover of the motor controller. These selections will protect the motor properly and allow it to develop its full horsepower rating, allowing for the service factor, if the ambient temperature is the same at the motor as at the controller. If the temperatures are not the same or if the motor service factor is less than 1.15, a special procedure is required to select the proper thermal unit.

Standard overload relay contacts are closed under normal conditions and open when the relay trips. An alarm signal is sometimes required to indicate when a motor has stopped due to an overload trip. Also, in some situations, it may be required to signal an overload condition rather than have the motor stop automatically. This is done by fitting the overload relay with a set of contacts that close when the relay trips, completing an alarm circuit. These contacts are appropriately called alarm contacts.

A magnetic overload relay has a movable magnetic core inside a coil which carries the motor current. The flux set up inside the coil pulls the core upward. When the core rises far enough, it trips a set of contacts on the top of the relay. The movement of the core is slowed by a piston working in an oil-filled dashpot mounted below the coil. This produces an inverse-time characteristic. The effective tripping current is adjusted by moving the core on a threaded rod. The tripping time is varied by uncovering oil bypass holes in the piston. Because of the time and current adjustment, the magnetic overload relay is sometimes used to protect motors having long accelerating times or unusual duty cycles.

PROTECTIVE ENCLOSURES

The correct selection and installation of an enclosure for a particular application can contribute considerably to the length of life and trouble-free operation. To shield electrically live parts from accidental contact, some form of enclosure is always necessary. This function is usually fulfilled by a general-purpose, sheet-steel cabinet. Frequently, however, dust, moisture, or explosive gases make it necessary to employ a special enclosure to protect the motor controller from corrosion or the surrounding equipment from explosion. In selecting and installing control apparatus, it is always necessary to consider carefully the conditions under which the apparatus must operate; there are many applications where a general-purpose enclosure does not afford protection.

Underwriters' Laboratories has defined the requirements for protective enclosures according to the types of hazardous conditions, and the National Electrical Manufacturers' Association has standardized enclosures based on these requirements.

NEMA 1—General purpose.   The general-purpose enclosure is intended primarily to prevent accidental contact with the enclosed apparatus. It is suitable for general-purpose applications indoors where not exposed to unusual service conditions. A NEMA 1 enclosure serves as protection against dust and light indirect splashing, but is not dusttight.

NEMA 3—Dusttight, raintight. This enclosure is intended to provide suitable protection against specified weather hazards. A NEMA 3 enclosure is suitable for application outdoors, such as in construction work. It is also sleet resistant.

NEMA 3R—Rainproof, sleet resistant. This enclosure protects against interference in operation of the contained equipment due to rain, and resists damage from exposure to sleet. It is designed with conduit hubs and external mounting, as well as drainage provisions.

NEMA 4—Watertight. A watertight enclosure is designed to meet a hose test, which consists of a stream of water from a hose with a 1-inch nozzle, delivering at least 65 gallons per minute. The water is directed on the enclosure from a distance of not less than 10 feet for a period of five minutes. During this period, it may be sprayed in any one or more directions as desired. There must be no leakage of water into the enclosure under these conditions.

NEMA 4X—Watertight, corrosion resistant. These enclosures are generally constructed similarly to NEMA 4 enclosures except they are made of a material that is highly resistant to corrosion. For this reason, they are ideal in applications such as chemical plants, where contaminants would ordinarily destroy a steel enclosure over a period of time.

NEMA 7—Hazardous locations, Class I. These enclosures are designed to meet the application requirements of the NE Code for Class I hazardous locations. In this type of equipment, the circuit interruption occurs in air.

NEMA 9—Hazardous locations, Class II. These enclosures are designed to meet the application requirements of the NE Code for Class II hazardous locations.

NEMA 12—Industrial use. This type of enclosure is designed for use in those industries where it is desired to exclude such materials as dust, lint, fibers and flyings, oil seepage, or coolant seepage. There are no conduit openings or knockouts in the enclosure, and mounting is by means of flanges or mounting feet.

NEMA 13—Oiltight, dusttight. NEMA 13 enclosures are generally made of cast iron, gasketed, or permit use in the same environments as NEMA 12 devices. The essential difference is that due to its cast housing, a conduit entry is provided as an integral part of the NEMA 13 enclosure, and mounting is by means of blind holes rather than mounting brackets.

NATIONAL ELECTRICAL CODE REQUIREMENTS

The National Electrical Code® deals with the installation of equipment and is concerned primarily with safety—the prevention of injury and fire hazard to persons and property arising from the use of electricity. It is adopted on a local basis, sometimes incorporating minor changes or interpretations, as the need arises. National Electrical Code (NEC) rules and provisions are enforced by governmental bodies exercising legal jurisdiction over electrical installations and used by insurance inspectors. Minimum safety standards are thus assured.

HVAC control equipment is designed to meet the provisions of the NEC. Sections applying to industrial control devices are found in Article 430 on motors and motor controllers and Article 500 on hazardous locations.

With minor exceptions, the NEC, together with some local codes, require a disconnect means for every motor. A combination starter consists of an across-the-line starter and a disconnect means wired together in a common enclosure. Combination starters include a blade-disconnect switch, either fusible or nonfusible, while some combination starters include a thermal-magnetic trip circuit breaker. The starter may be controlled remotely with push buttons, selector switches, and the like, or these devides may be installed in the cover. The single device makes a neat as well as compact electrical installation that takes little mounting space.

A combination starter provides safety for the operator because the cover of the enclosing case is interlocked with the external operating handle of the disconnecting means. The door cannot be opened with the disconnecting means closed. With the disconnect means open, access to all parts may be had, but much less hazard is involved inasmuch as there are no readily accessible parts connected to the power line. This safety feature cannot be obtained with separately enclosed starters. In addition, the cabinet is provided with a means of padlocking the disconnect in the OFF position.

TWO-WIRE CONTROL

Figure 13-6 shows wiring diagrams for a two-wire control circuit. The control itself could be a thermostat, float switch, limit switch, or other maintained contact device to the magnetic starter. When the contacts of the control device close, they complete the coil circuit of the starter, causing it to pick up and connect the motor to the lines. When the control device contacts open, the starter is deenergized, stopping the motor.

Two-wire control provides low-voltage release but no low-voltage protection. When wired as illustrated, the starter will function automatically in response to the direction of the control device, without the attention of an

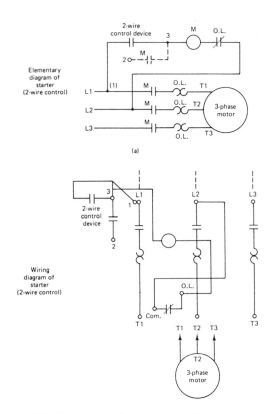

Figure 13-6   Elementary diagram of two-wire motor control.

operator. In this type of connection, a holding circuit interlock is not necessary.

THREE-WIRE CONTROL

A three-wire control circuit uses momentary contact, start–stop buttons, and a holding circuit interlock wired in parallel with the start button to maintain the circuit. Pressing the normally open (NO) start button completes the circuit to the coil. The power circuit contacts in lines 1, 2, and 3 close, completing the circuit to the motor, and the holding circuit contact also closes. Once the starter has picked up, the start button can be released, as the now-closed interlock contact provides an alternative current path around the reopened start contact.

    Pressing the normally closed (NC) stop button will open the circuit to the coil, causing the starter to drop out. An overload condition, which causes the overload contact to open, a power failure, or a drop in voltage to less than the seal-in value would also deenergize the starter. When the starter drops out, the interlock contact reopens, and both current paths to the coil, through the start button and the interlock, are now open.

Since three wires from the push-button station are connected into the starter—at points 1, 2, and 3—this wiring scheme is commonly referred to as three-wire control (see Fig. 13-7).

The holding circuit interlock is a normally open auxiliary contact provided on standard magnetic starters and contactors. It closes when the coil is energized to form a holding circuit for the starter after the start button has been released.

In addition to the main or power contacts, which carry the motor current, and the holding circuit interlock, a starter can be provided with externally attached auxiliary contacts, commonly called electrical interlocks. Interlocks are rated to carry only control circuit currents, not motor currents. Both NO and NC versions are available. Among a wide variety of

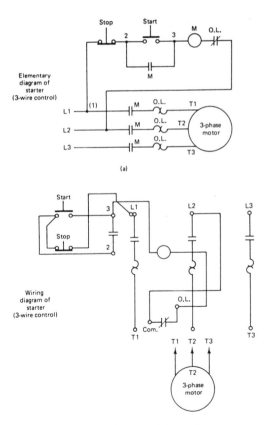

Figure 13-7 Elementary diagram of three-wire motor control.

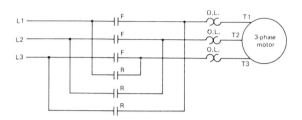

Figure 13-8   Diagram of a three-pole reversing starter used to control a three-phase motor for an air handling unit.

applications, interlocks can be used to control other magnetic devices where sequence operation is desired, to electrically prevent another controller from being energized at the same time, and to make and break circuits to indicating or alarm devices such as pilot lights, bells, or other signals.

The circuit in Fig. 13-8 shows a three-pole reversing starter used to control a three-phase motor. Three-phase squirrel-cage motors can be reversed by reconnecting any two of the three-line connections to the motor. By interwiring two contactors, an electromagnetic method of making the reconnection can be obtained.

As seen in the power circuit (Fig. 13-8), the contacts (F) of the forward contactors, when closed, connect lines 1, 2, and 3 to the motor terminals T1, T2, and T3, respectively. As long as the forward contacts are closed, mechanical and electrical interlocks prevent the reverse contactor from being energized.

When the forward contactor is deenergized, the second contactor can be picked up, closing its contacts (R), which reconnect the lines to the motor. Note that by running through the reverse contacts, line 1 is connected to motor terminal T3, and line 3 is connected to motor terminal T1. The motor will now run in reverse.

Manual reversing starters are also available. As in the magnetic version, the forward and reverse switching mechanisms are mechanically interlocked, but since coils are not used in the manually operated equipment, electrical interlocks are not furnished.

CONTROL RELAYS

A relay is an electromagnetic device whose contacts are used in control circuits of magnetic starters, contactors, solenoids, timers, and other relays. They are generally used to amplify the contact capability or multiply the switching function of a pilot device.

The wiring diagrams in Figs. 13-9 and 13-10 demonstrate how a relay amplifies contact capacity. Figure 13-9 represents current amplification. Relay

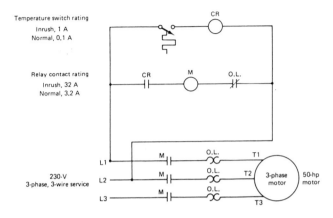

Figure 13-9   Relay amplifying contact capacity.

and starter coil voltage are the same, but the ampere rating of the temperature switch is too low to handle the current drawn by the starter coil (M). A relay is interposed between the temperature switch and the starter coil. The current drawn by the relay coil (CR) is within the rating of the temperature switch, and relay contact (CR) has a rating adequate for the current drawn by the starter coil.

Figure 13-10 represents voltage amplification. A condition may exist in which the voltage rating of the temperature switch is too low to permit its direct use in a starter control circuit operating at a higher voltage. In this

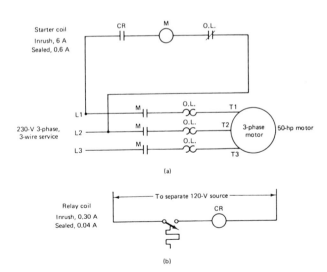

Figure 13-10   Circuit amplifying voltage.

application, the coil of the interposing relay and the pilot device are wired to a low-voltage source of power compatible with the rating of the pilot device. The relay contact, with its higher voltage rating, is then used to control operation of the starter.

OTHER CONTROLLING EQUIPMENT

Timers and timing relays. A pneumatic timer or timing relay is similar to a control relay, except that certain of its contacts are designed to operate at a present time interval after the coil is energized or deenergized. A delay on energization is also referred to as "on delay." A time delay on deenergization is also called "off delay."

A timed function is useful in applications such as the lubrication system of a large machine, in which a small oil pump must deliver lubricant to the bearings of the main motor for a set period before the main motor starts.

In pneumatic timers, the timing is accomplished by the transfer of air through a restricted orifice. The amount of restriction is controlled by an adjustable needle valve, permitting changes to be made in the timing period.

Drum switches. A drum switch is a manually operated three-position three-pole switch which carries a horsepower rating and is used for manual reversing of single- or three-phase motors. Drum switches are available in several sizes and can be of spring-return-to-off (momentary contact) or maintained-contact type. Separate overload protection, by manual or magnetic starters, must usually be provided, as drum switches do not include this feature.

Push-button stations. A control station may contain push buttons, selector switches, and pilot lights. Push buttons may be of momentary- or maintained-contact type. Selector switches are usually maintained-contact type but can be spring-return type to give momentary-contact operation.

Standard-duty stations will handle the coil currents of contactors up to size 4. Heavy-duty stations have higher contact ratings and provide greater flexibility through a wider variety of operators and interchangeability of units.

Limit switches. A limit switch is a control device that converts mechanical motion into an electrical control signal. Its main function is to limit movement, usually by opening a control circuit when the limit of travel is reached. Limit switches may be momentary-contact (spring-return) or maintained-contact types. Among other applications, limit switches can be used to start, stop, reverse, slow down, speed up, or recycle machine operations.

Snap switches.   Snap switches for control purposes are enclosed, precision switches which require low operating forces and have a high repeat accuracy. They are used as interlocks and as the switch mechanism for control devices such as precision limit switches and pressure switches. They are also available with integral operators for use as compact limit switches, door-operated interlocks, and so on. Single-pole double-throw and two-pole double-throw versions are available.

Pressure switches.   The control of pumps, air compressors, and machine tools requires control devices that respond to the pressure of a medium such as water, air, or oil. The control device that does this is a pressure switch. It has a set of contacts which are operated by the movement of a piston, bellows, or diaphragm against a set of springs. The spring pressure determines the pressures at which the switch closes and opens its contacts.

Float switches.   When a pump motor must be started and stopped according to changes in water (or other liquid) level in a tank or sump, a float switch is used. This is a control device whose contacts are controlled by movement of a rod or chain and counterweight, fitted with a float. For closed-tank applications, the movement of a float arm is transmitted through a bellows seal to the contact mechanism.

ELECTRONIC CONTROLS

In recent years, many solid-state devices and circuits have entered the motor control and HVAC field, reducing previously bulky equipment to compact, efficient, and reliable electronic units. In fact, most sophisticated HVAC utilize solid-state, computerized controls.

14
Balancing the System

Once an HVAC system has been completely installed with all ductwork, control wiring, and the like, the final step before acceptance by the owners, architect, and engineers is to balance the system. In general, balancing means to test the system to insure that the correct amount of air is reaching each room or area and then to make the proper adjustments to achieve this goal.

Balancing the system begins with the air-handling unit. The engineer or designer of the system should have made careful calculations during the design stage, and then selected an air-handling unit or fan that delivers the correct amount of air at the proper velocity to provide satisfactory heating and cooling within the building. However, in many cases, the air-handling units will need a minor final adjustment to achieve the desired results. In most cases, this adjustment is merely a matter of changing the pulleys on the fan and motor.

HEATING SYSTEM BALANCE

The speed of the air-handling unit or fan should permit a temperature rise across the heating surface of between 90 degrees F to 100 degrees F. In most cases, the temperature should not vary outside of these boundaries, for safety reasons and to avoid damage to the heat exchanger or heating coils.

To perform such a test, a temperature reading is taken at the return duct just prior to entering the air-handling unit. Another temperature reading is taken at the supply duct immediately upon leaving the air-handling unit. Then these two readings are compared. If the difference is greater than 100 degrees F, the fan speed should be increased. On the other hand, if the difference is less than 90 degrees F, the fan speed should be decreased to allow more time for the air to pick up heat from the heating surfaces.

The next step is to set the fan cut-in switch at approximately 110 degrees F, but this setting can be varied depending upon certain factors. If high wall outlets are used in the majority of building areas, set the cut-in between 100 and 105 degrees F; if low wall outlets are used, set the cut-in for about 112 to 115 degrees F.

The fan cut-out switch, naturally, should be set at approximately 10 to 15 degrees lower than the cut-in temperature. With the temperature difference between the cut-in and cut-out switches, the fan should run for long periods and stop for short periods. Continuous or almost continuous fan operation is desirable for heating because it tends to prevent cold drafts.

Set the high limit bonnet temperature control according to the manufacturer's recommendations, but in most cases, this setting will be approximately 190 degrees F. Then adjust the supply registers and dampers, using the appropriate instruments for testing.

BALANCING INSTRUMENTS

The simplest method of balancing the system in residential and small commercial applications is by the thermometer method. In general, the following steps should be used to perform the tests and balancing procedures:

1. Make certain the entire system has been deenergized, and no air is flowing.
2. Place a suitable thermometer in each room or area that is to be conditioned by the HVAC system. A thermometer should also be placed at the thermostat, and at the same level. If more than one zone is involved, test each zone individually.
3. Open all dampers and registers.
4. Once all of the preceding steps have been done, the system should be energized and allowed to operate until the temperatures have stabilized at each thermometer. This phase should take a minimum of 30 minutes.

5. Record the temperature readings from each room or area, and at the thermostat; that is, at each of the thermometers previously placed at various locations.

6. If the temperature readings vary from room to room, slightly close the damper in the rooms or areas where the temperature readings are higher than the reading of the thermostat. Closing the damper slightly allows less heat to enter this particular area, and permits more heat for other areas with a lower temperature.

7. Repeat this procedure until the temperature variation from room to room is less than 3 degrees F.

Experienced technicians sometimes use what is known as the short method of balancing an air-conditioning system, since this method usually saves time over other methods. In general, the longest duct runs are determined, and the dampers on these longest runs are opened to the full position. Next, the shortest duct runs are determined, and the dampers on these ducts are opened between 1/4 to 1/2 position. Dampers in the medium duct runs are opened to 1/2 to 3/4 position, depending on the number of direction changes in the ductwork. Readjustments are then made as necessary, according to the preferences of the architect, owner, and consulting engineer.

Most consulting engineering firms require that the system be tested with a velometer and an anemometer before final acceptance. These instruments are made by different manufacturers, and their exact use will depend on the brand. However, the following should suffice for our purposes. In general, good results can be achieved by taking readings with either of the two instruments at the return grilles. However, if outside makeup air is used, the readings should be taken at the supply registers. With these thoughts in mind, proceed as follows:

1. Take a reading with a velometer at several places across the face of the supply registers. Total the readings and then determine the average reading by dividing by the number of readings taken.

2. Multiply the average velocity reading calculated by the square feet of the effective area of the register. Refer to the manufacturer's specifications for the effective area of each register. The resulting value is the cubic feet of air per minute (cfm) passing through the register. The cubic feet of air thus obtained should be compared with the design cfm required for the space, which was obtained during the heating and cooling calculations.

3. If the cfm is smaller than the design cfm for that particular register, slightly change the setting of the damper in the branch run to the register toward full open. If the cfm is larger, change the damper setting toward the closed position.

4. Take a second velometer reading. Determine cfm as before; compare this reading with the design cfm. Continue this procedure until the design cfm is achieved at each register within 2 or 3 cfm.

An anemometer can also be used to take velocity readings across the face of a register, but the results do not reflect the actual velocities. Since the grille bars in the face of the register deflect the air stream, the result may not be the actual velocity. For this reason, correction factors are used in conjunction with the anemometer to accurately determine cfm.

Pilot tubes are another means used to aid the technician when balancing an air-conditioning system, especially those with extensive duct runs. A pilot tube, in conjunction with an instrument called a manometer, can measure static pressure, velocity pressure, and total pressure in a given duct. Measurements are normally taken at both the return and supply ducts immediately before and after the air-handling unit. The resulting values are used to determine the various fan pressures and capacities, and the air quantities being supplied to each branch duct. The total quantities can be compared to the design calculations performed during the design phase of the system, and then compared to the actual measurements taken at each register or diffuser. If the total is satisfactory, the registers may then be tested with the velometer as previously described. On the other hand, should a deficiency occur, dampers must be adjusted in the main duct unit to be certain sufficient air is supplied to each branch.

COOLING SYSTEM BALANCE

The tests and adjustments recommended for balancing a heating system are very similar to adjustments recommended for balancing the cooling system. However, if cooling conditions do not prove satisfactory, or if the system is initially balanced during the cooling season, the fan should be set at the lowest speed that gives adequate cooling. The dampers and registers should be set according to any of the three methods given previously.

The BASIC program gives a general guide for the approximate temperature drop required across the cooling coil under three varying conditions. The resulting values give approximate, but not final, fan speed settings. If a greater temperature drop is required across the coil to maintain satisfactory cooling conditions, the fan speed should be decreased until satisfactory results are obtained. If a smaller drop is needed, the fan speed should be increased.

To begin the balancing of a cooling system, set the thermostat at the desired temperature, which is usually between 75 and 85 degrees F. Before testing, however, allow the system to operate approximately 24 hours. Then test the cooling conditions in the room or area with a sling psychrometer.

The dry-bulb temperature should be between 75 to 80 degrees F, and the relative humidity should be 50 percent. If the humidity reading is higher than 44 percent to 60 percent, the volume of air should be reduced. If the humidity is lower than 40 percent to 45 percent, the volume of air should be increased. This is accomplished by increasing or decreasing the fan speed, which is normally done by changing the pulleys.

When any of the previously described instruments are purchased for use, always study the manufacturer's instructions that accompany these instruments. Upon reviewing the instructions, charts, and other materials, the programmer should have several items that could be incorporated into a master HVAC BASIC program.

15
Residential Estimating

The business of residential HVAC contracting obviously demands efficient job management procedures and the use of trained, experienced workers. However, unless a rapid, accurate estimating system is adopted, no amount of efficiency and worker expertise can insure survival in this highly competitive field. The main objective of this chapter is how to come up with a workable selling price.

BASIC CONSIDERATIONS

HVAC estimates may be classified into several types, depending on the purpose and the degree of accuracy required. Most frequently used methods fall into the following categories:

1. *Detailed unit quantity estimate:* This method consists of finding the costs of a work unit involving material, labor, and equipment. These costs are multiplied by the number of units on the job.
2. *Detailed total quantity estimate:* The total quantity of material, labor, and equipment costs are found and then added together for the total estimate.

3. *Quantity survey:* This method consists of a complete estimate of all the quantities of material required for a given project. The labor units are added to each material item, material is priced, and then overhead and profit are added for a selling price.

4. *Square-ft and cubic-ft methods:* These are crude methods used to check other types of estimates.

5. *Progress estimates:* These are periodic checks on work progress to determine the amount of payment due the contractor at the time the estimate is made.

Qualifications of the Residential Estimator

Since the estimate is made before the actual work is started, an estimator's ability to visualize the phases of construction is of utmost importance. The following are other necessary traits:

• An orderly mind
• Ability to concentrate
• Patience
• Neatness
• Reasonable amount of mathematical ability
• Experience in the HVAC field
• Knowledge of the details of construction
• Ability to collect, classify, and file data
• Knowledge of labor, equipment, and construction materials
• Good judgment in selecting workers, materials, and equipment

There is no substitute for experience; potential estimators should work as an apprentice, under an HVAC designer, or under a veteran estimator. To arrive at a reasonable price for a given project, an estimator must rely on not only what can be obtained from the specs and drawings, but also on personal knowledge of HVAC construction details.

Estimating Errors

Serious mistakes in estimating can result in loss of contracts, or in contracts that can be fulfilled only at a loss to the contractor. Common estimating errors can be reduced to a negligible amount if a few simple precautions are taken.

The use of proper forms will greatly reduce or eliminate errors and omissions, regardless of the size of the project. Repeated use of the same forms and work sheets will result in a more accurate and more detailed estimate made with greater confidence than if a hit-and-miss method is used for each job.

Mathematical errors—especially improper location of the decimal point—haunt all estimators. Use of an electronic calculator in extending prices and totaling columns can do wonders to keep such errors to a minimum; however, the calculator is no magic box—it depends on the accuracy of the user's input.

The best method of detecting mathematical errors is to have another person go over the calculations. If this is not possible, they should be checked by the estimator using a slightly different procedure—summing a column from bottom to top instead of top to bottom, for example. There are many other possible errors:

1. Omitting overhead and profit.
2. Not allowing for waste material.
3. Neglecting job factors, such as weather conditions, performance of general contractor, labor strikes, types of structure, and so on.
4. Neglecting transportation costs, storage costs, and so on.
5. Changing prices of labor and materials.
6. Errors in copying items.
7. Omitting rent or purchase of special tools required on a unique project.
8. Not knowing the correct overhead factor to apply to a certain size project.

There are other sources of errors, of course, but those just listed should be sufficient to provide a basis for evaluating the accuracy of existing procedures.

Profit and Loss

Profitable operation of a contracting business demands the ability to honestly apply the following:

$$Material + Labor + Direct\ Job\ Expense + Overhead = Cost$$

$$Cost + Profit = Selling\ Price$$

Because of the highly competitive field of residential HVAC contracting, the contractor must be extremely careful about applying accurate costs and a reasonable profit in calculating the selling price for a given project. If the costs are overestimated, the contractor does not get the job; if the costs are underestimated, he or she may get the job but with too low a profit—or with a loss. It doesn't take too many low-profit or loss-inflicting jobs to force the contractor out of business.

There are very few occasions that might make it beneficial to take a project at cost or at a small profit. One could be that a highly qualified contractor would like to "get in" with a certain home builder who has been giving all the HVAC work to part-time workers (moonlighters) at a low price. If the qualified contractor feels that the builder can be convinced because of better service and higher-quality work, it may be feasible to take one or two jobs—and only these—at a reduced price.

There is also a tendency among smaller HVAC contractors to take jobs at cost or a very low profit when work is slack. This should be avoided. It's a bad feeling to be hungry—perhaps causing a contractor to take jobs at a very low profit—but remember, it's worse to be both *tired* and hungry! In other words, if you are not going to make any money from a job, why go to all the trouble to do it?

Other operations involved in profit and loss that should be considered involve the following:

1. Buy materials in large quantities when possible—not on speculation, but when it can reasonably be predicted that material will be used for several projects in the near future.

2. Select materials that will save installation time. For example, a certain type of inlet or outlet may require less time to install than another. If the saving in labor is more than the additional cost of the item, then it will probably pay to use the time-saving material. Also, when it is known that a certain project is going to require many duct elbows of a certain size, usually some labor can be saved by prefabing all of them at the same time and storing them for future use, rather than to fabricate them as they are needed. Once the shop has set up to form a few of them, much time can be saved by forming enough to last the entire job or several jobs.

3. Keep all tools in good working condition. Workers using a drill motor with a defective switch cannot do their best work if they have to operate the switch several times to make contact each time they use it.

4. Look into the possibility of building custom tools to help reduce labor. Many such tools have been invented by experienced workers but were never manufactured for one reason or another.

5. Don't purchase unnecessary tools, but don't be stingy either. Many special tools can make the contractor additional money.

6. Use an estimating method specifically designed for residential work where accurate estimates can be turned out in the shortest possible time. Many HVAC contracts have been awarded on the spot when the contractor was able to come up with a selling price in only a few minutes.

UNIT PRICING

HVAC installations in most commercial and industrial buildings vary so greatly that a definite standard of unit pricing is not practical. However, for the more standard operations of residential work, unit pricing provides a simple, fast, and reasonably accurate method of estimating—an absolute necessity in this highly competitive field.

In general, unit pricing is the process of combining items of material that are commonly used together in a given section of an HVAC system, assigning material and labor values to each group or section, and then using this price as a unit when the particular group or section comes up in the estimating process. Once the material price has been calculated for a particular installation group or device, the labor units should be applied, including the labor for installing the ductwork. This will have to be determined by the installation situation; that is, whether the installation is in new construction, where all partitions are open, if there is adequate working space, if the ductwork must be installed in concealed partitions, and so on. Possible variations will be covered later. For now, let's assume that the residential installation will be in new work with average working conditions. It has been found that the average worker familiar with residential installations will average 1.55 manhours per ceiling diffuser. If the worker gets paid $10 per hour, the labor on the outlet will then cost $10 × 1.55 or $15.50 per outlet. Add to this figure your direct job expense, overhead, and profit. These figures, of course, will vary from contractor to contractor, but if yours happens to be $4.56, the total unit price per outlet will be $5.50 (labor) + $4.56 + the actual cost of materials.

Obviously, a few of the items indicated in the material list could change. For example, a few outlets spaced close together could require only a few feet (say, 4 feet or less) of duct, while a longer run might take 50 feet or more of ductwork. However, in the average overall residential HVAC system, such changes will be insignificant, as with enough outlets, the normal run should average out to about 23 feet. Therefore, once the unit price has been worked out, this will be the average selling price. For example, if the total costs came to $120 per outlet, and a residence has ten outlets, the cost of furnishing material and installing these ten outlets will be $1,200.

In old work, or renovation projects, where the duct must be "fished" in concealed partitions, the labor may go up to 2.30 manhours per outlet, making it necessary to raise the total selling price per outlet. Also, in renovation projects, where only a few outlets are encountered, the length of duct runs will probably justify a detailed estimate, giving the exact amount of ductwork required for the installation.

The intelligent contractor also will compare actual material and labor costs after each job has been completed to keep a close watch on the unit prices as well as to improve estimating skill and management ability. If there is a problem, the contractor can then correct it before too much damage has been done.

Other residential units will include concrete pads for condensing units, the installation of a particular type of wall thermostat, a certain size supply or return outlet (grille, diffuser, and so on).

One point to remember about unit prices is that most of them are calculated on an average complete installation. If the project, for example, only required one diffuser for a room addition, the unit prices would be extremely low—probably not even paying for the gas to drive the truck to the work location. So keep in mind that unit prices are suited only for a complete residential HVAC project having a complete HVAC system installed.

When the number of rooms are fewer than eight—such as a modernization project—the estimate should reflect an increase in each unit price used, or a contingency factor should be added to the overall bid according to the judgment of the contractor.

INSTALLATION VARIABLES

Although a residential installation generally lends itself favorably to estimating by unit pricing, there are variables—especially with regard to labor cost for old work or modernization of existing buildings—that must be considered and for which adjustments must be made.

Some of the principal causes of variation in labor cost between open area in new homes and the mostly concealed or hard-to-get-to areas of work in existing buildings are:

1. The nature of the building construction and the various building materials encountered.
2. The accessibility of the areas where work is to take place.
3. The extent of concealed ductwork.
4. Restricted work space.
5. Care required to avoid damage to existing finishes and, in some cases, furnishings.
6. Difficulties encountered by the workers due to the inaccessible and restricted work space.

There are almost an unlimited number of installation situations that can affect the labor cost for any given type of diffuser, grille, duct run, and so on. However, to keep this list to a practical length, the large number of conditions can be divided into four installation situation groups for all practical purposes. These groups will be designated 1, 2, 3, and 4, with group 1 representing the installation requiring the least amount of labor, and group 4 requiring the most manhours for the same type of installation.

Assume that a contractor is to install six outlets consisting of ceiling and wall diffusers and one return-air grille. Since group 1 represents the least amount of labor required, all working areas will be open and readily accessible to the workers. There also will be no restricted work areas. Typical examples would include practically any area in a new home before the wall partitions are concealed, a basement in an existing home with exposed floor joists for easy accessibility to the outlets and the routing of the ductwork, an unfinished attic, or the unfinished side of a finished room.

Situations in group 2 would include work in areas that are partially accessible but require minor fishing of ductwork in concealed partitions. One example of this group is the installation of a duct from one floor to another up through a finsihed partition which is accessible from both the top and bottom; however, the duct will have to be pushed or fished up through the finished partitions.

The same applies to ductwork from an open basement to an outlet in the finished living area where minor fishing of ductwork is necessary. The installation of surface ductwork tapped from existing trunk and requiring some changes of direction will also fall into group 2; the working space should be relatively unlimited.

Working situations falling into group 3 usually involve the installation of concealed ductwork in partially inaccessible spaces, such as installing ductwork from below a floor in a crawl space. Although the work area is open, the cramped work space slows up workers enough to warrant this situation to be in group 3. Other situations include notching of fire-stops or diagonal bracing to get ductwork in finished wall spaces, installing equipment on masonry walls where furring strips have been applied, and installing ductwork in attic or basement where both horizontal and vertical surfaces have been closed in. The working space in all of these situations is limited to some extent.

Relatively difficult wiring situations fall into the group 4 installation—ductwork run through masonry walls that have to be drilled, removal of floor boards to route ductwork, or cutting and patching of finished surfaces to conceal new ductwork.

When arriving at the cost of work in an existing home, the estimator should keep in mind that all of the work probably will not fall into any one installation group. Several situations or work groups may be encountered in one project. The estimator must face each of these situations, as well as others not listed here that are difficult to categorize, and use good judgment to group the situation correctly.

MATERIAL COST AND PRICING

Standard materials commonly used in residential HVAC systems include nearly all types of ducts, elbows, boots, connectors, grilles, diffusers, and other components. Very seldom do any of these items have to be custom built, and therefore the prices for all of them are readily available without a special quotation from suppliers on each job. This, of course, facilitates unit pricing for residential construction.

In some instances, however, the HVAC contractor may be able to obtain a better discount by buying large quantities of materials for several residential projects at one time; then a special quotation from HVAC suppliers is warranted. When such a situation occurs, it is recommended that the contractor not change the normal unit pricing of materials (unless it means losing a very important project). Rather the savings should be put into the contractor's business either to help cover some of the firm's operating expenses or to increase the firm's yearly profits.

To help keep abreast of the constantly changing prices of HVAC materials, practically all HVAC contractors involved primarily in residential and small commercial projects subscribe to one of the price services publishing current prices of most standard HVAC products. Most of the price service firms offer an extremely rapid accurate reporting service to keep the contracting and wholesale industries continuously up to date with the constantly changing prices of HVAC construction materials.

Regardless of how you choose to go about it, you must know the exact price of your materials to stay in business. In fact, most of the contractors who go out of business each year do so because they do not know their costs accurately enough to bid work at a profit. Your competitors' bids cannot be used as a basis for bidding your work. The one you pattern your bids after may be taking work at a loss and could cause both of you to go out of business.

On some residential projects the materials may call for specialized items. In cases like this, the contractor should request quotations as early as possible from the manufacturer and obtain written confirmation of all quotes. The contractor may even want shop drawings to make certain that specialized items are in compliance with job requirements. Whenever possible, a guarantee should be obtained of the quoted price for a definite period of time in case the architect/engineer/owner is tardy in awarding a contract.

The HVAC contractor should also consider the ability of the manufacturer or supplier to deliver the specialized items on time. Many manufacturers have, unfortunately, taken months longer than bargained for to deliver specialty items. Their customers find themselves in the position of having to seek the items from another source of supply, often at a higher price.

Although it has been a practice in the past to try to keep the material inventory stock as low as possible so as not to impair the contractor's working capital, it is a good idea to keep quantities of the most often used items in stock to keep lost time on the jobs to a minimum, as well as to gain a price advantage. The contractor should then have some means of inventory control to replenish the items as they are reduced to a certain minimum. A record of the exact cost of these items should be kept for billing and bidding purposes.

DIRECT JOB EXPENSE

To operate a successful contracting business, a thorough understanding of direct job expense is necessary, since these costs must be recovered from the job bids or contracts. Direct job expenses are all of the costs in addition to material and labor that have to be met directly because of the job and that would not exist if the job had not been undertaken. All other expenses would fall under overhead, which will be discussed later.

Items that should always be considered as direct job expenses in estimating residential HVAC construction are bid bonds (if required), inspection fees, work or building permits, special licenses (other than the normal HVAC contracting license), and labor adders for payroll. The latter item will include social security, workmen's compensation, unemployment insurance, employee's liability, and certain other dues and assessments paid in the form of a percentage of the productive labor payroll.

In addition, there are items that lie in the fringe area between direct job costs and overhead expenses. When the exact amount of costs for these items can be allocated to a particular job, they should become direct job expenses. However, because of the difficulty in doing so, they are most often charged against overhead. These items include layout and job super-vision, freight and postage for materials shipped for several jobs at once, estimating charges, interest on borrowed money, supplemental drawings, job truck, and depreciation and consumption of tools.

To illustrate, let's assume that a truck is used for two full days to carry men and materials to a residential project. The expense of operating the truck definitely can be charged to direct job expense, as can a certain percentage of the depreciation calculated for the truck. However, if the truck was used to service many jobs in one day, it would be difficult to accurately charge the truck expenses for the day to the various jobs on which it was used.

Another example would be the use of tools. On small jobs, where tools and equipment are used only for a relatively short period of time, it is probably impractical to charge an item of tool depreciation as a direct job expense. But a pro rata amount of the tool cost could be charged and used in the estimate to help recover the original cost of the tool. One of the best ways of doing this is to establish a monthly cost of rental charge per tool calculated on the basis of its useful life, then further break this cost down into hours. With such figures at hand, it will be much easier for the accounting department to determine how much direct job expense to charge each job.

A drill motor may cost the contractor $100. If the average life of a 1/2-inch drill motor used on residential construction is approximately 18 months, the cost of using each drill will be $100/18, or $5.55 per month—or about 25 cents per working day. If two drills were used on a residential project for two days, it would be reasonable to charge about 2 × $0.25 × 2 or about $1.00 against the job for direct job expenses. This sounds like small change, but the net effect of such items as step ladders, trucks, and electric generators used on a project can cut down the firm's overhead expenses if they are charged to each individual project on which they are used. Remember, someone has to pay for the tools, and it might as well be your customers.

Where a contractor furnishes a company truck to transport workers to or from out-of-town projects, any expense incurred should definitely be charged as a direct job expense, not to overhead.

In rare instances of residential construction, it may become necessary for workers to spend the night at out-of-town locations. These workers must be compensated for room and board in addition to the travel expenses. The estimator or contractor should try to foresee such instances and include an amount in the total contract (under direct job expenses) to cover the costs incurred.

Other residential projects may require supplemental drawings to guide the workers in making the proper installation. In most cases, only a few additional hours of time will be required. An HVAC contractor should be able to judge fairly accurately the extent of such job drawings or supervision and make a proper allowance for it in the total project price.

On larger residences designed by architects, the architect or engineer may require that shop drawings of various pieces of HVAC equipment be submitted for approval. This is going to require some time and calls for an additional amount to be added to the direct job expense. In some cases, the HVAC contractor may be required to furnish complete working and in-place drawings to the architect for approval. If this is overlooked, the contractor could wind up paying an engineering firm for detailed working drawings, eliminating much or all of the profit.

You may be thinking by now that if you included in your estimate all the necessary items of direct job expense, you would never get a contract. But look at it this way. Whenever you fail to include any item of direct job expense that is going to have to be paid directly or indirectly, you are giving your customer money—your money. You wouldn't think of grabbing $50 out of the cash drawer and throwing it out the window, but the effect is the same when you don't figure all of your direct job costs and include them in your bid.

OVERHEAD COSTS

In general, overhead expenses are items that cannot be charged to a particular job or project but must be paid to remain in business. Therefore, the contractor's first problem is to determine the overhead, and then find practical methods of fairly distributing this amount to the various jobs performed over a period of a month, three months, or a year. From this, we can see that the most practical method would be to add a certain percentage of the yearly overhead to each contract.

The following items are usually considered as overhead expenses, and a definite amount of money is spent to defray them by all HVAC contractors, regardless of their size. Each of these will be discussed in turn.

Advertising. Any sales promotion—whether devices or services— used to obtain or increase business falls under this heading. Such items include newspaper ads, radio or TV commercials, classified photo directory listings, business cards, direct mail brochures, circulars, signs, and truck advertising. Letterheads may also be listed under the heading of advertising, since they do display the firm's name; but they are usually listed under office expenses. The average residential HVAC contractor normally spends about 1 percent of the gross sales for advertising, larger contractors spend much less.

Association dues and subscriptions. Business clubs, chambers of commerce, HVAC associations, and similar dues would be considered under this heading. Also, the subscription to trade journals, if necessary for the operation of your business, should be charged under this heading and will therefore be valid as a tax exemption.

Automobiles and trucks. Items like state inspection fees, licenses, registration fees, gas, oil, minor repairs, and similar costs of automobiles and trucks used in the normal operation of business are included here.

Bad debts. This account should be debited each month for uncollectable or doubtful accounts. The HVAC contractor should make an allowance each year for such bad debts and proportionate part included in each job estimate.

Charitable contributions. All donations to charitable or educational organizations as defined by the federal (and/or state) income tax regulations are included under this heading.

Collections. The cost of collecting past-due monies are charged to this account—that is, legal fees, commissions paid for collections, and so on.

Defective, lost, obsolete, or stolen goods. The actual value falling under any or all of these categories is chargeable to overhead and may be deducted from income taxes.

Delivery costs. The total expense of all freight, express mail, and postage that cannot be charged to a given job as direct job expense belongs here.

Depreciation. This account may be debited with the amount of depreciation on buildings, autos, trucks, equipment and heavy tools, office furniture, and office equipment based on the estimated useful life of each.

Insurance. Many contractors break this category down into several parts (general insurance, workmen's compensation, and so on), but insurance fees should be charged as overhead (unless a percentage of them can be charged as direct job expense). Some types include fire, theft, liability, and the like.

Interest. The amount of interest paid or accured on outstanding interest-bearing obligations of the business—with the exception of interest that may be charged to a particular job—is charged here.

Legal and accounting fees. As the names imply, all accountant fees, as well as those of an attorney, fall under this heading.

Lost productive labor. Idle time or time lost in correcting defective work or materials, inventory taking, and similar instances where worker's time cannot be charged directly to a job falls under this category.

Office expenses. This includes the cost of such supplies as pencils, pens, staples, printed forms, and similar items. It does not include office equipment (typewriters, computers, calculators, file cabinets, and so on).

Rent. The total amount paid for rental or lease of buildings, land, storage space, and so on, used in the operation of the business but not chargeable to one particular job is included here.

Repairs and maintenance. The total cost of all repairs and maintenance to buildings, equipment, furniture, tools, and so on, used in the operation of the business is charged to this account.

Salaries and commissions. This includes salaries and commissions not readily chargeable to jobs. A secretary's salary would normally fall under this heading, but if a secretary was, say, typing written specifications for a particular project, that time could be charged directly to the job.

Sales discount. Discounts allowed for either materials or services should be charged to overhead.

Small tools. Tools that do not have a prolonged life and are not capital expenditures may be charged under this heading, provided that they are not charged to a particular job as direct job expense.

Taxes. Any city, county, state, federal, and other taxes not charged directly to a job should be included under this division. Many contractors break this category down into general taxes and payroll taxes.

Travel and transportation. Transportation, meals, and other incidental expenses not directly chargeable to a job but necessary for the operation of the contractor's business are charged to this account.

Telephone. Charge this account with all telephone expenses (including answering service) that cannot be charged directly to a job.

Miscellaneous. This includes all expenses allowed by the IRS not otherwise provided for in the preceding categories.

The first step in determining the amount of applicable overhead for each job is to determine a base cost including material cost, labor cost, direct cost, and so on, to which the overhead percentage rate is to be applied. For new contractors, this percentage will have to be estimated, based on good judgment and from an examination of records or experiences of other contractors. Once the contractor has his or her own records, however, overhead can be determined more accurately. This determination should be based on several years' operations rather than on only a few months.

The contractor should then determine whether a single rate of overhead can be equitably applied to all work or whether—because of both large and small jobs being performed—it is necessary to develop more than one rate.

The next step is to determine the total normal overhead expense of the business consistent with the total base rate developed previously.

The final step is to apportion the total general overhead cost to the overhead cost totals for large and small jobs respectively on the basis of percentages used in segregating the rate base for each type of work. The rate base applicable to that type of work is applied accordingly.

PROFIT AND SELLING PRICE

While many HVAC contractors derive pleasure from operating a successful business, few would continue their operation if a reasonable profit could not be made. This is the main reason for being in business—to make money.

The amount of profit that a firm makes over a given period depends on many factors such as the amount of work performed, the amount charged for the work, correct job management, and buying materials correctly and at the right price. One of the most important, however, is the ability to determine the correct selling price for the greater part of the work performed. You might miss a few, but the majority of your bids must be performed within a certain predetermined budget if you and the firm are to make a profit.

In general, the percentage of profit that a contracting firm should realize depends mainly on the gross amount of work the firm will perform during a year's time. For example, if a contractor could make $25,000 a year while working for another contractor, it stands to reason that he or she should at least aim for $35,000 annually, considering the headaches of running a firm. Often, the first year or two will be low on profits; but after that time, the contractor should be putting more money into his or her own pocket than could be made working for someone else.

A contracting firm that grosses, say, $750,000 each year may get by charging between 10 to 15 percent profit on its work, while a firm doing half this amount will have to charge at least 25 percent, and so on.

The first question that probably comes to mind is how, then, can the smaller contractors compete with the larger firms if they have to charge twice as much profit on each job? The answer is simple! Usually, the larger a contracting firm, the less efficient it is. A large firm's percentage of overhead is usually much more than the smaller firm. Therefore, what the smaller firm has to charge in the way of profits can usually be made up by charging less overhead and by performing the work more efficiently.

The calculation for determining the cost of construction is

Materials + Labor + Direct Job Expense = Prime Cost

To determine your selling price:

Cost + Anticipated Profit = Selling Price

It may seem very simple to run an HVAC contracting business, but the truth is that there are many complications. Items such as constantly fluctuating material prices and labor problems are prime examples. A further complication arises from the fact that the average contractor (and especially one involved in residential construction) has difficulty in determining overhead expenses accurately and more often than not underestimates them. Since the costs are higher than anticipated, the profits are naturally lower.

The business is further complicated by intense competition in residential construction, which makes it compulsory to come up with a correct price—an almost exact price. To illustrate: if contractors overestimate costs, they do not get the job; if they underestimate the costs, they may get the job, but with either too low a profit or loss.

To obtain the amount of profit that you want out of the business, you must be able to buy materials at the best possible cost, have workers trained in residential wiring, and practice good job management. These are the basic steps. Then you must know, almost exactly, what your materials are going to cost for any given job; you must apply the correct labor units to these figures; and finally, you must add all direct job expenses to come up with a prime cost for the project.

By making careful records of your business over periods of time, you should know almost exactly what your current overhead is and what percentage must be added to the prime cost of each job. This figure varies considerably between residential contractors. Most of them are able to keep their overhead at about 25 percent of the prime cost of their gross income. Some new shops may go as high as 40 percent, but this is unusual; few have an overhead less than 15 percent to 20 percent.

When the overhead is applied to the prime cost, you come up with a price that should enable you to break even. That is, if you took the job calculating all materials, labor, direct job expense, and overhead, you should be able to do the job without losing any money. You will not, of course, make any profit, as this has yet to be added.

Now comes the profit and selling price that can be determined only by you. Few contractors who specialize in residential and small commercial projects can get by on less than 20 percent profit because their gross sales are seldom over $200,000 annually. Many charge 25 percent to 30 percent profit, depending on the type of work and how much the builders or general contractors are willing to pay.

When you have decided on your own figure, this should be added to the prime cost. The result (hopefully) is the selling price that will yield the profit that you have anticipated.

Whether you are new in the business or an old timer, you should still keep records of each job, giving a cost breakdown on the various stages of construction. Then, if you're making a mistake in your estimates, you should be able to detect the problem immediately and rectify it. This way, you may lose some money on one or two jobs, but if you know your problems and correct them, you can make this money up on future jobs. Remember: this loss goes into overhead.

ESTIMATING AND CONTRACTING FORMS

Many calculations and records must be made during the process of estimating residential HVAC construction (or any other type of HVAC construction, for that matter). Such calculations are best performed when the systematic pattern is followed, using appropriate forms. In general, all forms have spaces for the name of the project, the date, the names of the estimator, foreman, and other standard data. Forms are available from HVAC societies and business supply houses. Obtain and study their catalogs for the type of forms that best suits your business.

COMPUTER ESTIMATING

The personal computer lends itself nicely to residential estimating applications as well as job management and bookkeeping applications for the HVAC contractor. Software is currently available for nearly any application the contractor may have, or you can have custom programs made to handle your own needs.

There are also many firms that specialize in estimating systems for the HVAC contractor. You should contact them directly for details. Brief descriptions of some follow:

Contractors Computers Systems, 842 Goodale Blvd., Columbus OH 43212. This firm supplies hardware and software computer systems with programs for estimating payroll and job costing, accounting, inventory, T/M, bid day summary, and word processing.

Contractors Management Systems, 1760 Reston Ave., Reston VA 22090. Handles both personal and general business computers along with estimating equipment.

Datatrak, 1700 Stierlin Rd., Mountain View CA 94043. Sells Radio Shack and IBM computers with application software for estimating, T/M billing, HVAC design, payroll, job costing and accounting programs for the HVAC contractor, and direct scaling probes.

The Elecon System, 714 E. Evelyn Ave., Sunnyvale CA 94086. Handles accounting systems, computers, estimating services, word processors, complete in-house computer system encompassing payroll, accounts payable, accounts receivable, general ledger, word processing, job costing, estimating tools, automatic billing, asset management, report generator, and spreadhseet, all fully integrated.

Estimatic Corporation, 5350 S. Roslyn St., Englewood CO 80111. One of the oldest firms in the estimating business. Provides estimating systems, pricing and labor manuals, computer estimating services, estimating and job management workshops, labor reporting and scheduling forms, computerized payroll and labor/material cost control systems, along with computer-related hardware.

Estimation, Inc., 805 L Barkwood Court, Linthicum Heights MD 21090. Furnishes computer systems with single-station or multistation, multitasking capabilities and powerful estimating programs, job management systems, computerized payroll with labor distribution and other accounting functions; complete library of programs for HVAC contractors.

16
Office Facilities and Management

The HVAC contractor's office, whether large or small, is required to perform at least the following functions:

1. Business administration
2. Supervision and job management planning
3. Design
4. Estimating

The contractor may occupy a single room where there may be enough space for all necessary activities, or an entire floor or whole building may be needed. There are several factors that dictate the size of the office, such as volume of business, cash flow, the way in which the business is operated, and the newness of the firm. The organization of the estimating facilities will also vary.

Ideally, a separate estimating room should be provided that is out of the way of the usual office routine. It should be illuminated with approximately 150 footcandles of glare-free light, painted a pleasing color, be provided with a well-designed heating, cooling, and ventilating system, and be of sufficient size to accommodate all tools and materials needed for estimating all types of projects.

Basically, the room should be furnished with a drawing board, throw-off table or desk, and a comfortable stool or chair. Bookshelves for catalogs, estimating manuals, and pricing data should be placed near the desk in easy reach of the estimator. Filing cabinets and plan files complete the basic furnishings.

The floor plan of one estimating area shown in Fig. 16-1 is ideal for one estimator and deserves a closer look.

A 12-foot blank wall space between two windows was chosen for the location. The built-in estimating work center consists of a 30- by 12-ft countertop with filing and storage drawers below and bookshelves above. A drawing board (30 × 42 in.) was placed in the center of the countertop, with a two-lamp bookshelf-type fluorescent fixture mounted on the wall above it. This left more than 4 ft of throw-off space on each side of the board.

The bookshelves contain reference books, manufacturers' catalogs, price service book, estimating manuals, and so on. The drawers below contain drafting tools, estimating tools, estimating forms, plans, and the like. Using a chair equipped with rollers, the estimator can maneuver the chair along the 12-ft countertop without getting up. This makes for rapid estimating.

Figure 16-2 shows the floor plan of another estimating room large enough to accommodate four estimators. Notice that U-shaped counters are built along one entire wall, giving the estimators an L-shaped work area. Drawing boards (30 × 42 in.) are mounted on one leg of the countertop; the remaining section is used as a reference or throw-off space.

Above the countertops are several duplex receptacles for electric erasers, electronic calculators, and similar items requiring electrical power. The wall opposite the counters or work areas contains bookshelves for the storage of manufacturers' catalogs and equipment data. One section was

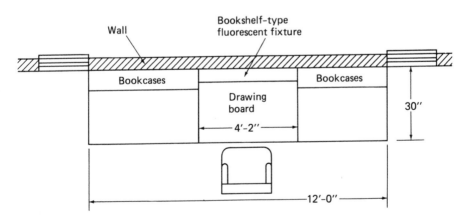

Figure 16-1 Small estimating area.

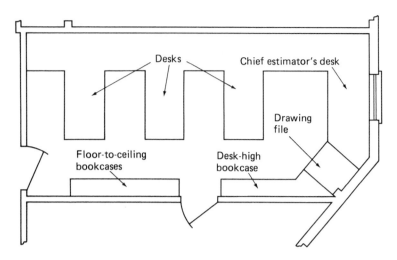

Figure 16-2   Floor plan of office serving four estimators.

built from floor to ceiling, while the other (the one nearest the window) is approximately 30 in. high. This section also serves as a narrow countertop where pencil sharpener, staple machine, and similar items are stored and used by all occupants in the room. At the end of each drafting counter is a built-in bookcase the same width and height as the counter itself. These bookcases contain reference books most frequently used by the estimator at each space.

The end area next to the window, somewhat larger than the remaining areas, was planned for the chief estimator, who handles more drawings and must have more work space to organize the drafting/estimating procedures. The "stick" plan file to the immediate right contains drawings of projects under construction. The chief estimator has convenient access to these drawings for quick reference when questions are phoned in by the workers on the jobs.

Between the plan file and the chief estimator's drawing board is a small counter space that contains a telephone, an electronic calculator, and a tape recorder for dictation.

To the immediate left of the drawing board is a large throw-off or reference space along with a 16-compartment roll plan file. The reference space usually has piles of work in progress, while the roll file contains new work that will be started as soon as time permits.

Directly beneath this reference countertop lies a flat file where tracings are stored. The walls above contain charts in large print of the most-used labor units and other estimating and design data for quick reference. Two-drawer, legal-size filing cabinets installed under the countertops are used for storage of job files and reference material.

Lighting fixtures are standard, surface-mounted, four-lamp fluorescent fixtures. However, they are mounted at a 15-degree angle to the wall to help eliminate unwanted shadows. The illumination level averages approximately 200 fc. The combination of diffused illumination and the mounting method eliminates the need for individual table lamps.

The entire area is heated and cooled by an electric forced-air system using ceiling supply-air diffusers.

The higher efficiency of the work provided by such facilities more than offsets the cost of construction and will pay for itself at a very early date, for both large and small shops.

Each estimator should be equipped with a reliable electronic calculator. The use of such calculators reduces human error, helping to eliminate costly mistakes. Savings will pay for the calculator many times over.

The estimating area should also be equipped with drafting instruments and supplies, along with a tabulator for counting outlets and other electrical components; a rotameter, metal tape graduated to 1/8- and 1/4-in. scales; and various colored pencils.

Circuits and feeders are usually measured with the rotameter, which indicates the actual footage of the run when graduated to the proper scale. However, since these meters are not inexpensive, a rotameter graduated in inches may be the most economical buy. Such a meter may be used on any drawing, regardless of its scale. The inches read on the meter are converted into actual footage of installed circuit and feeder runs on the actual project in accordance with the scale used on the plans.

The colored pencils are helpful in checking or indicating the outlets, circuits, and other electrical equipment as they are taken off and accounted for on the take-off forms or work sheets.

While these spaces were designed primarily for estimating facilities, the same layout would also suffice for a small consulting/engineering firm. In this case, the estimators would be replaced with engineers, designers, and draftsmen, but practically everything else would remain the same.

PROGRAMS FOR HVAC OFFICE MANAGEMENT

There are dozens of software packages available which will help tremendously in any phase of HVAC design, estimating, and business administration. Many of these programs are briefly described at the end of this chapter. However, there may be times when it is desirable to write custom-made programs to suit an individual's needs. We will deal with a few that should prove useful to all firms involved in HVAC designs or installations.

One type of basic program that is always helpful is one dealing with payroll. The program in Fig. 16-3 is designed to calculate gross pay for a group of employees. The program uses data statements to introduce the data

```
10 CLS
100 REM ***BUSINESS PROGRAM FOR HVAC BOOK 1986***
110 REM THIS PROGRAM CALCULATES GROSS PAY FOR A GROUP OF EMPLOYEES
120 REM C$ COMPANY NAME
130 REM D$ DATE OF WEEKENDING
140 REM H FOR HOURS WORKED
150 REM N$ FOR EMPLOYEE NAME
160 REM R HOURLY PAY RATE
170 REM N EMPLOYEE NUMBER
180 REM P FOR PAY
190 REM P1 FOR OVERTIME PAY
200 REM P2 FOR GROSS PAY ACCUMULATION
210 REM P3 ACCUMULATED OVERTIME
220 REM H1 ACCUMULATED TOTAL HOURS
230 REM H2 ACCUMULATED OT HOURS
240 REM W1 COUNTING EMPLOYEES WORKING OT
250 REM C COUNTER FOR NUMBER OF EMPLOYEES
260 PRINT
270 REM ****INITIALIZE VARIABLES****
275 P2=0
280 P3=0
290 H1=0
300 H2=0
310 W1=0
320 C=0
321 F0$=''##.##''
325 F1$=''$###.##''
330 F2$=''######.#''
340 F3$=''$#####.##''
350 F4$=''$#####.##''
360 F5$=''######.#''
370 F6$=''######.#''
380 F7$=''$#####.##''
390 REM ****PRINT HEADERS****
400 READ C$,D$
410 PRINT TAB(29);C$
420 PRINT
430 PRINT TAB(23);''GROSS PAY FOR WEEK ENDING '';D$
440 PRINT
450 PRINT TAB(4);''NAME'';TAB(25);''NUMBER'';TAB(35);''HOUR S'';
    TAB(44);''PAY RATE'';
460 PRINT TAB(56);''GROSS PAY''
470 PRINT
480 REM ****MAIN PROGRAM****
490 READ N$,N,H,R
500 IF N$=''ZZZ'' THEN 690
510 IF H>40 THEN 550
520    P=H*R
```

Figure 16-3 BASIC program designed to calculate gross pay for a group of employees.

```
530    GOTO 630
540 PRINT
550    P=40*R
560    P1=(H-40)*(R*1.5)
570    P3=P3+P1
580    H2=H2+(H-40)
590    W1=W1+1
600    P=P+P1
610    GOTO 630
620 PRINT
630 C=C+1
640 H1=H1+H
650 P2=P2+P
660 PRINT N$;TAB(25) TAB(36);H;TAB(46);
661 PRINT USING F0$;R;
662 PRINT TAB(57);
670 PRINT USING F1$;P
680 GOTO 490
690 REM ****PRINT TOTAL****
700 PRINT
710 PRINT
720 PRINT TAB(5);''TOTAL HOURS WORKED'';TAB(28);
730 PRINT USING F2$;H1
740 PRINT TAB(5);''TOTAL GROSS PAY'';TAB(28);
750 PRINT USING F3$;P2
760 PRINT TAB(5) ''AVERAGE PAY'';TAB(28);
770 PRINT USING F4$;P2/C
780 PRINT TAB(5);''AVERAGE HOURS''TAB(28);
790 PRINT USING F5$;H1/C
800 PRINT TAB(5);''AVERAGE OT HOURS'';TAB(28);
810 PRINT USING F6$;H2/W1
820 PRINT TAB(5);''AVERAGE OT PAY'';TAB(28);
830 PRINT USING F7$;P3/W1
840 PRINT
850 PRINT
860 STOP
870 DATA BURNER HEATING CO., 4/15/86
880 DATA MARY JONES, 34789,42.5,4.20
890 DATA A.FRANCIS, 51432,38,5.69
900 DATA JOHN GRINCH, 11234,40,4.82
910 DATA JAMES ARLO, 71642,40.5,5.30
920 DATA J.B. MACKS, 45687,43,6.20
930 DATA JERRY ALLEN, 12869,54,7.50
940 DATA B.L.TURBE, 54320,32,4.75
950 DATA H.S. WARREN, 32156,48,6.10
960 DATA F. FUZZ, 54641,55,5.00
970 DATA U. STUD, 34512,45,7.10
980 DATA H. RUNNER, 11234,40,4.65
990 DATA ZZZ,,,
1000 END
```

Figure 16-3 cont'd

into the program. The program then reads the data statements, calculates the gross pay for each employee, and prints the data. In use, after the last data card has been read and the last detail line printed, the following data will be calculated and printed:

1. Total hours worked
2. Average hours worked
3. Average overtime hours for those who worked overtime
4. Total gross pay
5. Average gross pay
6. Average overtime pay for those who worked overtime

The printout in Fig. 16-4 shows all of the above information. To use this program, it is first loaded and then the entire program is listed. Since the

BURNER HEATING CO.

GROSS PAY FOR WEEK ENDING 4/15/86

NAME	NUMBER	HOURS	PAY RATE	GROSS PAY
MARY JONES	34789	42.5	4.20	$183.75
A. FRANCIS	51432	38	5.69	$216.22
JOHN GRINCH	11234	40	4.82	$192.80
JAMES ARLO	71642	40.5	5.30	$215.98
J.B. MACKS	45687	43	6.20	$275.90
JERRY ALLEN	12869	54	7.50	$457.50
B.L. TURBE	54320	32	4.75	$152.00
H.S. WARREN	32156	48	6.10	$317.20
F. FUZZ	54641	55	5.00	$312.50
U. STUD	34512	45	7.10	$337.25
H. RUNNER	11234	40	4.65	$186.00

TOTAL HOURS WORKED	478.0
TOTAL GROSS PAY	$ 2847.10
AVERAGE PAY	$ 258.83
AVERAGE HOURS	43.5
AVERAGE OT HOURS	6.9
AVERAGE OT PAY	$ 63.44

Figure 16-4 Printout showing averages and totals of hours and wages of a group of employees.

Programs for HVAC Office Management   **263**

data statements are at the end of the program, these will appear on the monitor screen for the operator to correct; that is, enter the total hours worked for each employee. Of course, a change in pay rate may also be made at this time or employees may be added or deleted. When the data statements have been corrected, the program is run to obtain the required information.

A possible modification to this program would be a breakdown of each employee's hours as to the projects on which each employee worked. For example, if a draftsman worked on four different projects during the week, it may be advantageous to list the total hours spent on each one. This would help to give an accurate cost of each project.

All businesses need financial records, and the computer is ideally suited for this task. Many good software packages are available, but the simple program in Fig. 16-5 can be of immediate use for filing financial records. Only a few items of interest have been listed, but others should come to mind and may be added in the data statements at the end of the program.

```
10 REM ****BUSINESS PROGRAM FOR VNR HVAC BOOK****
20 REM ****THIS PROGRAM IS DESIGNED TO RECORD FINANCIAL INFORMATION****
30 PRINT
40 M=1000
50 PRINT ''DO YOU WISH TO PRINT ALL ENTRIES (Y OR N)?''
60 INPUT A0$
70 IF A0$=''Y'' THEN 170
80 PRINT ''SHALL I PRINT CREDIT CARDS (C), INSURANCE (I),''
90 PRINT ''          SECURITIES (S), OR MORTGAGES (M)?''
100 INPUT A1$
110 IF A1$=''C'' THEN 180
120 IF A1$=''I'' THEN 360
130 IF A1$=''S'' THEN 530
140 IF A1$=''M'' THEN 700
150 PRINT ''INPUT NOT RECOGNIZED''
160 GOTO 50
170 PRINT
180 PRINT
190 PRINT
200 PRINT
210 PRINT''BANK CREDIT/LIMIT'';TAB(22);''CONTACT/NOTIFY'';TAB(40);
    ''NUMBER'';
```

Figure 16-5 BASIC program designed for filing financial records.

```
220 PRINT TAB(55); ''PHONE NO. ''
230 PRINT ''----------------''; TAB(22); ''----------------''; TAB(40);
240 PRINT ''------------''; TAB(55); ''-----------''
250 FOR I = 1 TO M
260     READ T$
270     IF T$=''END'' THEN 340
280     READ N$, H$, A$, D$, A, L$
290     IF T$<>''C'' THEN 330
300     PRINT N$; TAB(22); H$; TAB(40); A$; TAB(55); D$
310     PRINT A; TAB(22); L$
320     PRINT
330 NEXT I
340 IF A0$<>''Y'' THEN 850
350 RESTORE
360 PRINT
370 PRINT
380 PRINT''INS TYPE/AMT''; TAB(19); ''INSURED/COMPANY''; TAB(37);
    ''POLICY #'';
390 PRINT TAB(52); ''DATE''
400 PRINT ''----------------''; TAB(19); ''----------------'';
410 PRINT TAB(37); ''---------''; TAB(52); ''----------''
420 FOR I =1 TO M
530     READ T$
440     IF T$=''END'' THEN 510
450     READ N$, H$, A$, D$, A, L$
460     IF T$<>''I'' THEN 500
470     PRINT N$; TAB(19); H$; TAB(37); A$; TAB(52); D$
480     PRINT A; TAB(19); L$
490     PRINT
500 NEXT I
510 IF A0$<>''Y'' THEN 850
520 RESTORE
530 PRINT
540 PRINT
550 PRINT ''SECURITY/PRICE''; TAB(20); 'COMPANY/LOCATION''; TAB(50);
    ''QTY''; TAB(60);
560 PRINT ''DATE''
570 PRINT ''----------------''; TAB(20); ''----------------'';
    TAB(50);
580 PRINT ''------''; TAB(60); ''--------''
590 FOR I =1 TO M
600     READ T$
610     IF T$=''END'' THEN 680
620     READ N$, H$, A$, D$, A, L$
630     IF T$<>''S'' THEN 670
```

Figure 16-5 cont'd

```
640   PRINT N$; TAB (20) ; H$; TAB (50) ; A$; TAB (60) ; D$
650   PRINT A; TAB (20) ; L$
660 PRINT
670 NEXT I
680 IF A0$<>''Y'' THEN 850
690 RESTORE
700 PRINT
710 PRINT
720 PRINT ''PROPERTY/AMOUNT''; TAB (19) ; ''NAME''; TAB (37) ; ''YRS''
730 PRINT TAB (52) ; ''PRCH DATE''
740 PRINT ''------------------''; TAB (19) ; ''---------------''; TAB (37) ;
750 PRINT ''-----''; TAB (52) ; ''---------''
760 FOR I = 1 TO M
770     READ T$
780     IF T$=''END'' THEN 850
790     READ N$, H$, A$, D$, A, L$
800     IF T$<>''M'' THEN 840
810     PRINT N$; TAB (19) ; H$; TAB (37) ; A$; TAB (52) ; D$
820     PRINT A; TAB (19) ; L$
830     PRINT
840 NEXT I
850 PRINT
860 PRINT
870 PRINT
880 STOP
890 PRINT
900 DATA I, LIABILITY, BURNER HVAC, 11-12345, APR 5 1986, 250000
910 DATA STATE FARM INSURANCE CHARLOTTESVILLE VIRGINIA
920 DATA C, JEFFERSON NAT. BANK, JOHN BRUBAKER, 47 1458, 743-5886
930 DATA 50000.00, LURAY VA 22835
940 DATA S, COMMON STOCK, BURNER HVAC, 500, JUN 5 1979, 1234.46, SAFE
    DEPOSIT BOX
950 DATA C, SOVRAN BANK   , JOHN ADAMS, 11 123 11, 652-8111
960 DATA 10000, BOX 678 RICHMOND VA
970 DATA M, 3478 BECAN HILL , BURNER HVAC INC, 20, JUN 11 1979, 135000
980 DATA MORTGAGE AAA SERVICE ENGLEWOOD TN 32401
990 DATA END
6894 BECAN HILL BURNER HVAC      30            JUN 11 1979
```

Figure 16-5 cont'd

During use, this program accepts all entries from data statements previously provided and prints all entries, or selected categories of entries. A separte processing area exists for the handling of each type of record. More could easily be added as the need arises. In each area headings are printed, formatting is accomplished, and the items are printed. Figure 16-6 shows the printout for each heading incorporated into the program.

DO YOU WISH TO PRINT ALL ENTRIES (Y OR N)?
? N
SHALL I PRINT CREDIT CARDS (C), INSURANCE (I),
SECURITIES (S), OR MORTGAGES (M)?
? C

BANK CREDIT/LIMIT	CONTACT/NOTIFY	NUMBER	PHONE NO.
JEFFERSON NAT. BANK 50000	JOHN BRUBAKER LURAY VA 22835	47 1458	743-5886
SOVRAN BANK 10000	JOHN ADAMS BOX 678 RICHMOND VA	11 123 11	652-8111

Break in 880
Ok
RUN ' 'PRNSCRN

DO YOU WISH TO PRINT ALL ENTRIES (Y OR N)?
? N
SHALL I PRINT CREDIT CARDS (C), INSURANCE (I),
SECURITIES (S), OR MORTGAGES (M)?
? I

INS TYPE/AMT INSURED/COMPANY	POLICY #	DATE
LIABILITY BURNER HVAC 250000 STATE FARM INSURANCE CHARLOTTESVILLE VIRGINIA	11-12345	APR 5 1986

Break in 880
Ok

RUN ' 'PRNSCRN

RUN

DO YOU WISH TO PRINT ALL ENTRIES (Y OR N)?
? N
SHALL I PRINT CREDIT CARDS (C), INSURANCE (I),
SECURITIES (S), OR MORTGAGES (M)?
? S

SECURITY/PRICE	COMPANY/LOCATION	QTY	DATE
COMMON STOCK 1243. 46	BURNER HVAC SAFE DEPOSIT BOX	500	JUN 5 1979

Figure 16-6 Printout showing headings in previous program.

MAILING LISTS

Mailing lists are invaluable to HVAC contractors for both advertising and billing purposes. Many types of systems are available, but the computer is one of the best. One type of mailing list can be compiled from the word-processing mode, but the one shown in Fig. 16-7 is written in BASIC and can be very helpful to the HVAC contractor.

In general, the program in Fig. 16-7 produces alphabetical listings of names and addresses provided in data statements. The program determines, through the question-and-answer sequence, the format of the printed output. Test prints are also provided for verification and alignment. To use, enter the names and addresses as data prior to running the program. This program has several options. For example, the computer will print all entries or a single entry. You then have the capability of listing the number of vertical lines per address, the number of addresses per line, and the tab position of each column, for printing directly onto mailing labels, envelopes, or the like.

```
10  REM ****MAILING LIST PROGRAM****
15  OPEN ''COM1:1200,E,7,1'' FOR OUTPUT AS #1
20  LET N3=5000
30  PRINT ''WOULD YOU LIKE TO SEE INSTRUCTIONS''
40  INPUT G$
50  IF G$=''N'' THEN 130
60  PRINT ''THIS PROGRAM PRODUCES ALPHABETIC LISTINGS OF NAMES AND''
70  PRINT ''ADDRESSES PROVIDED IN DATA STATEMENTS. TO ENTER THE DATA''
80  PRINT ''ENTER THE NAMES AND ADDRESSES BEGINNING IN LINE''
90  PRINT ''NUMBER 2000. FOR EVERY NAME ENTER THE NUMBER OF LINES OF''
100 PRINT ''INFORMATION THAT IT WILL INCLUDE.''
110 PRINT ''END YOUR DATA ENTRIES WITH A DATA 0 CARD.''
120 PRINT
130 PRINT
140 PRINT
150 PRINT ''DO YOU WANT TO PRINT ALL OF THE RECORDS''
160 INPUT G$
170 IF G$=''Y'' THEN 280
180 PRINT ''ENTER STARTING AND ENDING RECORD NUMBERS (IE 4,55)''
190 INPUT N0,N3
200 PRINT
210 IF N0=<1 THEN 280
220 FOR I = 1 TO N0-1
230    READ N1
240    FOR J= 1 TO N1
250       READ G$
260    NEXT J
```

Figure 16-7 BASIC program designed to store names and addresses.

```
270 NEXT I
280 PRINT
290 GOSUB 540
300 DIM A$(N2,C)
310 PRINT
320 LET N=(N3+1-N0)/C
330 FOR I= 1 TO N
340    FOR K=1 TO C
350       READ N1
360       IF N1=0 THEN 420
370       LET R0=R0+1
380       FOR J= 1 TO N1
390          READ A$(J,K)
400       NEXT J
410    NEXT K
420    LET J=0
430    LET J=J+1
440    FOR K= 1 TO C
450       PRINT #1,TAB(T(K)) A$(J,K);
460       A$(J,K)='' ''
470    NEXT K
480    PRINT #1,CHR$(10)
490    IF J<N2 THEN 430
500    IF N1=0 THEN 520
510 NEXT I
520 PRINT R0 ''RECORDS WERE PRINTED''
530 STOP540 PRINT
550 PRINT ''ENTER THE NUMBER OF VERTICAL LINES PER ADDRESS''
560 INPUT N2
570 PRINT ''ENTER THE NUMBER OF ADDRESSES PER LINE''
580 INPUT C
590 DIM T(C)
600 DIM X$(12)
610 PRINT ''ENTER THE TAB POSITIONS OF EACH COLUMN''
620 FOR I= 1 TO C
630    INPUT T(I)
640 NEXT I
650 LET X$(1)=''111111111111111111111111''
660 LET X$(2)=''222222222222222222222222''
670 LET X$(3)=''333333333333333333333333''
680 LET X$(4)=''444444444444444444444444''
690 LET X$(5)=''555555555555555555555555''
700 LET X$(6)=''666666666666666666666666''
710 LET X$(N2)=''************************''
720 PRINT ''POSITION PAPER NOW''
730 LET I0=N2
740 INPUT G$
750 C1=0
```

Figure 16-7 cont'd

```
760 FOR M=1 TO 2
770    FOR I= 1 TO I0
780       FOR J= 1 TO C
790          PRINT TAB(T(J)) X$(I);
800       NEXT J
810       PRINT
820    NEXT I
830 NEXT M
840 PRINT ''ARE THE NUMBER OF VERTICAL LINES CORRECT''
850 INPUT V$
860 IF V$=''Y'' THEN 900
870 PRINT ''ENTER THE NUMBER OF VERTICAL LINES PER ADDRESS''
880 INPUT N2
890 GOTO 710
900 PRINT ''ARE THE HORIZONTAL TABS CORRECT''
910 INPUT H$
920 IF H$=''Y'' THEN 970
930 PRINT ''RE-ENTER TABS''
940 FOR I= 1 TO C
950    INPUT T(I)
960 NEXT I
970 PRINT ''WOULD YOU LIKE ANOTHER TEST PATTERN PRINT''
980 INPUT G$
990 IF G$=''Y'' THEN 710
1000 LET C1=C1+6
1010 IF C1=2*N2 THEN 1050
1020 PRINT
1030 LET C1=C1+1
1035 IF C1>6*N2 THEN 1050
1040 GOTO 1010
1050 RETURN
1060 PRINT
1070 PRINT
1080 PRINT
1090 PRINT
1100 PRINT
1110 PRINT
2000 DATA 3
2001 DATA ''John Zimmerman''
2002 DATA ''PO Box 628''
2003 DATA ''Sebastian, Fl 32958''
2004 DATA 4
2005 DATA ''Dave Thompson''
2010 DATA ''PO Box 628''
2015 DATA ''15329 NE 62nd Ct.''
2025 DATA ''Redmond, WA 98052''
2035 DATA 3
2045 DATA ''The Gun Garage''
2055 DATA ''Box 73 RD 1''
2065 DATA ''Danielson, CT 06239
```

Figure 16-7 cont'd

```
2075 DATA 3
2085 DATA ''Jim Spurling''
2095 DATA ''8921 Grandstaff Ct.''
2105 DATA ''Springfield, VA 22153''
2115 DATA 3
2125 DATA ''Dormay Inc.''
2135 DATA ''PO Box 167''
2145 DATA ''Williamson, NY 14589''
2155 DATA 3
2165 DATA ''Ron Glenn''
2175 DATA ''3324 Winona Rd.''
2185 DATA ''Grants Pass, OR 97526''
2195 DATA 3
2205 DATA ''Don Findley''
2215 DATA ''5312 84th St.''
2225 DATA ''Lubbock, TX 79424''
2235 DATA 0
```

Figure 16-7 cont'd

COMPUTER SOFTWARE

There are hundreds of software packages available for use in HVAC applications, ranging from bookkeeping and estimating to computerized drafting. Here is a brief description of some that are available.

Lotus 1-2-3. This package is from Lotus Development Corp. and provides three business tools in a single, integrated package; that is, spreadsheet, an information management component, and a full range of business graphics features. Begin by using the spreadsheet for analyzing, forecasting, or planning. Then sort or select from the results with the information management component. Finally, use the graphics feature to translate the work into presentation-quality graphs and charts.

Visi On. Visi On software from VisiCorp gives the ability to perform multiple applications simultaneously on the computer. It allows switching back and forth between multiple windows on the screen to perform spreadsheet analysis, word processing, and graphics, without abandoning any application or changing a disk.

Peachtree. This is one of the most useful software packages for HVAC business applications. Two packages are designed to fill a variety of needs.

1. Job Cost System provides a reliable means of entering estimates and cost transactions for tracking job-to-job cost and profitability.
2. Calendar Management System automates all scheduling and time planning activities.

The Job Cost System includes the following files and reporting capabilities:

- Detail File—contains a record for each transaction occurring on a job.
- Job Total File—contains detailed estimated and actual job costs.
- Job Master File—contains summaries of estimated and actual job costs.
- Job Cost Report—provides summary of the status of a job, including comparison of job costs with project receipts.
- Job Estimate Worksheet Report—gives estimates for each cost category of the project.
- Cost Comparison Reports—provide information on levels and categories of costs and variance from original estimates.

Accounting software from Peachtree offers six important programs to help run the business more efficiently. The six basic packages include:

1. General Ledger
2. Accounts Payable
3. Accounts Receivable
4. Inventory Control
5. Sales Invoicing
6. PeachPay Payroll System

Other software packages include the following:

Advanced Information Management from Aims Plus. A database manager for storing and retrieving information. Lets you merge data into word-processing documents.

Data Base Manager II—The Integrator from Alpha Software Products. A menu-driven file management system, designed for the nontechnical user working with Lotus 1-2-3, Wordstar, and Multiplan.

AutoCAD 2.1 with ADE 2 from Autodesk, Inc. A computer-aided drafting and design system for architectural and landscape drawing, engineering applications, and printed circuit design.

AutoCAD 2.1 with ADE 2 and 3 from Autodesk, Inc. All the features of AutoCAD 2.1 with ADE 2 plus many extras.

Master Tax from CPaids, Inc. Gives you the power to prepare federal tax returns. Helps you process 33 forms and schedules, including those for itemized deductions, depreciation, and amortization.

Accounts Receivable from CPaids, Inc. A flexible accounts receivable system that handles any combination of open item, balance forward, or contract receivables. Lets you deal with finance charges and account aging.

HVAC SPECIFICATIONS

The specifications for a building construction project are the written description of what is required by the owner, architect, and/or engineer. Together with the drawings, the written specifications form the basis of the contract construction requirements.

A set of written specifications will vary in size considerably, depending on the size of the project. For the smaller residential installations, perhaps less than a dozen pages will complete the written specifications. On the larger commercial and industrial projects, especially those involving government contracts, the written specifications may consist of several volumes of written instruction.

Computer software packages are now available for writing specifications for HVAC systems. However, most engineering firms prefer to write their own, inserting important items based on their past experience. The computer is well adapted to such applications, and there are several techniques that may be used. Of course, a BASIC program may be written for writing HVAC specifications, leaving variables out so they may be inserted at will. However, in this case, the word-processing application would seem to be the most feasible.

USING THE GLOSSARY FEATURE

On the Wang word-processing system, the glossary feature enables storage of commonly used text, such as standard paragraphs in written specifications. This eliminates the need for repetitive typing because text stored in glossary documents can be recalled and entered into another document with just two keystrokes. The glossary may also be used to perform common editing functions.

To use the glossary entry on the Wang PC, perform the following steps:

1. Select Create New Document from the WP menu and press EXEC.
2. Type the document name and press EXEC.
3. When the document screen appears, press GL (for Glossary)—the system prompts "Which Entry?"

4. Type any capital letter to identify the glossary entry, such as A, B, S, Y, Z, and so on.

5. Type in the written specification paragraph when a variable is encountered. Note the variable, "shall be manufactured by (specify manufacturer)."

6. At this point the monitor will prompt the operator for information, and the name of the manufacturer may be typed in, then the standard text continues to be printed until another variable is encountered.

REPLACE, INSERT, AND DELETE FEATURES

The replace feature is available on most word-processing systems and may be used to replace text in a set of written specifications. To use, a standard set of written specifications is typed on the keyboard and stored on discs. As a new project is encountered, the document is read on the monitor until a change is necessary, then the replace feature is used to replace the existing text. By the same token, unwanted text may be deleted from the master set, or new text may be inserted as needed. Once the entire set has been edited to suit the project at hand, the printer will print the document ready for copying or printing.

The following sample illustrates the general wording and contents of a typical heating and ventilating specification. This may be used to write your own specifications, but several modifications will probably be necessary.

DIVISION 15—MECHANICAL

Heating and Ventilating

1. GENERAL:
   A. The "Instructions to Bidders, General Conditions" of the architectural Specifications govern work under this Section.
   B. It is understood and agreed that the Contractor has, by careful examination, satisfied himself as to the nature and location of the work under this Section and all conditions which must be met in order to carry out the work under this Section of the Specifications.
   C. The Drawings are diagrammatic and indicate generally the locations of materials and equipment. These Drawings shall be followed as closely as possible. The architectural and structural Drawings of other trades shall be checked for dimensions and clearance before installation of any work under this Section. The Heating and Ventilating Contractor shall cooperate with the other trades involved in carrying out the work in order to eliminate interference between the trades.

D. The Drawings and Specifications are complementary each to the other, and work required by either shall be included in the Contract as if called for by both.

E. It shall be the responsibility of the Heating and Ventilating Contractor to obtain drawings of equipment and materials which are to be furnished by the Owner under separate contract, to which this Contractor is to connect, and for which it is necessary that the Heating and Ventilating Contractor coordinate the work under this Section.

F. All services that are interrupted or disconnected shall be rerouted and reconnected in order to provide a complete installation.

G. All work shall be performed by mechanics skilled in the particular class or phase of work involved.

H. All equipment shall be installed in strict accordance with the respective manufacturer's instructions or recommendations.

I. Where appropriate, all equipment shall be UL approved.

J. The Heating and Ventilating Contractor shall present five (5) copies of shop drawings or brochures for all fixtures, equipment, and fabricated items to the Engineer for the Engineer's approval. The Heating and Ventilating Contractor shall not proceed with ordering, purchasing, fabricating, or installing any equipment prior to the Engineer's approval of the shop drawings and brochures. Checking is only for general conformance with the design concept of the project and for general compliance with the information given in the contract documents. Any action shown is subject to the requirements of the Plans and Specifications. The Contractor is responsible for dimensions that shall be confirmed and correlated at the job site, fabrication processes and techniques of construction, coordination of his work with that of all other trades, and the satisfactory performance of his work.

K. All materials and equipment shall be new and undamaged and shall be fully protected throughout the construction period in order that all equipment and materials shall be in perfect condition at the time of acceptance of the building by the Owner. It shall be the responsibility of the Heating and Ventilating Contractor to replace any damaged equipment or materials he is furnishing.

L. The naming of a certain brand or manufacturer in the Specifications is to establish a quality standard for the article desired. This Contractor is not restricted to the use of the specific brand or manufacturer named. However, where a substitution is requested, a substitution will be permitted only with the written approval of the Engineer. The Heating and Ventilating Contractor shall assume all responsibility for additional expenses as required in any way to meet changes from the original materials or equipment specified. If notice of substitution is not furnished to the Engineer within fifteen (15) days after the General Contract is awarded, then equipment named in the Specifications and materials named in the Specifications are to be used.

M. Excavation and Backfilling:

(1) The Heating and Ventilating Contractor shall do necessary excavation, shoring, and backfilling to complete the work under this Section of the Specifications under the supervision of the General Contractor. No foundation or structural member shall be undermined or weakened by cutting, unless provisions are made to strengthen the member so weakened as necessary.

(2) Excavation shall be cut to provide firm support for all underground conduit, pipe, etc.

(3) Backfill shall be provided as specified under "Backfilling."

N. Codes and Standards: All materials and workmanship shall comply with all applicable codes, Specifications, industry standards, and utility company regulations.

(1) In cases of differences between the building codes, Specifications, state laws, industry standards, and utility company regulations in the Contract Documents, the most stringent shall govern. The Contractor shall promptly notify the Architect in writing of any such existing difference.

(2) Noncompliance: Should the Contractor perform any work that does not comply with the requirements of the applicable building codes, state laws, industry standards, and utility company regulations, he shall bear the cost arising from the correction of the deficiency.

(3) Applicable codes and all standards shall include all state laws, utility company regulations, and applicable requirements of the following nationally accepted codes and standards:

a. National Building Code

b. National Electrical Code

c. Industry codes, Standards, and Specifications:

1. AMCA—Air Moving and Conditioning Association

2. ASHRAE—American Society of Heating, Refrigeration, and Air Conditioning Engineers

3. SMACNA—Sheet Metal and Air Conditioning Contractors' National Assocation.

O. This Contractor shall do all cutting and patching of work as necessary to complete the work under this Section. All finished work in conjunction with this work shall be repaired to perfectly match adjoining finished work. This work shall conform to each respective Specification Section for the particular phase involved. The Heating and Ventilating Contractor shall employ tradesmen skilled in the particular trade involved in carrying out this work. This work shall proceed only with the approval of the Architect. This Contractor shall perform the work under this Section of the Contract in such a way that the amount of cutting and patching of other work shall be kept to an absolute minimum.

P. This Contractor shall obtain all permits and arrange for all inspections necessary for the installation of this work. All fees in this relation shall be paid for by the Heating and Ventilating Contractor. This Contractor shall provide the Owner with certificates of inspection from all authorities having jurisdiction. This Contractor shall be responsible for notifying the authorities having jurisdiction at each inspection stage, and no work shall progress until the inspection has been completed and the work approved.

Q. Coordination:

(1) It is called to the Heating and Ventilating Contractor's attention that the ductwork and piping shown on the base bid plan have extremely close clearance.

(2) It shall be the responsibility of the Heating and Ventilating Contractor to coordinate the work under this Section with the Plumbing Contractor and Electrical Contractor and other subcontractors.

(3) This Contractor shall check approved equipment drawings of other trades so that all roughing-in work shall be of proper size and in the proper location, for all specific equipment used.

(4) The Heating and Ventilating Contractor shall furnish necessary information to the related trades and shall properly coordinate this information.

(5) The Heating and Ventilating Contractor shall cooperate with the other trades involved in order to eliminate any interference between the trades. This Contractor shall make minor field adjustments to accomplish this.

(6) This Contractor shall cooperate with the other subcontractors in order to establish the responsibilities of each so that work can be completed without delay or interference by this Contractor.

2. WORK INCLUDED:

A. The work in this Section shall include furnishing all labor, equipment, materials, supplies, and components for complete heating and ventilating systems as indicated on the Drawings and Specifications.

3. ELECTRICAL WORK:

A. The Heating and Ventilating Contractor is to furnish and attach all necessary components for the heating and control system. The control wiring is to be performed by a qualified electrical contractor employed by the Heating and Ventilating Contractor.

B. The Heating and Ventilating Contractor is to furnish all motor starters and control components that are specified in the Mechanical

Section of these Specifications or shown in schedules on the Drawings.

C. The Electrical Contractor shall furnish all other starters and disconnect switches. The Heating and Ventilating Contractor shall be responsible for the electrical connections and for the electrical wiring between the elements of the pneumatic control system.

D. The Electrical Contractor shall furnish all conduit, fittings, and materials for the electrical work to connect to the heating and ventilating equipment.

E. The electrical work required in the Heating and Ventilating Electrical Section of these Specifications.

F. All equipment shall be suitable for 208-volt, three-phase, 60-hertz electrical characteristics except motors under 1/2 hp, which are to be 120-volt, single-phase, 60-hertz. Motors of other characteristics are to be used only where specifically indicated.

4. EQUIPMENT:

A. Ventilating units:

(1) Ventilating units shall be the draw-through type as scheduled on the Drawings.

(2) Units shall be installed in accordance with the manufacturer's recommendations and be factory assembled and tested.

(3) Casings shall be constructed of steel, reinforced and braced for maximum rigidity. Casings shall be of sectionalized construction and have removable panels for access to all internal parts.

(4) Fans shall be DIDW Class 1 centrifugal and shall be statically and dynamically balanced at the factory. Fan shafts shall run in grease-lubricated ball bearings, the grease line for internal bearings being brought out to the exterior of the casing.

(5) The interior of the unit casing shall be insulated with one-inch blanket fiberglass insulation, coated to prevent erosion.

(6) Casings and all accessories, with the exception of the coils described in the following paragraphs, shall be galvanized steel or shall be given a protective baked-enamel finish over a suitable rust inhibitor.

(7) Coils shall have seamless copper tubes and aluminum fins. Fins shall be bonded to tubes by mechanical expansion of the tubes. No soldering or tinning shall be used in the bonding process. Coils shall have a galvanized steel casing no lighter than 16 gauge, shall be mounted so that they are accessible for service, and shall be removable without dismantling the entire unit. Steam coils shall be a nonfreeze, distributing type. Hot-water coils shall be type WS, and the steam coils shall be type NS steam distributing.

(8) Heating coils for hot-water service shall be pitched in the unit

casing for proper drainage, and tested at 250 psig air pressure under water.

(9) Each unit shall be provided with an adjustable-speed V-belt drive, having a variable-pitch motor sheath to provide approximately 10 percent variation in speed above and below the factory setting. Drive shall be protected by a suitable guard with openings at fan and motor shafts for use of a tachometer.

(10) Motor shall be general-purpose, squirrel-cage type with same type bearings as air-handling unit. Nameplate rating of motor shall not be exceeded by fan BHP requirements.

(11) See details on Drawings for mounting and isolation of units.

(12) Filter boxes shall be furnished with throw-away filters, as scheduled. Filter area shall be such that filter velocity is an accordance with the filter manufacturer's recommendation. Filter boxes shall have access doors on both sides. Filters shall fit snugly to prevent air bypass. Both sides of the filter box shall be flanged for fastener holes. Filter shall be not less than two inches thick.

B. Converter:

(1) Convertor shall be designed for heating hot water with steam. The unit shall be constructed in accordance with ASME Code and labeled for 150-psi working pressure in shell and tubes.

(2) Materials of construction shall be as follows:

    a. Water chamber—cast iron.

    b. Shell—carbon steel.

    c. Tube sheet—rolled steel.

    d. Support and cradles—steel or cast iron.

    e. Tubes—3/4-inch O.D. 18-gauge seamless drawn copper.

    f. Tube spaces—soft bronze or copper alloy.

(3) Capacity given in schedule on Drawings shall be based on a fouling factor of 0.0005.

(4) A valved ____ No. 60 vacuum breaker shall be provided on shell. At each convertor in water piping, a ____ Series 240 Relief valve, ASME rated and sized for full capacity of convertor, shall be installed and set to relieve at pressure shown on Drawings. Valve shall be located so it cannot be valved off from convertor. Pipe discharge shall be full size to the floor drain.

(5) The Contractor shall provide a stand for support of convertor, constructed of welded structural steel or steel pipe.

(6) Convertor shall be as manufactured by ____ Company, Type SU1.

C. Pumps:

(1) Base-mounted pumps shall be ____ "Universal" of vertical split-case design, equipped with mechanical seals for 225°F

279

operating temperature and built for not less than 125-psi working pressure. Motor shall be 1750 rpm, drip proof, and specifically designed for quiet operation. The coupler between motor and pump shall be ____ flexible type. Spring-type couplers will not be acceptable. Pump and motor shall have oil-lubricated bronze sleeve bearings. Pump shall have removable bearings frame to permit disassembly of pump without disconnection of piping, hydraulically balanced bronze impeller, and solid cast-iron volute. Pump and motor shall be mounted on a steel base plate.

(2) Base-mounted pumps shall have pump connectors as manufac-tured by ____ and shall be stainless steel, Type SPCF. They shall be sized the same as the connecting pipe.

D. Cabinet Unit Heaters:

(1) Cabinet unit heaters shall be self-contained and factory assem-bled, and shall consist generally of a filter, heating coil, fan with driving motor, and casing. Heater element shall consist of nonferrous fuses and fins.

(2) Cabinet shall be of steel and be wall mounted or ceiling mounted as indicated on the Drawings.

(3) Front of cabinet shall be removable and not lighter than 16-gauge steel. The back shall be not less than 18-gauge steel. Cabinet shall be provided with steel supports for fan, heating coil, and filter, and shall be steel-reinforced members as re-quired to provide a rigid exposed casing and silent operation.

(4) Enclosures shall be complete with inlet and outlet grilles and with doors for access to valves. The element shall be easily accessible for repair after installation of unit. Enclosures shall be galvanized, bonderized, or painted with rust-inhibiting paint at factory, and finished in baked enamel in standard color selected.

(5) Fans shall be centrifugal type with one or more wheels mounted on a single shaft. Fan wheels, shaft, bearings, and fan housing shall be mounted as an integral assembly on a heavy steel mounting plate and securely fastened to enclosures. Bearings of fan and motor shall be self-aligning, permanently lubricated ball type, or sleeve type with ample provision for lubrication and oil reservoirs. Bearings shall be effectively sealed against loss of oil and entrance of dirt.

(6) Filters shall be of the permanent type, mounted in tight-fitting slide-out frames arranged to permit filter renewal or cleaning without removal of front panel.

(7) Heaters shall be tested and rated in accordance with standard test codes adopted jointly by the Unit Heater Division, Air Moving and Conditioning Association, and the American So-

ciety of Heating, Refrigeration, and Air Conditioning Engineers.

(8) Motors shall be resilient mounted on a cushion base, shall be for constant or multispeed operation, and shall have overload protection.

(9) See Drawings for capacity, type, and arrangement.

E. Fin-tube Radiation: Fin-tube heating elements and enclosures, together with required mounting components and accessories, shall be furnished and installed as indicated on plans. Material shall be as manufactured by _____ Radiator Company or approved equal.

(1) Nonferrous Heating Elements: Nonferrous heating elements shall consist of full-hard aluminum plate fins, permanently bonded to copper seamless-drawn tube and guaranteed for working pressure at 300°F not less than 150 psi for 1-inch tube and 200 psi for 1-1/4-inch tube. Fins shall be embedded in copper tube at least .007 inch.

(2) Enclosures and Accessories: Enclosures and accessories shall be of style and dimensions indicated on plans and shall be fabricated from electrozinc-coated, rust-resistant, bonderized steel. Enclosures shall be 14 gauge. Enclosure louvers shall be "pencil-proof" type. On wall-to-wall application, enclosures shall be furnished in one piece up to a maximum of 10-feet enclosure length for rooms or spaces measuring a maximum of 10 feet 10 inches in wall length, and a 6-inch end trim shall be used at each end. Enclosures shall be furnished in two or more lengths for wall lengths exceeding 10 feet 10 inches. Corners and end enclosures shall have same method of joining. End trims, furnished with roll-flanged edges, shall be used between ends of enclosures and walls on wall-to-wall applications. End trims shall be 6 inches maximum length and shall be attached without visible fasteners. Corners and end enclosures shall be furnished where indicated, shall be the same gauge as enclosures, and shall fit flush with enclosures.

(3) Enclosure Supports: Type-A Dura-Mount Back: Enclosures shall be supported at top by means of a 20-gauge roll-formed continuous mounting channel fabricated from electrozinc-coated, rust-resistant, bonderized steel. There shall be a minimum of eight bends forming strengthening ribs running the length of the channel. The top projection of channel shall position the enclosure 7/8 inch from wall to prevent gouging of walls when enclosure dirt sealer shall be provided to the offset section of channel premanently anchored to wall, allowing enclosure installation or removal without disturbing the sealer.

Dirt sealers attached to rear flange of enclosure are not permitted.

(4) Enclosure Brackets and Element Hangers:

    a. Enclosure brackets and element hangers shall be installed not farther than 4 feet. Brackets shall be die formed from 3/16-inch-thick stock, 1-1/2 inches wide, and shall be lanced to support and position lower flange of enclosure. Enclosures shall be firmly attached to brackets by setscrews, operated from under the enclosure. Devices that do not provide positive fastening of enclosures are not acceptable. Brackets shall be inserted in prepunched slots in mounting channel to ensure correct alignment and shall be fastened securely to wall at bottom.

    b. Sliding saddles shall support heating element and provide positive positioning of element in enclosure to ensure maximum heating efficiency while preventing any possibility of fin impingement on brackets or enclosure joints during expansion or contraction. Element supports shall be double-saddle design fabricated from 16-gauge electrozinc-coated, rust-resistant, bonderized steel. Saddle shall slide freely on saddle support arm bolted to support bracket. Support arm shall allow 1-1/2-inch height adjustment for pitch. The element support saddle shall allow 1-5/8-inch lateral movement for expansion and contraction of heating element. Rod or wire hangers are not acceptable.

(5) Access Doors: Access doors shall be provided where noted on plans. Doors shall be at least 8 by 8 inches, shall be located in 12-inch-long access panels, and shall have the same gauge as enclosures.

(6) Enclosure Dampers: Enclosure dampers shall be provided where indicated. Damper blades shall be fabricated from 18-gauge electrozinc-coated, rust-resistant, bonderized steel, flanged for added rigidity, and shall be permanently attached to enclosures. Threaded damper screw and trunion shall provide positive operation of blade in any position between open and closed. Damper shall be operated by knob.

F. Fans: Fans shall be provided as shown and scheduled on Drawings. Care shall be taken when mounting in-line fans between joists to provide access to all parts of the fan. (No fan shall be mounted on roof.)

(1) In-line Fans: All these fans shall be equal to ____ "Square Line Centrifugal Fan" with backward-inclined centrifugal wheel, belt-driven Model SQ.B. See Schedule on Drawings.

(2) Fume Centrifugal Fan: (Welding Fumes) This fan shall be equal to "ILG" Type PE-Belted with cast-iron wheel. See Drawings for capacity and mounting.

(3) Propeller Fans: See Drawings for location and capacity.

(4) Note: See Drawings for mounting and isolation.

G. Underground Pipe Conduit: (See Alternate A)

(1) Scope: The underground conduit shall include reinforced concrete foundation slabs, unit cast-iron pipe supports, unit sleeve-alignment guides, unit pipe anchors and tile conduit envelope, and shall be insulated as specified in these Specifications.

(2) The tile shall be "Therm-O-Tile," or approved equal, and shall be vitrified and equal to or better than "extra strength" clay pipe of the same diameter as per ASTM Specification C-278. All joints in the conduit envelope shall be sealed with _____ cement mortar mixed in the proportion of one part _____ cement to two parts clean, sharp sand, and coated after cement has set with "Therm-O-Mastic" compound. Additional weatherproofing consisting of one layer of 30-pound felt shall be applied completely over the tile and lapped over the concrete foundation slab. Laps shall be at least 3 inches and shall be sealed with "Therm-O-Mastic" or hot asphalt.

(3) The Conduit Foundation: The foundation slab shall be at least 4-inch-thick concrete as specified under Section 3, reinforced with 6 by 6 by No. 10 welded wire mesh, and shall have on emergency drain throughout its run. The foundation slab shall extend through building or manhole walls and shall rest on the masonry of these walls. The emergency drain shall be continued to building or manhole sumps, to sewers, to dry wells, or to outfalls. Where conduit passes under roadway, it shall be reinforced with an envelope of concrete, 4 inches thick.

(4) Pipe Supports, Anchors, and Guides: These accessories shall be as regularly furnished by the manufacturer of the "Therm-O-Tile" conduit and especially designed to fit within the conduit envelope. Location shall be as shown on the Plot Plan. There shall be two guides on each side of each drop.

(5) Conduit shall be sized per the manufacturer's recommendations for the pipe sizes enclosed.

(6) Shop Drawings: The successful Contractor for the conduit work will be required to furnish, for approval, scale drawings showing cross sections through each separate conduit run and giving all required dimensions of the conduit and centers on which each pipe line will be located within it.

(7) Wall Openings: The space around the conduit where it enters walls shall be closed with brick and mortar and completely covered with weatherproof mastic. The space on the inside of the conduit on the inside of building or manhole wall shall be filled with brick and mortar.

(8) Backfilling: Backfilling shall be done carefully, and the surface restored to its original condition. Backfilling and tamping shall proceed simultaneously on both sides of the conduit (lengthwise of the trench) until the arch is covered to a depth of at least 18 inches. Rock or stone that might damage the tile shall not be used in the backfill. Backfilling shall comply with Section 2 of the Specifications.

(9) Expansion joints shall be furnished or installed where indicated on Drawings. Model and size shall be as shown on Drawings. Expansion joints shall be as manufactured by ____ Company.

(10) Conduit and accessories shall be installed in accordance with the manufacturer's recommendations.

H. Steam Pressure Reducing Valve Assembly:

(1) SPRV: Valve shall be as manufactured by ____ Specialty Manufacturing Corp. Valve body shall be iron and shall have flanged connections. Valve shall be single seated and shall have a stainless-steel valve and seat and deep glad packed stuffing box for minimum friction on valve stem. Valve shall have minimum working pressure of 250 psig, an initial pressure of 75 psig, and a reduced pressure of 10 psig. All parts shall be renewable and interchangeable, and valve seat and disc shall be such that they can be changed without removing valve body from the line. Valve shall be ____ No. 7000 3-inch size, capacity 8,600 pounds condensate per hour.

(2) Components of pressure-reducing valves shall be installed as recommended by the manufacturer.

(3) Safety valve on reduced-pressure side of pressure-reducing station shall be as manufactured by ____ Company, ASME tested and rated, having cast-iron body and 250-pound flanged inlet connection. Valve shall be Catalog No. 630 and shall have capacity indicated on Drawings based on a 3 percent accumulation. Pipe discharge of safety valve shall be full size to exterior of building.

I. Steam Specialties:

(1) High-pressure Steam: Traps shall be ____ side inlet inverted bucket traps. Traps shall be built for up to 125-psig working steam pressure.

(2) Low-pressure Steam: Traps shall be ____ B series, float and

thermostatic type, built for up to 15-psig working steam pressure. Traps shall be sized at 1/4 pound of differential.

(3) Traps shall have cast-iron or semisteel body with stainless-steel trim.

(4) Flash tank shall be as detailed on the Drawings.

J. Heating Water Specialties:

(1) Hot-water expansion tank shall be ___ built for 125-pounds water working pressure, and shall be equipped with proper size "Airtrol" tank fitting and air charger fitting. Tank shall be ___, ASME of size as indicated on Drawings.

(2) Air separaters shall be ___ "Rolairtrol." They shall be installed as instructed by manufacturer and shall afford adequate clearance to remove built-in strainer.

(3) Water makeup pressure-reducing valves shall be ___ Type 12, with screwed ends.

(4) Air vents installed on heating coils and at high points in water piping and on all upfeed radiation units shall consist of an air chamber and manual air vent of a type suitable for the particular application where used.

(5) Balancing Fittings: The Heating and Ventilating Contractor shall furnish and install ___ Series 700 flow meter fittings as a permanent part of the water piping systems for use with ___ No. SD-400-4 flow meter in determining and balancing water flow in all systems. These fittings shall be at points indicated on Drawings and shall be located so as to provide 15 diameters upstream and 5 diameters downstream of uninterrupted straight pipe. The systems shall be balanced as closely as practicable by use of the aforementioned flow meter.

(6) Water relief valves shall be ___ Series 230 or 240 as indicated on Drawings. Valves shall be set to relieve at the pressures indicated on Drawings. Pipe discharge shall be full size to floor drain.

(7) Thermometers: Thermometers shall be ___ Type 105 straight form or Type 115-90 degree back angle form, as applicable, industrial type, with standard separable socket, 9-inch scale, 30°F to 240°F range, cast-aluminum case, with red-reading mercury tube.

(8) Pressure Gauges: Pressure gauges for pipe lines shall be ___ drawn case gauges, No. 1000 for pressure, No. 1002 for vacuum, and No. 1004 for compound. Pressure gauges shall have brass bourdon tube soldered to socket and tip, brass movement, and white-coated metal dial 3-1/2 inches in diameter, graduated to meet system design requirements, normal operating pressure being indicated middial. ___ No. 1106B brass

pulsation dampener shall be provided on gauges near pumps and ___ No. 1092 T-handled cock in 1/4-inch line to all pressure gauges. No. 1100 pigtail siphon shall be provided on all steam gauges.

K. Condensate Pump:

(1) One duplex condensation pump shall be furnished and installed where shown on the Plans. The pump shall be manufactured by the ___ Co. The pump shall be driven by open, drip-protected ball-bearing motors, rated for single-phase, 60-hertz, 120-volt ac operation. Each pumping unit shall have capacity at 205°F as indicated. The Heating and Ventilating Contractor shall furnish combination starters with disconnect switch and motor overload protection.

(2) The equipment is to include one cast-iron receiving tank, two pumping units, and the following accessories:

a. The pumping units shall be bronze fitted throughout, shall be of the centrifugal type, and shall have rotating parts that have been dynamically balanced. The receiving tank, pumping units, and motors shall be assembled by the manufacturer to form an integral unit. A strainer with movable screen is to be installed in the receiving tank.

b. Automatic controls shall consist of a float switch, combination starters, and alternator. Controls shall provide automatic alternation between one pump motor and the other.

(3) If requested, the installing contractor shall secure from the pump manufacturer a factory test report which is to be submitted to the specifying engineer for approval. This report shall show the actual condensate capacity for the pumping units and the power input to the units, all as determined by tests of the actual equipment furnished. The test report is to be certified by the manufacturer as to its correctness in all particulars.

L. Diffusers, Registers, and Grilles:

(1) Diffusers: Diffusers shall be ___ type SFSV with deflectrol, No. 7 finish. Dropped collar shall be provided where called for on Drawings.

(2) Exhaust Registers: Exhaust registers shall be ___ type GMRV or GFRV, No. 4 finish. Grille in Dark Room shall be light tight.

(3) Supply Registers: Supply registers shall be ___ type GMAV with No. 4 finish.

(4) Exhaust Grilles: Exhaust grilles shall be ___ type EMR or FGR with No. 7 finish.

(5) Door Grilles: Shall be provided by General Contractor. (See Drawings for location only.)

M. Mechanical Expansion Joints: Mechanical expansion joints shall be provided as called for on Drawings. Size, capacity, and type are given on Drawings. Expansion joints and guides shall be equal to ____.

N. Flexible Connections: Bronze unbraided flexible metal nipples shall be provided to connect to steel heating piping below floor and shall extend from 3/4-inch inlet to fin tube radiation above floor. See detail on Drawings. Nipples shall be furnished in 18-inch length, 3/4-inch hex male end, and suitable for temperatures up to 350°F.

O. Unit Heaters: Horizontal hot-water-type heaters shall be provided by ____ or equal. See Drawings for model number, size, and capacity.

P. Fan-coil Units: Two units of the following type and capacity shall be provided: Model OH 600, 4.2 GPM, 42.2 mbh, 200°F EWT, 180°F LWT, P.D.-12 feet, three-speed, and a return-air plenum with permanent filter and a fan-control switch. Motor shall have split capacitor, 1/20 hp, 120 volt/1hp.

Q. Automatic Temperature Controls:

   (1) General: The system shall be a complete system of automatic temperature regulation of the pneumatic type with electric accessories and components as indicated. Component parts of the system shall be manufactured by ____; the base bid shall be ____ and can be considered as an alternate at the option of the Contractor. The entire system shall be installed by the Control Manufacturer. All control items except room thermostats shall be properly identified with engraved plastic nameplates permanently attached. Room thermostat locations shall be coordinated to align vertically or horizontally with adjacent light switches or control instruments. Room thermostats shall be 5 feet 6 inches (nominal) above the floor. Room thermostat covers shall be open.

   (2) Materials: (Thermostats)

       a. Firestats shall be UL approved, manual-reset type T-7602 with an adjustable temperature setting. Range hood shall be set at 250°F; all others at 125°F.

       b. Freezestats shall be T-7606 with 20-foot temperature-sensitive element, located downstream from the coil. If any portion of the element senses a temperature below its setting, the contacts shall break.

       c. Unit heater thermostats for space mounting shall be T-7162, line-voltage type with SP-ST switching action rated 6 amperes for full load and rated 36 amperes at 120 volts for lock rotor.

       d. Surface-mounted aquastats shall be type T-7912 with adjustable set point and 10° differential. Contacts shall be rated 10 amperes at 120 volts.

e. Thermostatic sensors shall be T-5210 style "B" bulbs with 5-1/2 inch and 4-foot capillaries or 8-foot and 17-foot averaging element. Sensors shall be designed to measure a temperature and to convert the measurement to an air-pressure signal that is transmitted to a receiver, a 3- to 15-psi signal. The sensor shall have pneumatic feedback.

f. Fluidic controlling receivers shall be T-9000. The instrument shall accept a 3- to 15-psi pneumatic signal from one or two temperature-relative humidity or pressure transmitters, and have pneumatic feeback and enclosed fluidic circuitry.

g. Receiver controller shall be T-5312 and shall accept a 3- to 15-psi signal from a remote transmitter.

h. Pneumatic thermometer shall be T-5500 to provide visual indication of the temperature. The thermometer shall accept a 3- to 15-psi signal from a remote transmitter. The T-5500 shall be for flush-mounted applications.

i. Day-night thermostats shall be T-4502 equipped with two (2) separate bimetallic elements for day and night operation. The thermostats shall be equipped with an indexing switch for changing the thermostat to day or night operation as desired, or from a control location by changing the air pressure from 15 to 20 pounds.

j. Remote capillary pneumatic thermostats shall be T-8000 for direct or reverse acting. The T-8000 shall be equipped with the proper capillary, B bulb for sensing outside air and water temperature, and also of the averaging type for all other applications.

k. Remote capillary pneumatic thermostats for two-position applications shall be T-8000.

(3) Valves:

a. Valves shall be sized by the control manufacturer and shall have threaded connections, except valves over 2 inches shall have flanged connections. Valve packing shall be U-cap silicone except where indicated. Maximum allowable pressure drop shall be 5-feet water column for water valves and 60 percent steam pressure.

b. Valve operators for valve 1/2 inch to 2 inches shall be V-3000 piston operated. The diaphragm shall be manufactured by Butyl rubber enclosed in a heavy die-cast aluminum housing.

c. Valves for steam or water service shall be V-3752 normally-open type. The valve shall be equipped with a V-3752 piston operator. The V-3752 bodies shall be of high-grade cast red brass in sizes 1/2 inch through 2 inches and shall have a back-setting feature that permits changing the stem packing without interrupting service to the system. The modulating plug shall have a replaceable composition disc, especially compounded for steam or hot water, and shall provide an equal percentage relationship between valve lift and flow at a constant pressure drop.

d. Connector valves shall be V-3800 for steam or water with restrictor mounting space. The valve shall be equipped with a heavy-duty moulded rubber diaphragm of the oval-piston type. The valve body shall be of cast red brass in sizes 1-2 inch through 2-3/4 inch.

e. Valve for steam or water service shall be V-3970 normally-closed type. The valve shall be equipped with a V-3000 piston operator. The V-3870 bodies shall be of high-grade cast red brass in sizes 1/2 inch through 2 inches and shall have a back-setting feature that permits changing the stem packing without interrupting service to the system. The modulating plug shall have a replaceable compulsion disc especially compounded for steam or hot water, and shall provide an equal percentage relationship between valve lift and flow at a constant pressure drop.

f. Three-way mixing valves shall be V-4322 and 1/2 inch through 2 inches in size. The body shall be three-way with screwed ends and made of high-grade cast red brass. The body shall be suitable for pressure to 150 psi.

(4) Dampers and Damper Motors:

a. Automatic control dampers shall be interlocking and air-tight. They shall be of opposed-blade construction for modulating service and of parallel-blade construction for two-position service. Dampers shall be of the multilouver construction with brass bearings, channel iron frame, and maximum width of 6 feet.

b. Control dampers shall be D-1200 or D-1300 and manufactured specifically to control the air flow in heating, ventilating, and air-conditioning systems.

c. Frames shall be made of No. 13 galvanized sheet steel, formed into channels and riveted. In addition to the rigid frame construction, corner brackets shall be used to maintain alignment of the damper.

d. Blades shall consist of two formed No. 22 galvanized sheets, spot-welded together for strength to withstand high velocities and static pressures. Square blade pins shall be furnished to ensure nonslip pivoting of the blades when a damper is used as a single module or when it is interconnected with others.

e. Bushings shall be made of oil-impregnated sintered bronze and shall provide constant lubrication.

f. Synthetic elastomer seals shall be provided on the blade edges and on the top, bottom, and sides of the frame, and shall be capable of withstanding air temperatures from −20 to 200°F or from −65 to 400°F, as required for the application. The material and extruded form of the blade-edge seals shall create a positive seal when the blades are closed. The seals shall be replaceable if they become damaged. Leakage shall be less than 0.5 percent when closing against 4-inch w.g. static pressure, based on conventional velocity of 2,000 fpm.

g. Damper motors shall be provided for all automatic dampers and shall be of sufficient capacity to operate the connected damper. Where required, damper motors shall be equipped with positive positioners.

h. Automatic control dampers are specified to be provided as an integral part of the air units.

(5) Panels:

a. Control cabinets shall be furnished where specified. In general, it is the intention of these Specifications that control cabinets be furnished for each air-handling unit, major equipment components, and elsewhere as specified. Control cabinets shall be fabricated of extruded aluminum or steel. The cabinets shall have a face panel for flush-mounting gauges and a subpanel for mounting of controllers, relays, and so on. Those controls which require manual positioning or visual indication shall be flush mounted and identified with engraved nameplates on the face panel. The controls that must be accessible for maintenance and calibration only are to be mounted on the subpanel inside cabinet. Each item shall be identified by engraved nameplates.

(6) Control Piping:

a. Control piping shall be hard-drawn copper tubing where exposed and may be either hard- or soft-drawn copper tubing where it is to be concealed. Either solder or compression fitting shall be used. Tubing shall be run in a neat and workmanlike manner and shall be fastened securely to the building structure. All tubing in finished rooms shall be concealed. Where exposed in unfinished rooms, tubing shall be run either parallel to or at right angles to the building structure. In lieu of copper tubing, plastic tubing may be used in end compartment of unit and in control panel.

  b. Plastic tubing: In lieu of copper tubing, high-density virgin polyethylene may be substituted, subject to the following requirements. The tubing shall be rated 600-psi burst pressure at 72°F and 300-psi burst pressure at 140°F. Each tube shall be individually numbered at intervals not exceeding 1 inch. All tubing except tubing in control panels and junction boxes shall be installed in EMT conduit in sizes of 1/2 inch through 2 inches. Standard electrical fittings shall be used. All bends for conduit 1 inch and larger shall be standard purchased bends. There shall not be more than three 90-degree bends between pull boxes. Termination shall be made in standard electric junction boxes or enclosed control panels. Where connections are made from plastic to copper, protective grommets shall be used to prevent electrolysis. The conduit installation shall conform to the same standard as set forth in the copper piping requirements.

(7) Installation:

  a. Exposed:

   1. Single polyethylene tubing and soft copper aluminum tubing may be run exposed for a length of 18 inches or less. For lengths that exceed 18 inches, the lines shall be run within enclosed trough or conduit, and this tube carrier system shall be installed in a workmanlike manner, parallel to building lines, adequately supported, and so on. All connections, except for terminal connections to valves, damper operators, and so on, shall be made inside troughs, junction boxes, or control cabinets.

   2. Factory-manufactured bundles of polyethylene tubing, with protective outer sheath and hard copper or aluminum tubing, may be installed without an additional trough or conduit envelope, provided that the tube system is installed in same workmanlike manner as previously specified for trough and conduit systems.

  b. Concealed-accessible:

   1. Single polyethyelene tubing and soft copper or aluminum tubing, either individual or bundled, shall be installed in a workmanlike manner, securely fastened to fixed members of the building structure at sufficient points to avoid excessive freedom of movement. Field-frabricated bundles shall be tied together with a sufficient number of nylon ties to present a neat, uniform appearance.

c. Concealed-inaccessible: Single polyethylene tubes shall be run within enclosed trough or conduit. Factory-manufactured bundles of polyethylene tubing, with protective outer sheath and soft copper or aluminum tubing, may be installed without an additional trough or conduit envelope. Fitting connections to polyethylene tubing shall not be made within the inaccessible area.

d. Piping Test: The piping system shall be tested and made tight under pressure of 30 psi. Leakage will not exceed 10 psi in 12 hours.

(8) Miscellaneous relays, pressure switches, disconnect switches, PE and EP relays, time clocks, and other items shall be provided as required for the sequence of control indicated. Time clock shall be seven-day type. The PE relays shall be located within 5 feet of the motor control device.

(9) Air Compressor: Air compressor shall be of the electric type complete with tank, gauges, combination pressure-reducing valves, low-pressure relief valve, filter assembly, and necessary accessories. The unit shall be of ample capacity to automatically maintain the desired air pressure with an idle period equal to at least twice that of the operating period. Compressor shall be single-stage, high-pressure (60- to 75-psi) type fitted with galvanized ASME reservoir. Motor shall be provided with built-in overload protection. Compressor and motor shall be sized so that their capacity is sufficient for future addition to building.

(10) Work by Others:

a. Dampers and valves will be installed by the Mechanical Contractor.

b. Temperature-control wiring shall be the responsibility of the Temperature Control Contractor. This responsibility shall consist of wiring the following items:

1. PE switches
2. EP switches
3. Firestats
4. Freezestats
5. Air compressor
6. All interlocking wiring required for the system to function properly

c. The Electrical Contractor shall be responsible for all power wiring to the equipment.

(11) Sequence of Operation:

a. Air-handling Unit Control: When the unit fan is started, EP-1 in energized to position the outdoor air damper open through D-1 and through PE-1 on units 7 and 8 which energize their respective exhaust fans. When the unit fan is stopped, PE-1 is deenergized and the outdoor air damper is positioned fully closed. Firestat T-3, located in the filter discharge, stops the fan if the discharge temperature rises above 125°F. T-1, located in the discharge duct, controls V-1 modulator to bypass an increasing amount of water around the coil. T-2, with its element located on the face of the heating coil, prevents the discharge temperature from falling below 35°F by overriding T-1 and modulating V-1. Five (5) untis have hot-water coils and require three-way valves; three (3) units are steam coils and require steam valves.

b. Radiation Control: During the day operation, T-1 controls V-1 to maintain the desired space temperature. During the night operation, T-1 controls V-1 to maintain a reduced night temperature of 60°F.

c. Exhaust Fan Control: T-1, located in the intake of each exhaust fan, stops the unit fan should the intake temperature rise above 125°F.

d. Pump Bypass Control: T-1, with its sensor located in the supply and return lines, controls V-1 to maintain the desired differential pump pressure.

e. Convertor Control: T-1, with its sensor TT-2 located in the convertor supply, is reset inversely with changes in the outside air temperature by TT-1, to control V-1 and maintain the desired convertor discharge temperature inversely with changes in the outside air temperature. T-2 located in the outside air, stops the pump should the outside air temperature rise above 70°F. When the pump is stopped, EP-1 is deenergized to position V-1, fully closed.

f. Domestic Hot-water Control: T-1, located in the discharge of the convertor, controls V-1 to maintain the desired domestic hot-water temperature. T-2, located in the tank, starts the circulating pump if the temperature rises above a predetermined setting. Aquastat T-3 starts the recirculating pump if the temperature rises above the predetermined setting.

g. Air Supply: During the day, seven-day time clock C-1 is energized. In turn, it energizes EP-1 which positions VA-1 to supply 15 pounds of air to day-night thermostats for day operation. During the night operation, C-1 is deenergized. In turn, it deenergizes EP-1 which positions VA-1 to supply

20 pounds of air to day-night thermostats for night operation.

h. Valve and Mechanical Rooms Exhaust-fan Control: T-1
cycles the fan to maintain a desired temperature of 85°F. A
motorized damper, located at the outside air-intake louver,
interlocks with fan to open when fan is energized and to
close when fan is deenergized. A low-limit thermostat,
located downstream of the damper in the outside air duct,
shuts off fan if temperature drops below 35°F.

i. Fan-coil, Unit-heater, and Cabinet Unit-heater Control: T-1
cycles fans to maintain the space temperature. Aquastat T-2
stops the fans if the supply-water temperature falls below
90°F.

(12) Service and Guarantee: The entire control system shall be
serviced and maintained in first-class condition by the Control
Manufacturer for a period of one (1) year after acceptance at no
extra cost to the Owner. At the end of the one-year guarantee
period, the Control Contractor must be capable of furnishing
emergency service within a normal requested time.

5. DUCTWORK:

A. Duct thickness, duct breaking, duct joints (both longitudinal and
transverse), duct hangers, and all general ductwork shall be in
accordance with the recommendations of "Duct Manual and Sheet
Metal Construction for Ventilating and Air-Conditioning Systems,"
as prepared by the Sheet Metal and Air-Conditioning Contractors'
National Association.

B. Ductwork shall be galvanized steel, manufactured in gauges recommended in the previously mentioned manual.

C. Duct fittings shall be equivalent to Air Distribution Institute Standard fittings as a minimum requirement.

D. Where mains split, splitter dampers must be furnished.

E. All duct joints are to be airtight at 1/2-inch water pressure.

F. Turning Vanes: ____ or ____ air-turns are to be used in all elbows
except round pipes.

G. External Duct Insulation:

(1) Exposed Ductwork: Supply ducts and outside air ducts shall be
insulated on the outside with 1-inch-thick J-M No. 814, nonflex-
ible, SPIN-GLAS fiberglass duct insulation. Insulation shall
have factory-applied facing—FSK (Foil Skrim Kraft). Insulation shall have an average thermal conductivity not to exceed
.23 Btu-inch per square foot per °F per hour at a mean
temperature of 75°F. All insulation shall be applied with edges
tightly butted. Insulation shall be impaled on pins welded to the

duct and secured with speed clips. Pins shall be clipped off close to speed clips. Spacing of pins shall be as required to hold insulation firmly against duct surface, but not less than one pin per square foot. All joints and speed clips shall be sealed with ____ 207 glass fabric set in ____ 30-35, on a 3-inch-wide strip of same facing adhered with ____ 85-20 adhesive.

(2) Concealed Ductwork: Supply ducts and outside air ducts shall be insulated on the outside with 1-inch-thick J-M flexible Microlite or approved equal. Insulation shall be cut slightly longer than the perimeter of the duct to ensure full thickness at corners. The insulation shall have an average thermal conductivity not to exceed 0.25 Btu-inch per square foot per °F per hour at a mean temperature of 75°F. All insulation shall be applied with edges tightly butted. Insulation shall be secured with ____ 85-20 adhesive. Adhesive shall be applied so that insulation conforms to duct surface uniformly and firmly. All joints shall be taped and sealed with 3-inch-wide strips of the facing applied with 85-20 adhesive.

H. Where ducts change shape, enlarge, or reduce, transition is to be made with a maximum angle of 15 degrees, except where it is specifically shown otherwise.

I. Volume-control Duct Dampers and Duct Damper Hardware: Volume-control duct dampers shall be placed as indicated on Drawings and constructed as shown in the *SMACNA Duct Manual,* Plate No. 28 and multiple-plate volume dampers *SMACNA Duct Manual,* Plate No. 29. Vent-lock control hardware shall be appropriate for specific use.

J. Fire Dampers:

(1) Fire dampers shall be installed at locations indicated on the Plans, in full conformance with *NFPA Bulletin No. 90-A,* and in complete accordance with city, state, and local codes.

(2) All fire dampers shall bear label of UL and be listed under the continuing inspection service of UL, where applicable, and shall have been successfully tested for 1-1/2 hours, up to 1800°F. In mounting conditions not in conformance with UL testing, units shall be built in full conformance with standards of the American Insurance Association and the *NFPA Bulletin No. 90-A.*

(3) Fire dampers shall be as manufactured by "Fire-Seal" damper. Dampers shall be provided with interlocking blades to form a solid coating of steel when closed. When open, the blades are to be completely concealed in the head of the frame, allowing total undisturbed air flow with minimum turbulence. Entire assembly shall be galvanized for corrosion resistance and shall conform to ASTM Specification A-90-63-T.

K. Control Dampers: Control dampers shall be furnished to the Mechanical Contractor by the Control Manufacturer and shall be installed in accordance with the Control Manufacturer's instructions in the duct system.

L. Canvas Connections: Canvas connections shall be Vent-Fabric "Vent-Fab," 20-ounce waterproof and fireproof canvas approved by Underwriters' Laboratories. Each air-handling unit return and supply shall be connected with canvas connection.

M. Sawdust Ductwork: Sawdust ductwork shall be round, 16 gauge with fittings as shown. Ductwork shall be equal to ____. All joints shall be welded airtight. Welding frame fume exhaust shall be of same material.

N. Flexible metal exhaust duct shall be equal to ____ or ____.

O. This Contractor shall provide all louvers equal to Air Balance, 4 inches deep, rain and storm check, and of all-aluminum construction. Installation in wall shall be done by the General Contractor.

P. Paint Spray Booth Vent: Paint spray booth vent shall be fabricated of 20-gauge galvanized sheet steel equal to vent manufactured by ____. Vent shall be furnished with a roof flange and weather canopy with rain guard, as manufactured by ____. See Drawings for support detail.

6. WIRING DIAGRAMS:

A. This Contractor shall furnish to the Architect for the Architect's approval five (5) copies of wiring diagrams (i.e., all individual wires diagrammed) showing the complete control wiring system diagram for the heating and ventilating systems. The Contractor shall furnish a framed, glass-protected copy of this wiring diagram for the complete system as installed. This Contractor shall place this wiring diagram in the Equipment Room.

7. TESTS, CLEANING, AND GUARANTEE:

A. This Contractor shall provide all pumps, gauges, and other instruments necessary to perform tests as required.

B. This Contractor shall hydrostatically test the piping of the steam system and hot-water system, to a pressure of 150 percent of the system working pressures. The pressure test shall be for at least eight hours, at which time pressure shall remain constant without additional pumping. After satisfactorily completing tests and before permanently connecting equipment, this Contractor shall blow and flush piping thoroughly so that interiors of all piping shall be free of foreign matter. All traps, strainers, and so on shall be cleaned at the time of flushing.

C. The Contractor shall adjust and regulate the completed system under actual heating and ventilating conditions to produce a satisfactory system. All automatic temperature controls shall be adjusted for satisfactory operation during the first heating and ventilating seasons. This Contractor shall make all necessary adjustments during the first heating and ventilating seasons without additional cost to the Owner. (This does not mean that the Heating and Ventilating Contractor is responsible for any negligence of operation by the Owner.)

D. This Contractor shall furnish complete instructions covering the operation of the heating, ventilating, and control systems.

E. A framed,glass-protected copy of operating instructions is to be placed in the Mechnical Equipment Room by this Contractor.

8. PERFORMANCE TESTS:

A. This Contractor shall provide all necessary instruments to perform tests as required.

B. The Heating and Ventilating Contractor shall conduct the following tests upon completion of installation of the system under the direction of the Architect.

(1) Air-distribution System: Performance test after proper balancing of system, showing air-flow measurements through each supply and return.

(2) Ventilation Systems: Performance test after proper balancing, showing air-flow measurements through each exhaust grille.

(3) Heating System: Operating test of the entire system during cold weather with final adjustment to outdoor design conditions as necessary and to the heating system. In the event the weather prevents testing before acceptance of the building, the building will be accepted subject to successful completion of the preceding tests.

(4) Air-handling Equipment: Air-flow tabulation and listing of outlet and inlet temperatures and heating medium inlet-outlet temperatures.

C. Performance tests shall include the complete heating and ventilating systems and all their parts, including thermostatic and electrical controls, in order to determine that the systems are in compliance with the Contract. Tests shall show that the heating and ventilating systems are acceptable before the installation is approved for acceptance by the Owner. The Contractor shall furnish the Owner with four (4) copies of the findings of the approved texts, including tabulation of all readings for the job and computations. Final payment to the Contractor, less an amount to cover the cost of certain tests, shall be made when weather conditions have caused postponement of certain tests.

D. The heating units shall be checked for performance to determine that the Specifications are met in every respect.

E. This Contractor shall guarantee all materials and equipment installed by him, and all workmanship for a period of one (1) year after final acceptance of the heating work against all defects occurring during that period.

F. The heating and ventilating systems shall be tested under operating conditions for a period of five eight-hour days or as necessary to demonstrate that the requirements of the Contract are fulfilled.

G. This Contractor shall adjust and regulate the completed system under actual heating conditions to produce a satisfactory system. All automatic temperature controls shall be adjusted for satisfactory operation in the first heating season. This Contractor shall make all necessary adjustments in the first heating season without additional cost to Owner. (This does not mean that the Heating Contractor is responsible for any negligence in operation by Owner.)

9. MARKING OF CONTROLS, VALVES, AND ELECTRIC CONTROLS:

A. All valves, electric controls, and electric starters and switches are to be marked with permanent metal tags. The tags shall be black-enameled finish with engraved, white-enameled letters that are at least 1/4-inch high.

B. The location in ceiling of all damper electric controls and balancing valves and duct-balancing dampers shall be marked above the ceiling with tag, as previously described and screwed to the metal ceiling runners at each location.

10. TEMPORARY HEATING:

A. The General Contractor shall be responsible for furnishing temporary heating throughout the period of construction of the building.

11. PAINTING:

A. Factory-painted equipment and materials shall receive primer coat and two coats of enamel, factory applied.

B. Factory-painted equipment shall be touched up as necessary and where factory-painted color does not match the Architect's color scheme in finished area.

C. Factory-primed equipment and materials shall be painted with two coats of enamel in accordance with the Painting Section of these Specifications. This paint shall be applied by the Painting Contractor, who shall use experienced painters for this purpose in accordance with the Painting Section of these Specifications.

D. Unpainted equipment and materials shall receive one coat of primer and two coats of enamel in accordance with the requirements of the Painting Section of these Specifications for exposed metal. This paint shall be applied by the Painting Contractor, who shall use experienced painters for this purpose in accordance with the Painting Section of these Specifications.

E. The inside of all ductwork visible in finished building shall be painted dull black, the paint to be applied in accordance with painting Section of the Specifications.

F. All colors shall be as approved by the Architect.

12. TEMPORARY POWER:

A. The General Contractor shall provide, as required, 208/120-volt, single-phase, 60-hertz temporary power for use of the Heating and Ventilating Contractor.

13. LUBRICATION PRIOR TO START-UP:

A. Prior to start-up, the Heating and Ventilating Contractor shall fully lubricate all equipment under this Section in accordance with the respective manufacturer's recommendations.

17
HVAC Drafting

The smaller HVAC contractors have seldom found it necessary to set up a complete drafting department in their firm. However, when the work load begins to increase, many residential contractors have found it desirable to furnish a certain number of layout drawings to cut down on the amount of supervision necessary to complete the various projects. In doing so, good management is extremely important to keep expenses down, and to make the practice worthwhile.

The residential HVAC contractor should strive to keep the board time to a minimum, yet increase the understanding of the drawings by field personnel. All this is possible by incorporating certain techniques within the drafting/design department.

Drafting time may be kept to a minimum by using one or all of the following drafting aids: stick-ons printed with symbol lists, equipment schedules, HVAC details, and other frequently used data; easy-to-draw mechanical symbols and construction details to better convey the information to the workers on the job; mechanical lettering machines for notes on drawings rather than hand lettering; and special time-saving drafting instruments and supplies.

Most of these drafting practices will find immediate use in all mechanical drafting departments—even those turning out a minimal amount of drawings. However, some of the more expensive equipment can only pay for itself if a sufficient amount of drafting is done.

THE VARI TYPER

The Vari Typer is a mechanical-lettering device that reduces the time involved in lettering drawings where neat, printed-looking results are desired. The machine is particularly valuable for filling in bills of materials, specifications, and notes, as well as for inserting dimensional figures. It is operated much like a conventional electric typewriter except that the carriage will accept drawing paper of practically any size, and the type compares to regular drafting-lettering styles in a variety of different sizes. Since this machine produces uniform, clean, and sharp composition of type directly on the tracing, it is especially useful for lettering drawings which are to be microfilmed.

A typical application of this machine would be as follows: The draftsman, using lines and symbols, draws all necessary data on the tracing paper in the usual way. All notes, dimensions, and similar data requiring lettering are omitted. A print of the tracing is made (for reference) and then all notes, dimensions, and other data are written in longhand on the reference print in the location desired. This is normally done using a colored pencil or pen. The typist then attaches the reference print on a wall directly behind the lettering machine for easy viewing, inserts the original tracing in the carriage of the Vari Typer, and types the data supplied by the draftsman. The draftsman may also use a code to indicate the size type to be used for each note or dimension.

For firms requiring this type of lettering machine, they can be leased for around $100 per month. Many suppliers also have a lease/purchase plan; that is, you lease the machine, say, for three years, at the end of that time, the machine is owned outright. Free maintenance of the machine is usually included during the leasing period.

USING CONVENTIONAL TYPEWRITER FOR LETTERING

Many residential HVAC contractors may not turn out enough drawings to warrant the leasing or purchasing of a Vari Typer. However, much board time can be saved by grouping as many notes as possible in one location on the drawing. Then have these notes typed on stick-on paper which will be attached to the original tracing.

The typewriter stick-on method is utilized by having the draftsman complete all lines, symbols, dimensions, and short notes in the usual manner. However, space is left on the drawing to attach a sheet of stick-on notes. Then, rather than hand lettering long notes at various locations on the drawings, the draftsman letters "SEE NOTE No. 1." The typist then types the note on stick-on paper for attachment to the tracing at a later date.

When using this method, it is best to have the sheet of typewritten notes appear on the same sheet to which they apply. Sometimes, however, this is not possible, due to either the length of the note or the amount of line drawings on the tracing paper. In this case, all notes for the project can be attached to an extra sheet of tracing paper, usually at the end of the set of drawings. For example, if the project requires three drawing sheets for the mechanical design, a fourth sheet may be added for the notes. Then, where long notes are necessary on the other sheets, the draftsman letters, "SEE NOTE No. _____ ON SHEET M-4."

Where it is desired to have the written specifications incorporated into the set of drawings rather than in a separate booklet, this same method may be used. The specifications are typed on a certain size stick-on paper and then attached (in proper order) to the drawing sheets for reproduction on a white or blue printer. They may then be secured to the set of drawings, keeping all construction documents together.

TIME-SAVING MECHANICAL SYMBOLS

Although most designers attempt to use the symbols adopted by the American National Standards Institute, most consulting engineering firms, as well as mechanical contracting-design firms, frequently modify these standard symbols to fit a particular need. When standard symbols are modified, it becomes necessary to provide a symbol list or legend on the drawings so they may be interpreted by the workers using the drawings. Drawing and hand lettering such a symbol list on each set of drawings for different projects can be highly time consuming. Again, these lists may be duplicated on stick-on paper and merely attached to each new set of drawings—taking only minutes to do.

Selecting the proper symbol for a given item on an HVAC drawing should be given careful consideration. Ideally, the selected list of symbols should be:

1. Easy to draw.
2. Easily interpreted by workers.
3. Sufficient for most applications.

Obviously, the first item affects the draftsman's board time. Certainly all mechanical draftsmen would not think of using symbols for which templates are not available, but even with templates, certain modifications of the standard symbols can reduce board time considerably.

The second item, "easily interpreted by workers," not only affects labor on the job but also the time of the draftsman and other office personnel. To illustrate, a misinterpretation of a given symbol on a set of working drawings can mean a costly change to the contractor; if the workers cannot understand the meaning of a symbol, it means time lost by the workers as well as time wasted in calling the draftsman or designer to get an interpretation.

"Sufficient for most applications" as the final item means just what it says. It would be impractical to spend hours or days organizing what you consider to be a good modified symbol list, and then find out that it can be used only on one out of ten projects. The list in Chapter 2 of this book represents a good set of HVAC symbols and meets the previously mentioned criteria. Note the statement at the top of the list which states:

> NOTE: THESE ARE STANDARD SYMBOLS AND MAY NOT ALL
> APPEAR ON THE PROJECT DRAWING; HOWEVER, WHENEVER
> THE SYMBOLS ON THE PROJECT DRAWINGS OCCUR, THE ITEM
> SHALL BE PROVIDED AND INSTALLED.

This list of mechanical symbols should suffice for most mechanical drawings involving HVAC installations. When additional information needs to be included, a new symbol may be used, or a note may be placed on the drawing.

MECHANICAL DETAILS

Mechanical detail drawings of a separate item or portion of a mechanical system giving a complete and exact description of how workers are to install a certain portion of the system have been used for quite some time. Many firms, however, cut these details to a bare minimum due to the amount of drafting time required to produce most of them.

Much board time can be saved by having often-used details duplicated on stick-on paper and then filed. Whenever the detail is required, the backing paper is removed from the stick-on, and the detail drawing may then be applied to the drawing sheet.

Those details which are not used very often may be drawn freehand to a large scale, using scaled ruled paper. At full size, these freehand drawings look rather sloppy. However, when reduced on a reduction copier to 1/4 their original size, they will appear to have been drawn with a straight-edge and templates if the draftsman uses reasonable care on the enlarged version. This method has cut the time required for mechanical details in half.

The reduction in drawing time required for these detail drawings allows the firm to show more of them on a project, reducing both the labor and supervision time on the project as complex systems will be better understood by all concerned.

The draftsman should also make use of schedules on the working drawings whenever practical. When properly organized and presented, schedules are not only powerful time-saving devices for the draftsman and designer, but they also save the specification writer and the workers on the job much valuable time.

MAKING USE OF NEW TOOLS AND DEVELOPMENTS

Always look for new tools and supplies that will lessen board time while turning out neater and more accurate drawings. Templates, for example, are one of the best methods. One such template is the "Ductwork Fitting Template Timesaver" which has 1/8-inch scaled openings for elbows, turning vanes, damper blades, air outlets, splitter dampers, section arrowheads, and return air flow. This template alone will save the HVAC draftsman much valuable time in laying out and drawing duct systems on project drawings. The newer computer-aided drafting methods save even more time.

The many possibilities are almost endless, and we have but touched upon them. This material, however, should be sufficient to set drafting departments in the right direction.

DRAFTING FACILITIES

The drafting facilities also play an important role in productivity. The draftsmen should have a place to work in the contractor's office (just like the estimator), where they will not be disturbed by the usual office routine, such as the coming and going of salesmen and general shop activities.

A separate drafting room should be provided and, if possible, separate rooms for each draftsman/designer. The room should be provided with good illumination, heating, and air-conditioning facilities, and painted a pleasing color. A dingy, poorly lighted or ventilated drafting room is not conducive to the preparation of good drawings.

For further information on HVAC drafting techniques, obtain a copy of *Practical Drafting for the HVAC Trades* by John Traister, and published by Prentice Hall, Inc., Englewood Cliffs, NJ 07632.

COMPUTER-AIDED HVAC DRAFTING
TECHNIQUES: AUTOCAD

AutoCAD is a computer-aided drafting and design system that runs on many personal and professional computers, bringing the benefits of a high-performance CAD facility within the range of even the smallest drawing office. It can be used to great advantage when drawing or plotting duct layouts on construction documents. Furthermore, this system is suitable for a wide variety of applications, and is used by engineers and designers of every discipline. AutoCAD may be used to produce virtually any kind of drawing: mechanical, architectural, electrical, schematics, and flow charts of every description.

In general, AutoCAD handles drawings the way a word processor handles text. Drawings of any size are created and edited interactively, using a digitizer or mouse to point to the screen or tablet menu items and to move the drawing cursor around the screen. Once stored on a floppy or hard disk, the drawings may be plotted out at any scale, as required, and can be used freely as components in other drawings.

The basic AutoCAD drawing elements are lines, traces of any width, arcs, circles, solids, and inserts of other drawings. Drawings can be annotated with text of any size, position, and angle, from a variety of fonts and styles. Rectangular or circular repeats of objects such as elbows, air ducts, air-handling units, and the like can be generated automatically.

Drawing elements can be positioned on the screen by "freehand" pointing, with or without the use of GRID, SNAP, ORTHO, and other drawing aids, and in most cases they can be interactively "dragged" into position. Exact dimensions or position requirements can be entered through the keyboard, expressed either by absolute S,Y coordinates, lengths or angles, or as relative S and Y displacements or distance and angle from the last point.

Existing paper drawings can be copied into the system, in sections if necessary, using a digitizing tablet. A comprehensive set of editing commands allows drawn objects of any complexity to be moved, copied, repeated, changed, mirrored, rotated, partially or completely erased, and vertically or horizontally scaled. Any angular corner can be replaced by a fillet.

Drawings can be created on an unlimited number of layers, each with user-defined alphanumeric names. Different layers can be displayed and plotted with different noncontinuous line types, in different colors if the system's display and/or plotter allow. Layers can be turned on and off in any combination, providing selective display or plotting of drawings as if on transparent overlays.

Cross-hatching can be generated automatically at any angle and pitch, either from a library of more than 40 standard patterns, or from user-defined additions.

AutoCAD's dimensioning facility can automatically create linear, angular, and radial dimensions, with or without tolerances. Dimensions, data input, and a continuously updated display of current coordinates can be expressed in either metric units (0 to 8 decimal places), scientific/ exponential notation, or feet and inches. Angles can be displayed in degrees with decimal fractions, or in degrees, minutes, and seconds.

AutoCAD stores drawing data internally in full floating-point format, with an accuracy of 14 significant places and a ratio of over one trillion to one between the smallest and largest object. Accuracy of the final plotted output is limited only by the plotter resolution, not by the more limited display screen resolution.

DRAWING AIDS

An optional alignment GRID, with equal or different horizontal and vertical spacings, can be turned on and off at any time. SNAP can automatically align objects to the nearest grid point, and the grid can be rotated and the snap origin relocated. ORTHO forces lines and traces to run vertically and horizontally, or at corresponding angles if the grid has been rotated. Isometric drawings can be easily generated using AutoCAD's isometric GRID and SNAP facility.

A geometric or object snap locks drawing elements onto reference points on existing objects: endpoint of line or arc, midpoint of line or arc, center of arc or circle, quadrant of arc or circle, intersection of lines, arcs, or circles, insertion point of block, shape, or text, perpendicular from last point to line, arc, or circle, tangent from last point to arc or circle.

AXIS displays ''ruler lines'' along the edge of the graphics screen, with tick marks for desired spacing.

AutoCAD's bidirectional zoom facility allows drawing modification at any level of detail. Particular windows onto a drawing can be saved and later recalled as named views. The viewing window can be moved in any direction by the PAN command.

For jobs such as tracing in maps or contours, the system can be set into SKETCH mode, allowing totally freehand sketching on the screen via the digitizer or mouse.

A screen status line displays current X,Y coordinates, the current layer name, and the status of SNAP and ORTHO. While lines are being drawn interactively, with AutoCAD's RUBBER BAND line display, the status line switches to show the length and angle of the line instead of X,Y coordinates.

The LIST command displays the coordinates and other database details, of any objects in the drawing. Distance and area commands measure and display the distance and angle between two points, plus the area and perimeter of a polygon marked by any number of points.

STATUS reports on the current state of a number of drawing parameters, such as overall size, size of current window, base point, snap, grid, and axis spacing and status, current layer name, and color and line type. The limits, or overall size of a drawing, are set by default when it is first created, but may be expanded or contracted at any time.

The FILES command allows full or selective viewing of a disk directory, and renaming or deletion of files, without exiting AutoCAD.

Text styles give great flexibility for producing compressed or expanded, obliqued, mirrored or upside-down text. The five standard text fonts provided include italic and vertical; successive lines of text can be either left or right justified, centered, or scaled to precisely fit a particular space. QTEXT turns on quick text mode to optimize display speed on drawings containing substantial amounts of text.

AutoCAD includes powerful facilities for manipulating drawing data and exchanging them with other programs.

Blocks containing any selection of drawn objects can be designated and optionally written out to disk. Any number of attributes can be attached to these blocks. Attributes are text items for which the user defines the name, prompt, and default value, if any, and are typically such things as serial number, cost, power consumption and/or heat output, date of purchase, manufacturer code, individual's name and telephone extension.

Attributes may be visible or invisible on the drawing, and constant or variable. Whenever a block with variable attributes is inserted, AutoCAD automatically prompts for the values. Attribute values can be selectively edited, globally or individually.

Once a drawing containing blocks with attributes is completed, details of all or some of the attributes can be automatically extracted in a format that can be fed directly into a standard database management program for data analysis, sorting, or specialized calculations. This makes it exceptionally easy to extract component listings for producing bills of material and costings, calculate total power consumption or heat output in a machine room, produce a sorted list of staff with new internal telephone extensions after an office reorganization, and do stress analysis or other engineering calculations on assemblies.

HARDWARE

If you have a personal or professional computer, you already own the most expensive part of a CAD system. AutoCAD requires a minimum of 384K, but for the most satisfactory performance Autodesk recommends 512K RAM and hard disk.

AutoCAD also supports an exceptionally wide range of plotters, digitizing tablets, mice, and other pointing devices. The list of more than 50 devices includes digitizers and single or multipen plotters from A to E size, and from various industries.

On some professional or personal computers, AutoCAD can be run using either a monochrome or a color display, with screen resolution and size options in certain cases. Whether drawings are created on a monochrome or color screen, a multipen plotter always allows multicolor plots, using AutoCAD's layer facility.

All displays, plotters, and pointing devices for which AutoCAD software drivers have been written are rapidly and easily installed using AutoCAD's menu-driven configurator. This makes it easy to change or add devices at any time.

AUTOCAD APPLICATIONS

There are several application software that may be used with the basic AutoCAD program. One of the most useful for HVAC applications is the AutoCAD AEC architectural package. This program is suited to the specific needs of design professionals in architecture, engineering design, and facilities planning and management. Users can complete sets of drawings easily and quickly by selecting objects and commands from the Master Template Menu.

Users can draw one wall at a time, or two to three walls simultaneously to create a series of rooms. They can create and modify schematic diagrams, and then have them converted instantly to floor plans. Walls, rooms, and stairs can be generated automatically. Clean up of corners, intersections, and walls is automatic as well.

This system has shapes and symbols in its memory carrying user-defined specifications that can be extracted and read into a database system such as Lotus 1-2-3 or dBASE III for quick, accurate generation of contract documents. Because drawings are stored on hard and/or floppy disks, users have compact, consolidated archives of their drawings for later reference.

With CAD/camera system, existing paper drawings can be transferred into a CAD system within minutes. These transfers can then be modified and reprinted instantly.

Typical drawing symbols can be captured and made available for insertion in a drawing in less than a minute. A-size engineering drawings take approximately fifteen minutes to one hour; B-size drawings may take a few hours to complete.

For new users, a drawing exercise program is available that leads the user through the application of the AutoCAD commands to the completion of a drawing of a gear and cam assembly. The exercise also includes 3D visualization, blocks and inserts, attributes, and prototype drawings.

If the contractor already has a computer that will handle the AutoCAD software, then the basic system can be set up for less than $5,000. However, when starting from scratch, this figure can easily double.

The HVAC contractor who needs to turn out a large amount of drawings each year will probably come out ahead by utilizing an AutoCAD system. Those turning out a minimal amount of drawings will do better with another system.

MACINTOSH PLUS

The Macintosh Plus computer is very reasonable in price, and with the proper software, many drafting functions can be accomplished. A plotter or laser printer pushes the price of a complete system up to the $8,000 to $10,000 bracket, but if a sufficient amount of work is done, this expense will quickly be absorbed.

First consider the amount of drafting done or projected each year, and talk to a salesperson about the installation that would best fit your needs. Then weigh the results to see whether you really need a computer-aided drafting system.

Index

Accountmaster 8/16 (HVAC software), 96
Advertising, 249
Air, combustion, 7–8
Air conditioning (*see also* Cooling calculation)
Air-conditioning system: add-on, 141
Air density: equipment, effect, 80
Air-distribution ducts: damper, 155
    duct design, 154
    dimensions, 154
    duct layout, 154
    low static friction loss, 154
Air mixture, 79
Air-volume extractors, 193
Ambient-compensated bimetallic overload relay, 223

Architect's scales, 103
ASHRAE Guide, 157
Association dues and subscriptions, 249
AutoCAD application, 307–308
AutoCAD computer-aided drafting techniques, 304–305
Awning, 116

Balancing instruments: anemometer, 237
    pilot tube, 237
    short method, 236
    test and balancing procedures, 235–36
    velometer and anemometer: testing procedure, 236–37
Baseboard radiation system, 130–33

Baseboard radiation system
(*cont.*)
nonzoned single-loop system,
131
BASIC (computer language), 91
Bimetallic overload relay, 223
Boiler room, 128
Boss payroll management
(HVAC software), 97
Boss time billing system (HVAC
software), 97
Branch take-off:
air volume extractor, 193
fiberglass duct, 193
sheet-metal ductwork, 193
British thermal units (Btu), 8,
126
Btu per hour, heat loss, 103
Btu per pound of air, 80
Building energy analysis
program, 101
Bypass process, 79–80

Calorific value of fuel, 8
formula, 8–9
Carbon, 7, 8
Carbon dioxide, 7, 8
Cardfile (HVAC software),
99–100
Ceiling, 121–22
Ceiling diffuser, 170, 172–73
Central air-conditioning system:
do-it-yourself kit, 141–53
Central electric furnace:
advantage, 204
disadvantage, 204
operate, 205
Central heating unit, 5
fuel used, 5
Circular equivalent of
rectangular duct, 164,
(*figs*) 164–65, 166
Colorimeter, 8

Combination heating/cooling
unit, 5
Combustion, 7
air required, 7–8
carbon, 7, 8
carbon dioxide, 7, 8
hydrogen, 7, 8
incomplete, 8–9
nitrogen, 7, 8
oxygen, 7, 8
Complete combustion, 7, 8
Computer-aided HVAC drafting
technique:
AutoCAD, 304–305
Computer estimating, 254
HVAC computer estimating
firms, 254–55
Computer hardware, 306–307
Computer programs:
BASIC, calculate gross pay for
employees, (fig.) 260–61
printout, (fig.) 262
BASIC, filing financial record,
263–65
printout, (fig.), 266
drawing aids, 305–306
glossary software, 272–73
for HVAC, 90–91
for HVAC office management,
259–66
language, 91
BASIC, 91
mailing list, 267
BASIC program, (fig.),
267–70
preliminary planning, 91–92
software for HVAC, 96–101,
270–72
writing program for HVAC,
93–95
Computer software for HVAC:
Accountmaster 8/16, 96
boss payroll management, 97
boss time billing system, 97

building energy analysis
program, 101
cardfile, 99–100
construction management, 98
cost-acumen, 100
eagle software:
money decisions, 100
executive package, 96
E-Z Bid II, 98
4-Point graphics, 96
Labeltronics system 1000, 101
Labeltronics system 2000, 101
Lotus 1-2-3, 99, 270
Marketfax, 100
Microlink II, 99
MICS/1 job costing and
billing, 97–98
miscellaneous packages,
271–72
Notebook, 100
PC asynchronous
communication, 98
PC data base, 99
PC multiplan, 99
Peachtree, 270
Peachtree: calendar
management, 100
Peachtree: job costing, 97
Peachtree: peachpay payroll,
97
residential/commercial
services, 98
statistician, 99
TK!Solverpack-mechanical
engineering, 96
total accounting system, 97
Visi On, 270
Condensing unit, mounting, (kit),
143–44
Construction management
(HVAC software), 98
Contracting form, 254
Control circuit transformer,
213

Control diagram:
abbreviation, 64
symbols, 64, (fig) 64–65
Controlling equipment:
drum switch, 232
float switch, 233
limit switch, 232
pressure switch, 233
push-button station, 232
snap switch, 233
timer and timing relay, 232
Control relay:
purpose, 215
(see also Relay)
Converting to heating/cooling
system:
add-on, 141
basic steps, 142
cost, 142
do-it-yourself kit, 141–53
kit parts, 142–43
principle in converting, 141
proper size and type, 142
Cooling and dehumidifying,
80–81
latent heat, 81
sensible heat, 81
Cooling and humidifying, 80–81
psychromatic chart, 81
Cooling calculation, 114
ceiling, 121–22
central unit, 123
floors, 122–23
walls and doors, 119–21
window air-conditioning unit,
123
windows, 114, 116–19
Cooling coil, installing, (kit),
144–49
Cooling equipment:
selection, 123
Cooling system balance:
procedure for testing, 237–38
use of BASIC program, 237

Cooling tower, 81
Cost-acumen (HVAC software),
 100

Defective goods, 250
Delivery cost, 250
Depreciation, 250
Designing HVAC system, 11–12
 Architect's scales, 11–12
 components, 11
 floor plan, 11–12
Detail total quantity estimate,
 239
Detail unit quantity estimate, 239
Dewpoint temperature, 72, 73, 78
 how to determine, 74–75, 76
Diffuser:
 ceiling, 172–73
 location, 171–72
Do-it-yourself control
 air-conditioning kit,
 141–42
 checklist, 152
 installing the cooling coil,
 144–49
 installing the electric wiring,
 152
 installing the refrigerant
 tubing, 149–51
 mounting the condensing unit,
 143–44
 start-up procedure, 153
Doors, 121
 (*see also* Wall and door)
Double pole, double-throw
 (DPDT) switch, 64,
 (*fig.*) 65
Double pole, single-throw
 (DPST) switch, 64, (*fig*)
 65
Drafting:
 AutoCAD application, 307–308
 computer-aided technique, 304
 autoCAD, 304–305

computer drawing aids,
 305–306
computer hardware, 306–307
facilities, 303
Macintosh Plus, 308
mechanical details, 302–303
new tools and developments,
 303
symbols, 301–302
typewriter for lettering,
 300–301
vari typer, 299–308
Drum switch, 232
Dry-bulb temperature, 72
 of air mixture, 79
 calculating (outside) heating
 loads, 105
 how to calculate, 74, 76
Duct:
 combined, installation, 177
 fabricating fiberglass, 179–88
 installation, 174–76
 materials, 174–76
 planning installation, 177–78
 prefabricated round, 176
 rectangular, 177
 round, 176–77
 suspending rectangular,
 188–93
Duct design, 154
 architectural drawings, 155
 computer use in sizing, 156
 dimensions, 156
 location, 156
 size and shape, 156
Duct system, 114
Ductwork sizing:
 equal friction method, 157
 static regain method, 157
Dunham-Bush, 194

Eagle software:
 money decisions, 100

Electrical conductors:
 sizing, 213
 VA capacity equation, 214
Electrical diagram, 17
 component, 17
 flow, 17, (*fig.*) 17
 schematic wiring, 17, (*fig.*) 18
 single-line block, 17, (*fig.*) 18
 symbols, 17
Electrical symbols, 17–19, 64
 schematic drawing, (*fig.*) 19
Electrical wiring:
 ground, 139–40
 hot-water system, 138–40
 nameplate information, 139
 National Electric Code, 139
Electrical wiring diagrams, 67–69
Electric baseboard heater:
 advantage, 5, 83
 disadvantage, 5, 84
 mounting, 83–84
 wall discoloration, reasons, 84
Electric furnace, 87–88, (*fig.*) 87
 compact electric boiler, 87
 design, 87
 size, 87
 vertical model, 87
Electric heat:
 baseboard heaters, 83
 combination heating and
  cooling unit, 86
 expense, 83
 floor insert convection
  heater, 86
 forced-air wall heaters, 85
 furnace, 87
 infrared heaters, 85
 kick-space heaters, 86
 radiant ceiling heaters, 84
 radiant heating cable, 86
 radiant heating panels, 85
 units, 83, (*fig.*) 84
Electric heating unit, 204
 central electric furnace, 204

electric service, 205
 embedded heat cable, 205
 heating cable, 206–210
 heat panels, 205
 heat pump, 204
 infrared heater, 205
 installing combination units,
  205
 installing in existing structure,
  205
 installing in radiant heating
  cable, 206
 kick-space heater, 205
 through-wall combination
  heating/cooling unit, 205
Electric infrared heater, 85
 advantage, 85
 design, 85
 installation, 85
Electric kick-space heater, 86
 advantage, 86
Electric motor:
 overload protection, 221
Electric schematic diagram, 66
Electric wiring, installing, (kit),
  152
Electronic control, 233
Electronic graphic system,
  17–19, 64
 control diagram, 64
Enclosure:
 NEMA 1 general purpose, 225
 NEMA 3 dusttight, raintight,
  226
 NEMA 3R rainproof, sleet
  resistant, 226
 NEMA 4 watertight, 226
 NEMA 4X watertight,
  corrosion resistant, 226
 NEMA 7 hazardous location,
  Class I, 226
 NEMA 9 hazardous location,
  Class II, 226
 NEMA 12 industrial use, 226

Enclosure (*cont.*)
  NEMA 13 oiltight, dusttight,
    226
  protective requirements, 225
Energy source:
  coal, 1
  electricity, 1
  gas, 1
  oil, 1
  residential type, 1–2
  solar energy, 1
  wood, 1
Enthalpy, 80
Equal friction method:
  friction loss chart, 157, (*fig*)
    158
  rectangular main duct sizing,
    158–64
  round duct size, 158–59
Estimating forms, 254
Estimator qualifications, 240
Evaporative cooling, 78, 81
  (*see also* Cooling and
    Humidifying)
Executive page (HVAC
  software), 96
E-Z Bid II (HVAC software), 98

Fan-driven forced-air unit
  heater, 6
Fiberglass duct, 193
  fabrication, 179–88
Float switch, 233
Floor insert convection
  heater, 86
  advantages, 86
  installation, 86
Floor plan, 10–11
  heat loss, 103, 104
Floors, 122–23
  classification, 122
Flow diagram, 17, (*fig*) 17
Forced air heating, converting to
  heating/cooling, 141–43

Forced-air wall heater, 85–86
  type, 86
Forced hot-water system, 124,
  126, (*figs*) 125, 126, 127
  direct-return system, 127, (*fig*)
    128
  one-pipe design, 127
  reverse-return system, 127,
    (*fig*) 128
  two-pipe design, 127
4-Point graphics (HVAC
  software), 96
Fractional-horsepower manual
  starter, 217
Friction loss, 156–57
  excessive conditions causing,
    157
Friction loss chart, 157–58,
  (*fig.*) 158
Fuel:
  electric heat, 83
  heating equipment, 83
  types of, 1
Fuel heating system, 103
Fuses, uses, 222

Geographical heating loads
  calculation, 105, (*table*),
    106–109
Grains of moisture, 72, 73, 74
  how to calculate, 75
Graphical symbols for electrical
  diagrams, (*fig.*) 20–63
Gravity-flow heating system, 124
  (*fig.*) 125
Grille, 178
  capacity and throw chart, (*fig.*)
    172
  location, 170
  air patterns, 171
Grille and register sizing chart,
  175

Head pressure, 126–27

Heat, amount of, 8
Heat and humidity process, 78
Heat gain calculations:
  chart, shaded and unshaded,
    (*fig.*) 117
  shade line factor, 117
  window, 116–19
Heat gain chart, 117
Heating, ventilating, and
    air-conditioning (HVAC):
  residential construction, 2
Heating and cooling equipment:
  factors to consider, 82
  selection, 82
Heating and cooling system, 141
Heating and cooling unit,
    combination, 86–87
  advantage, 86
  selection, 87
Heating and humidifying, 80–81
  recirculating water spray, 81
  steam-water heater, 81
Heating cable:
  inspecting and testing cable,
    209
  installation in plaster ceiling,
    206–208
  calculation, 206
  installation procedure, 206–209
  installing in concrete floor, 208
  other heating uses:
    deicing roof and gutters, 210
    heating soil in hotbed, 210
    ice and snow removal, 210
    protect exposed water pipes,
      210
  proper voltage, 208
  proper wire size, 208
  repairing broken cable, 209
    thermoplastic tape, 209–210
  use of ohmmeter, 209
Heating calculation forms, (*figs.*)
    110, 112, 113
Heating calculations, 102

Heating equipment, 114
  type of fuel, 83
Heating loads calculating, 105,
    (*table*) 106–109
  geographical, 105
Heating system, 129–34
  baseboard radiation, 130–32
  best fuel, 103
  construction features of house,
    82–83
  good features, 102
  head pressure, 126–27
  heat loss, 126
  hot water, 129–30, 132–34
  hot-water combination, 134
  installation, 135–37
  pressure drop, 126
  size of equipment, 103
  type to use, 103
Heating system balance, 234–35
  fan cut-out switch, 235
  instruments, 235–37
Heat loss, 102
  determining, 126
  rate of, 126
  through roof, walls, floor, 126
Heat loss calculations, 102
  design conditions:
    inside, 105
    outside, 105
  duct system, 114
  floor plan, 103
    dimensions, 104
    outside perimeter, 104
  formulas, 110, 111
  heating calculation form,
    (*figs.*) 110, 112, 113
  heating equipment, 114
  how to, 105, 110–11
  information needed, 104, 105
  measures of rate:
    Btu per hour, 103
    in watts, 103
  steps in determining, 103

Heat-loss estimating form, 103,
  (*fig.*) 104
Heat loss formula:
  Btu, 103
  watts, 103
Heat measurement:
  British thermal unit (Btu), 126
Heat pump, 5
  advantage, 204
  disadvantage, 204
  operate, 205
High-velocity heating/cooling
    system, 6, 194, (*fig.*) 195
  adjustable damper, 200–201
  air outlets or terminators, 199,
    201
  components, 194
    blower coil unit, 195
    condensing unit, 195, (*fig.*)
      196
    controls, 196
    duct heater, 195
    plenum duct, 195
    return-air assembly, 194
    supply-air ducts, 196
    supply-air outlets plate,
      196
  condensing unit, 201–202
  controls, 202
  design, sizing, 196
  installation, 197
  layout, 196–97
  mounting blower unit, 197
    vibration isolators, 197
  outlets, 199–200, (*figs.*) 199,
    200, 201
  plenum duct, 198–99
  power wiring, 201–202
  single-story building, 202,
    (*fig.*) 197
  two-story building, 202
    two methods of installation,
      203
  tubing, 199

Hot-water baseboard heating:
  disadvantage, 5
  fuel source, 5
  temperature selection, 5
Hot-water boiler, 133
Hot-water combination unit:
  disadvantage, 134
  installation, 134
  operating cost, 134
Hot-water heating, 124–26
  direct-return system, 127,
    (*fig.*) 128
  forced hot-water system, 124,
    126, (*figs.*) 125, 126, 127
  gravity flow, 124, (*fig.*) 125
  reverse-return system, 127,
    (*fig.*) 128
  steam heating, 124, (*fig.*) 125
Hot-water system, 89, 129–34
  boiler, 89
  control buttons, 140
  cost, 89
  disadvantage, 89, 133
  electrical wiring, 138–40
  filter, 140
  installing unit, 135
    wall thickness, 135, (*figs.*)
      136
  location, 89
  operating and wiring diagram,
    (*fig.*) 88
  piping for steam or hot water,
    137–38
  temperature selection, 89
  zone thermostat, 89
HVAC:
  computer programming, 90
    preliminary planning, 91–9?
  contractor's office functions,
    256–59
  contractor's office
    management, 256–59
  writing computer program,
    93–95

HVAC computer software,
    96–101
Accountmaster 8/16, 96
boss payroll management, 97
boss time billing system, 97
building energy analysis
    program, 101
cardfile, 99–100
construction management, 98
cost-acumen, 100
eagle software, money
    decisions, 100
executive package, 96
E-Z Bid II, 98
4-point graphics, 96
Labeltronics system 1000, 101
Labeltronics system 2000,
    101
Lotus 1-2-3, 99
Marketfax, 100
Microlink II, 99
MICS/1 job costing and
    billing, 97–98
Notebook, 100
PC asynchronous
    communication, 98
PC data base, 99
PC multiplan, 99
Peachtree: calendar
    management, 100
Peachtree: job costing, 97
Peachtree: peachpay
    payroll, 97
residential/commercial
    service, 98
statistician, 99
TK!Solverpack—mechanical
    engineering, 96
total accounting system, 97
HVAC controls, 216
fractional-horsepower manual
    starter, 217
integral-horsepower manual
    starter, 217

integral-horsepower starters
    with low-voltage
    protection, 218
manual motor-starting switch,
    217
uses of, 217
operations of, 216
two- and three-pole starter,
    217–18
type and size, 216
HVAC design
psychrometric, 72
HVAC designer/engineer:
preliminary conference, 10–11
air conditioning, 10
ductwork, type of, 10
heating system, 10
inlets and outlets, 10
temporary electric
    facilities, 10
HVAC drafting, (see Drafting)
HVAC drawing, 69–71
plumbing, 69–71
HVAC estimates:
computer estimating, 254
HVAC computer estimating
    firms, 254–55
contracting forms, 254
detail total quantity, 239
detail unit quantity, 239
direct job expense:
bid bonds, 247–49
depreciation and
    consumption of tools,
    247–48
drawings, 247–48
freight, 247
inspection fees, 247–49
job truck, 247, 248
labor address for payroll,
    247–49
licenses, 247–49
permits, 247–49
supervision, 247

HVAC estimates (*cont.*)
errors, 240–41
proper forms, 240
mathematical, 241
estimating forms, 254
estimator qualifications, 240
four installation situation
groups, 245
installation variables, 244–45
labor cost, 244
new versus existing building,
244
material cost, 246
pricing, 247
overhead costs, 249–52
advertising, 249
association dues and
subscriptions, 249
automobiles and trucks, 249
bad debts, 249
charitable contributions, 250
collections, 250
defective, lost, obsolete, or
stolen goods, 250
delivery costs, 250
depreciation, 250
insurance, 250
interest, 250
legal and accounting fee, 250
lost production labor, 250
office expenses, 250
rent, 250
repairs and maintenance,
251
salaries and commissions,
251
sales discount, 251
small tools, 251
taxes, 251
travel and transportation,
251
telephone, 251
miscellaneous, 251–52

profit, 252–54
calculation to determine, 252
profit and loss, 241
cost, 241
operations to consider, 242
selling price, 241
progress estimate, 240
quantity survey, 240
selling price, 252–54
calculation to determine,
252–53
square-ft and cubic-ft methods,
240
unit price, 243–44
HVAC office management:
computer programs, 259,
262–63, 265
computer software, 270–72
HVAC specifications: 272
computer software for writing
specifications, 272–73
glossary software, 272–73
replace, insert, delete features,
273
sample specifications:
Division 15—mechanical,
273–98
HVAC symbols list, (*fig.*) 70
HVAC system:
blueprints, 13–71
comfort conditioning uses, 9
conveniences available, 10
designing, 11–12
drawing and diagrams, types,
13–71
floor plan, 10–11
general planning, 9–10
primary use, 9
type of, 10
Hydrogen, 7, 8

Incomplete combustion, 8–9
Infrared heater, 5

Installation cost variables,
    244–45
  four situation groups, 245
Insurance, 250
Integral-horsepower manual
    starter, 217
Integral-horsepower starter with
    low-voltage protection,
    218
Interest, 250
Isometric drawing, 14–15

Labeltronics system 1000, 101
Labeltronics system 2000, 101
Latent heat, 77–78
  cooling and dehumidifying, 81
  of fusion, 77–78
  of vaporization, 77–78
Legal and accounting fee, 250
Limit switch, 232
Lost goods, 250
Lost production labor, 250
Lotus 1-2-3 computer software,
    99, 270
Louvers and grilles, 129

Macintosh Plus, 308
Magnetic circuit:
  of controller, 219
  moving part:
    armature, 219
  stationary part:
    magnetic assembly, 219
Magnetic controller:
  magnet and armature
    assemblies in use, 218
  bell crank, 218–19
  clapper type, 218
  horizontal action, 218
  vertical action, 218
Magnetic pole face, (*fig.*) 220
Manual motor-starting switch,
    217

Manual starter:
  uses of, 217
Marketfax (HVAC computer
    software), 100
Masonry structure, 2, 3
Material cost and pricing, 246–47
Melting-alloy overload relay, 223
Microlink II (HVAC computer
    software), 99
MICS/1 job costing and billing
    (HVAC computer
    software), 97–98
Motor:
  nameplate information, 224
  (NEC) safety codes, 227
  starter and disconnect (NEC)
    requirement, 227

National Electrical Code®
    (NEC), 227
Nitrogen, 7, 8
Notebook (computer software),
    100

Oblique drawing, 14, 15
Obsolete goods, 250
Office expense, 250
Open-flamed equipment:
  confined spaces, 129–36
    all air from inside, 129
    all air from outside, 129
    louvers and grilles, 129
  general rules, 128
  installation of, 128
  unconfined space, 128
Orthographic-projection
    drawing, 16
Outlet:
  location, 170
Outlet types:
  ceiling diffuser, 170
  grille, 170
  register, 170
  (*see also* Supply-air outlets)

Overhanging roof, 116, 118
Overhead costs, 249–52
Overload relay, 222–23
Oxygen, 7, 8

PC asynchronous
    communications (HVAC
    software), 98
PC data base (HVAC
    software), 99
PC multiplan (HVAC
    software), 99
Peachtree computer software,
    270–71
  accounting, 271
  calendar management system,
    271
  job cost system, 271
Peachtree: calendar management
    (HVAC software), 100
Peachtree: job costing (HVAC
    software), 97
Peachtree: peachpay payroll, 97
Perspective drawing, 14, 15
Pictorial drawing, 13–15
  motor start, (fig.) 19
  types of, 14
    isometric, 14–15
    oblique, 14, 15
    perspective, 14, 15
Pipes:
  for steam and hot water
    systems, 137–38
Pneumatic timer, 232
Practical Drafting for the HVAC
    Trades, 303
Prefabricated structures, 2, 4
Pressure drop, 126
Pressure switch, 233
Progress estimate (HVAC
    estimating), 240
Psychrometric chart, 72–76,
    (fig.) 73

dry-bulb temperature of air
    mixture, 79
  evaporating cooling, 78
  heating and cooling
    changes, 77
  specific volume scale, 80
  wet-bulb temperature of air
    mixture, 79
Psychrometric concept:
  enthalpy, 80
  specific volume, 80
Psychrometric processes, 77–81
  bypass, 79–80
  cooling and dehumidifying,
    80–81
  heating and cooling
    changes, 77
  latent and sensible heat, 77
  heating and humidifying, 80–81
Psychrometrics, 72
  chart, 72
  dewpoint temperature, 72, 73
  dry-bulb temperature, 72, 74,
    76, 78
  grains of moisture, 72, 73
  relative humidity, 72, 73
  wet-bulb temperature, 72–73
Push-button station, 232

Quantity survey (HVAC
    estimating), 240

Radiant ceiling heater, 84–85
  installation, 85
  rating (watts), 84
  remote thermostat, 85
  uses, 84
Radiant heating cable, 6, 86
  installation, 206
  panel, 85
  mount, 85
  size, 85

Rectangular duct, 166, 177
  capacity and friction loss
    chart, (*fig.*) 167
  (*see also* Suspending
    rectangular duct)
Rectangular elbow, 166
  friction loss chart, (*table*) 168,
    (*fig.*) 169
Rectangular main duct sizing
  program, 158–64
Refrigerant tubing, installing,
  (kit), 149–51
Register, 170
Reinforced concrete, 2, 4
Relative humidity, 72, 73, 74,
  76, 78
  how to calculate, 74, 75, 76
Relay, 230
  amplifying contact capacity,
    231
  circuit amplifying voltage,
    231–32
  uses, 230
Rent (overhead costs), 250
Repairs and maintenance, 251
Residential/commercial service
  (HVAC software), 98
Residential construction:
  masonry, 2
  prefabricated structure, 2
  reinforced concrete, 2
  types, 2
  wood frame, 2
Residential Cooling Load
  Estimate form, 114, (*fig.*)
    115
Residential HVAC system:
  central heating unit, 5
  combination heating/cooling
    unit, 5
  electric baseboard heaters, 5
  fan-driven forced-air unit
    heaters, 6
  heat pump, 5

high-velocity and cooling
  system, 6
hot-water baseboard heating, 5
infrared heater, 5
miscellaneous heaters, 7
radiant heating cable, 6
solar heat, 6
(*see also* HVAC system)
Return-air inlets, 174
  grille and register sizing chart,
    175
Room (individual)
  air-conditioning, (*see*
    Window air conditioning)
Round duct, 166, 176–77
  capacity and friction loss
    chart, (*fig.*) 167
Round duct sizing, 158
  chart, (*fig.*) 159

Salaries and commissions, 251
Sales discount, 251
Schematic diagram, 65–67
Schematic drawing, (*fig.*) 19
Schematic electrical wiring
  diagram, 67–69
Schematic wiring diagram, 17,
  (*fig.*) 18, 65–67
Selling price (estimating), 252–54
Sensible heat, 77, 78
  cooling and dehumidifying, 81
Sensible heat factor line, 78
Shade-line factor, 114, 117,
  (*table*) 118
Shaded-pole principle, 219
Shading (windows), 116, 118–19
Sheet metal ductwork, 193
Single-line block diagram, 17,
  (*fig.*) 18
Single-pole double-throw (SPDT)
  switch, 64
Single-pole single-throw (SPST)
  switch, 64
Small tools, 251

Snap switch, 233
Solar heat, 6
Space-Pak kit (high-velocity
    heating/cooling system),
    194
Specific volume, 80
  air density, 80
Spray chamber, 80
  water spray coils, 80
Square-ft and cubic-ft method,
    240
Static pressure, 154, 156
Static regain method, 157
Statistician (HVAC software), 99
Steam-heating system, 124, 125
Stolen goods (overhead
    estimating), 250
Strap and angle system, 189
Strap and channel method, 189
Strap and pad system, 189
Strap and rail system, 189
Supply-air outlets, 166–67,
    173–74
  considerations, 173
  location, 170–73
  selection, 176
Suspending rectangular duct,
    188–93
  strap and angle system, 189
  strap and channel system, 189
  strap and pad system, 189
  strap and rail system, 189
  T-bar saddle method, 193
Symbol list or legend, 19, 64,
    (fig.) 20–63

Taxes, 251
T-bar saddle method, 193
Temperatures for calculating
    heating loads, (table)
    106–109
Thermostat:
  low-voltage combination of
    control, 215

Three-pole double-throw (3PDT)
    switch, 64, (fig.) 65
Three-wire control, 228
  holding circuit interlock, 229
  manual reversing starter, 230
  reversing starter, 230
Timer and timing relay, 232
Tinted glass, 116
TK!Solverpack—mechanical
    engineering (HVAC
    software), 96
Total accounting system (HVAC
    software), 97
"Trane Duct Sizer," 157
Transfers and secondaries, 211
  two common arrangements:
    continuous form, 212
    sectional, 211–12
Transformers:
  main purpose, 212
  selection, 212–13
Travel and transportation
    expense, 251
Two- and three-pole starter,
    217–18
Two-wire control circuit, 227–28

United States of America
    Standards Institute
    (USASI), 19
Unit pricing, 243–44

Velocity pressure, 156
Ventilation, 128
Visi On computer software, 270

Wall, construction and
    insulation, (fig.) 120, 121
Wall and door, 119–21
Wall thickness, 135
Wet-bulb temperature, 72–73,
    74, 78
  of air mixture, 79
  how to calculate, 75

Window, 114–19
  cooling calculation, 114,
    116–19
  exposure, 114
  heat gain, 116–17
  measuring area of, 114, 116–19
  shade-line factor, 117–18
  shading, 116
    awning, tinted glass, 116
    overhanging roof, 116–18
  unshaded glass, 118–19

Window air-conditioning unit:
  square-ft calculation, 123
Winter air conditioning, 76–77
  how to calculate, 76, 77
Wire size for electric power, 211
Wiring for light and power, 211
Wood frame, 2, (*fig.*) 3

Zone hydronic (hot-water)
    heating system, (*see*
    Hot-water system)